MOTION AND TIME STUDY

MOTION AND TIME STUDY

BY

RALPH M. BARNES, M.E., Ph.D.

Professor of Industrial Engineering and Director of Personnel
College of Engineering, University of Iowa

SECOND EDITION

NEW YORK

JOHN WILEY & SONS, Inc.

London: CHAPMAN & HALL, Limited

10/42

PRINTED IN U. S. A.

PREFACE TO SECOND EDITION

The favorable acceptance of the first edition of "Motion and Time Study" by men both in industries and in colleges has led me to attempt to extend its usefulness by enlarging upon certain of its features and by including more illustrative material.

The amplification of the material on process charts, operation analysis, and visual direction has been effected largely by the introduction of case material to show widely diverse applications.

The section on stop-watch time study has been enlarged, and two chapters have been added to illustrate the use of time values for combinations of therbligs in setting time standards.

Summarized results of research studies conducted in the Industrial Engineering Laboratory at the University of Iowa have been incorporated in the text. During the past three years more than a million measurements of hand motions used in factory operations have been made in the laboratory. Detailed reports of most of these investigations have been published in *Factory Management and Maintenance, Mechanical Engineering, Journal of the Society for the Advancement of Management, Proceedings of the Seventh International Management Congress, The Iron Age,* and in *University of Iowa Studies in Engineering.* These studies represent largely the work of Marvin E. Mundel, D. U. Greenwald, John M. MacKenzie, Harold T. Amrine, and James S. Perkins, whose painstaking thoroughness and diligence in the laboratory produced results that have already proved of value to industry.

Since the first edition was published, I have received helpful assistance from many people in the schools and industries where my book has been used. To these I am most grateful.

I am especially indebted to Harold Engstrom, Motion Study Supervisor, Bridgeport works of the General Electric Company, under whose direction were developed the methods and time values presented in Chapters 22 and 23.

Iowa City, Iowa
January, 1940

RALPH M. BARNES.

v

PREFACE TO FIRST EDITION

The present trend toward increased efficiency in all kinds of work has brought about a widespread interest in motion and time study. Wherever manual work is performed there is always the problem of finding the most economical way of doing the task, and then of determining the amount of work that should be done in a given period of time. This is ordinarily accompanied by some incentive plan of wage payment. Motion and time study provides a technique that is unequalled for finding methods of greatest economy and for measuring labor accomplishment.

The terms "time study" and "motion study" have been given many interpretations since their origin. Time study, originated by Taylor, was mainly used for rate setting; and motion study, developed by the Gilbreths, was largely employed for improving methods. One group saw time study only as a means of determining the size of the task that should constitute a day's work, using the stop watch as the timing device. Another group saw motion study only as an expensive and elaborate technique for determining a good method of doing work. Today the discussion of the comparative value of using either the one or the other of the two techniques has largely passed; industry has found that motion study and time study are inseparable, as their combined use in many factories and offices now demonstrates. Taking cognizance of present trends and recognizing the fact that motion study always precedes the setting of a time standard, we shall in this volume use the term "motion and time study" as referring to this broad field.

Since all manual work is done by means of the hands or other parts of the body, the study of body movements has been found to be a valuable approach to the problem of finding better ways of doing work. Training in the micromotion study technique is a valuable aid in analyzing and improving manual operations, i.e., in applying motion-economy principles. For this reason the technique of micromotion study has been presented in detail.

Micromotion study is defined as the study of the elements of an operation by means of a motion-picture camera and a timing device which accurately indicates time intervals on the motion-picture film. This, in turn, makes possible the analysis of the elementary motions recorded on the film, and the assignment of time values to each. Micromotion study may be used for two purposes: (1) to assist in finding the most efficient method of doing work; and (2) to assist in training individuals to understand the meaning of motion study and, when the training is carried out with sufficient thoroughness, to enable them to become proficient in applying motion-economy principles. The second purpose of micromotion study is by far the more important of the two.

The performance of manual work in an effective manner presupposes some understanding of the inherent capacities and abilities of the human body. Therefore, investigations bearing on manual work made by engineers, physiologists, and psychologists have been studied and such findings as seem most useful have been included in this volume. Although the material in Chapters 12, 13, and 14 has been discussed under the heading "principles of motion economy," it might, perhaps, have been more accurately designated as "some rules for motion economy and fatigue reduction." The writer has selected what material he could find that seemed to be useful in determining better methods of doing work. The twenty-two rules or principles presented in these chapters are not all of equal importance nor does this discussion include all of the factors which enter into the determination of better methods of doing work. However, it is hoped that this material may be of some value to those who have difficulty in finding a condensed treatment of the subject.

In presenting the technique of stop-watch study, the author has attempted to give those practices that result in most satisfactory time standards and to include simple examples to illustrate the methods.

The author has personally selected or developed the case material used for illustrations in this volume. Moreover, most of the material, in lithoprinted form, has had actual use in the classrooms of six colleges and universities and in many industries. The volume should, therefore, be of value to those supervising or engaged in manual work of any kind whatsoever. Workers as well as managers and engineers should profit from a study of this material. The many comments received from the users of the lithoprinted edition indicate that this material will serve not only as a textbook in technical colleges and universities but as a handbook in factories, stores, hospitals, homes, and on farms.

Over the period of several years during which this book has been in process of development, the author has had constant assistance and advice from industrial executives, engineers, and educators. To these he would express his great indebtedness. His special thanks for assistance received are due to Professor David B. Porter of the College of Engineering, New York University, and to L. P. Persing, supervisor of wage rates at the Fort Wayne works of the General Electric Company.

RALPH M. BARNES.

Iowa City, Iowa
    March, 1937

CONTENTS

CHAPTER   PAGE

1. Definition and Scope of Motion and Time Study   1

2. History of Motion and Time Study   7

3. Extent to Which Motion and Time Study May Be Profitably Used . 17

4. Process and Operation Analysis 22

5. The Use of Micromotion Study 54

6. Definition of Therbligs 62

7. Micromotion Study Equipment 67

8. Making the Motion Pictures 79

9. Film Analysis 86

10. The Use of the Therbligs 107

11. Fatigue 134

12. Principles of Motion Economy as Related to the Use of the Human Body 145

13. Principles of Motion Economy as Related to the Work Place . . 174

14. Principles of Motion Economy as Related to the Design of Tools and Equipment 216

15. Standardization—Written Standard Practice 245

16. The Relation of Time Standards to Wage Incentives 250

17. Making the Stop-Watch Study 255

18. Determining Rating Factor, Allowances, and Time Standard . . . 268

19. Determining Time Standards from Elemental Time Data and Formulas 288

20. The Use of Elemental Time Data and Formulas—Two Cases: Gear Hobbing and Soldering Cans 301

21. Determining Time Standards for Die and Tool Work 317

22. Determining Time Standards for Assembly Operations—Classification and Definition of Motions—Determination of Time Values . . . 333

23. Determining Time Standards for Assembly Operations—An Application 345

24. Training the Operator 359

Problems 371

Bibliography 379

Index 383

MOTION AND TIME STUDY

CHAPTER 1

DEFINITION AND SCOPE OF MOTION AND TIME STUDY

The terms "time study" and "motion study" have been given many interpretations since their origin. Time study, originated by Taylor, was mainly used for rate setting; and motion study, developed by the Gilbreths, was largely employed for improving methods. In recent years, the combined use of motion study and time study has become widespread. Common practice today requires that motion study and time study be used together since the two supplement each other. Taking cognizance of present trends and recognizing the fact that motion study always precedes the setting of a time standard, we shall in this volume use the term "motion and time study" as referring to this broad field and as having the following meaning.

Definition of Motion and Time Study. Motion and time study is the analysis of the methods, of the materials, and of the tools and equipment used, or to be used, in the performance of a piece of work —an analysis carried on with the purpose of (1) finding the most economical way of doing this work; (2) standardizing the methods, materials, tools, and equipment; (3) accurately determining the time required by an average worker to do the task; and (4) training the worker in the new method.

Motion and time study is composed of four parts as the above definition shows. Although these parts may be considered separately, no one of them can be omitted entirely without seriously impairing the value of the study. Each of the four parts will be explained more fully.

1. Finding the Most Economical Way of Performing the Operation. The best way of doing a specific task is determined by a scientific study of the methods, materials, tools, and equipment used. Since all operations require some human effort or attention (even an automatic machine requires some attention), a minute analysis of the movements made by the worker in performing his task is a valuable approach to the problem of finding the best way. This analysis of the movements of the operator is called motion study. Motion study is commonly defined as the study of the motions used in the performance of an operation for the purpose of eliminating all unnecessary motions and building up a sequence of the most useful motions for maximum efficiency.

A study of the motions of the operator naturally requires that the outside factors affecting these motions be considered also. The two are intimately connected, for when the operator moves his hand he makes contact with something. He assembles a part, uses a screwdriver, starts a machine, etc. A study of the materials, tools, and equipment, as well as of the motions themselves, is necessary. One material may have inherent qualities which make it superior to others for some specific use; so also may a tool or a machine. To illustrate, brass may be substituted for steel because its better machinability may more than offset its greater cost per pound; a high-speed steel drill may be substituted for a carbon steel one, or a semi-automatic machine may be used instead of a hand-operated one; all because in the particular case one material, tool, or machine is more economical than the other. And, furthermore, it is possible that conditions such as lighting, heating, ventilation, vibration, and noise which surround the job may affect the output. These conditions should be adjusted to insure the greatest comfort to the worker and to give the greatest overall economy.

"Best way," "optimum manner," and "method of maximum efficiency" are some of the terms used to denote the object of this first phase of motion and time study. To prevent confusion, it is important that a clear meaning be assigned to these terms. In all cases the object is to find the best way, *all factors* considered. That means that the economy in dollars and cents be considered as well as the economy in motions, materials, tools, and equipment used. For example, a magazine-fed, motor-driven pencil sharpener might be the *best* device for sharpening pencils, but for the small office the hand-operated one is *most economical*. Therefore, what may be the best way in one case may not be the best way in another case. It should also be added that the best method for one operator may not be the best method for another operator. The determination of the method of greatest economy for a specific job, giving consideration to all factors affecting the work and the operator, is the purpose of this first part of motion and time study.

2. Standardizing the Operation—Written Standard Practice. After the best method for doing the work has been determined, this method must be standardized. The particular set of motions, the size, shape, and quality of material, the particular tools, jigs, fixtures, gauges, and the machine or piece of equipment to be used must be definitely specified. All of these factors, as well as the conditions surrounding the worker, must be maintained after they have been standardized. A written standard practice giving a detailed record of the operation and specifications for performing the work is the most common and satisfactory way of preserving the standards.

3. Setting the Time Standard. Motion and time study may be used to determine accurately the standard number of minutes or hours that an average worker should take to perform the operation. This time standard converted into money value, as it often is, is called a piece rate. Piece rates are usually expressed as so many dollars per hundred pieces. In other cases, the standard time value is used as the basis for any one of the many different incentive wage-payment plans. This third part of motion and time study is commonly referred to as rate setting.

The most common method of measuring manual work is by means of a stop-watch study. The operation is divided into small elements and each of these elements is accurately timed with a stop watch. An average time value is found for each element and these are added together in order to get the total selected time for performing the operation. The skill and effort exhibited by the operator during the stop-watch study are rated or evaluated by the time-study observer and the selected time is adjusted by means of this rating factor so that an average operator can easily do the work in the specified time. This corrected time is called the base time. To this base time are added allowances for personal time, fatigue, and delay, the result being the standard time for the task.

' This standard time should permit the average employee to work indefinitely without undue fatigue. In fact, the time standard is usually set at such a level that 25 to 50 per cent of the working force can readily do a third more work than the standard requires. Therefore, when a wage incentive is used it is within the range of possibility for every first-class employee to do more work than the standard calls for and thus earn extra wages. The straight piece-rate plan of wage incentive, for example, rewards the worker in direct proportion to his output.

4. Training the Operator. A carefully determined method of doing work is of little value unless it can be put into effect. It is necessary to train the operator to perform the work in the prescribed manner.

Where but one or a few persons are employed on a given operation and where the work is relatively simple it is customary to train the operator at his work place. The supervisor, motion and time study analyst, a special instructor, or a skilled operator may act as the teacher. Where large numbers of employees must be trained for a single operation the training is sometimes carried on in a separate training department.

Written instruction sheets are valuable aids in training operators, and motion pictures are sometimes used for this purpose.

Scope. In order to gain perspective and to show relationships it seems desirable to illustrate in graphical form (see Fig. 1) the scope of the entire field of motion and time study. The process of making a motion and time study follows a fairly definite procedure and the several steps are shown on the chart in some detail. This chart also outlines the material to be presented in the remainder of the book.

Although motion and time study is most commonly applied in the shop and the office, the principles are universal in nature and may be equally effective wherever manual work is performed. For example, Professor R. H. Barrett at Massachusetts State College has shown some excellent effects from the application of these principles to the harvesting of vegetables and preparing them for market. Gilbreth at one time also made some investigations of picking berries. Miss A. G. Shaw at Metropolitan-Vickers in Manchester, England, has made substantial savings in time for serving food in the company's restaurants and canteens and has reduced operation costs through the application of motion and time study. Professor C. A. Koepke at the University of Minnesota has applied these principles to work in the hospital and hotel, and incidentally gives a course in motion and time study to a class of student nurses in the hospital. Mrs. Gilbreth has more recently given considerable attention to the proper design and arrangement of the home kitchen and laundry. There are many indications that the next few years will see widespread use for motion and time study in fields not now employing it.

Motion and Time Study but a Part of Industrial Engineering. Although the broad view of motion and time study has been presented, no attempt is being made to expand it to include the entire field of industrial engineering. In recent years there has been a tendency in this direction.

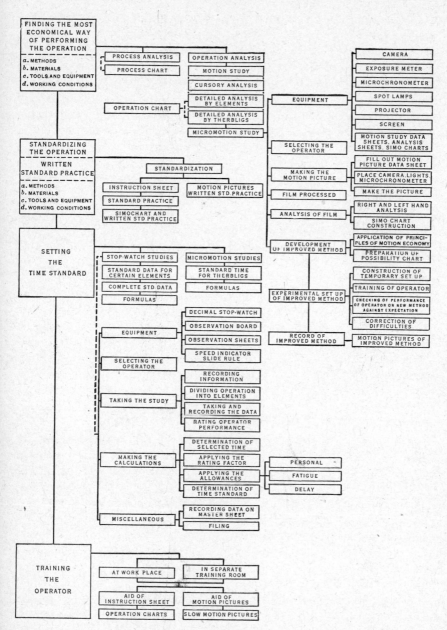

FIG. 1—Scope of motion and time study.

With competent engineers directing the use of motion and time study work, it frequently happens that a preliminary study of a single operation may quite properly lead to a complete investigation of an entire process, even involving the redesign of the product and an entirely new layout of manufacturing equipment. Such an investigation is beyond the scope of motion and time study and should more properly be classed under the broader field of industrial engineering.

CHAPTER 2

HISTORY OF MOTION AND TIME STUDY

In order to understand how time study has come to have the broad meaning presented in the preceding chapter, it is necessary to go back and investigate the origin, and examine the use that has been made of time study and motion study during the past fifty years.

TAYLOR'S USE OF TIME STUDY

It is generally agreed that time study had its beginning in the machine shop [1] of the Midvale Steel Company in 1881, and that Frederick W. Taylor was its originator. Taylor's definition and explanation of time study is as follows: [2]

Time study is the one element in scientific management beyond all others making possible the "transfer of skill from management to men." . . . "Time study" consists of two broad divisions, first, analytical work, and second, constructive work.

The analytical work of time study is as follows:

a. Divide the work of a man performing any job into simple elementary movements.

b. Pick out all useless movements and discard them.

c. Study, one after another, just how each of several skilled workmen makes each elementary movement, and with the aid of a stop watch select the quickest and best method of making each elementary movement known in the trade.

d. Describe, record, and index each elementary movement, with its proper time, so that it can be quickly found.

e. Study and record the percentage which must be added to the actual working time of a good workman to cover unavoidable delays, interruptions, minor accidents, etc.

f. Study and record the percentage which must be added to cover the newness of a good workman to a job, the first few times that he does it. (This percentage is quite large on jobs made up of a large number of different elements composing a long sequence infrequently repeated.

[1] Subcommittee on Administration of the A.S.M.E., "The Present State of the Art of Industrial Management," *Trans. A.S.M.E.*, Vol. 34, pp. 1197-98, 1912.
[2] *Ibid.*, pp. 1199-1200.

This factor grows smaller, however, as the work consists of a smaller number of different elements in a sequence that is more frequently repeated.)

g. Study and record the percentage of time that must be allowed for rest, and the intervals at which the rest must be taken, in order to offset physical fatigue.

The constructive work of time study is as follows:

h. Add together into various groups such combinations of elementary movements as are frequently used in the same sequence in the trade, and record and index these groups so that they can be readily found.

i. From these several records, it is comparatively easy to select the proper series of motions which should be used by a workman in making any particular article and, by summing the times of these movements and adding proper percentage allowances, to find the proper time for doing almost any class of work.

j. The analysis of a piece of work into its elements almost always reveals the fact that many of the conditions surrounding and accompanying the work are defective; for instance, that improper tools are used, that the machines used in connection with it need perfecting, and that the sanitary conditions are bad, etc. And knowledge so obtained leads frequently to constructive work of a high order, to the standardization of tools and conditions, to the invention of superior methods and machines.

From the above definition it is apparent that Taylor made some use of motion study as a part of his time study technique. However, he placed greater emphasis on materials, tools, and equipment in connection with the improvement of methods. It remained for the Gilbreths to develop motion study as we know it today.

As important as is Taylor's contribution in originating time study, this is only one of his many achievements. To him also goes the credit for inventing high-speed steel, discovering and evaluating the variables affecting the cutting of metals, originating the functional type of organization, and developing a system or philosophy commonly referred to as scientific management. These achievements were not accidental, but the result of a systematic study of the factors affecting the problem in each instance. Taylor's real contribution to industry was his scientific method, his substitution of fact-finding for rule-of-thumb procedure. His questioning attitude and his constant search for the facts gave him the high place which he reached and still holds as a proponent of science in management. He was a pioneer in applying science to that phase of industry which intimately affected the worker. He understood that he was dealing with a human problem as well as with materials and machines, and he approached the human side of his investigations with an understanding of its psychological aspects.[3]

So great has been Taylor's contribution to the whole problem of effective utilization of human effort in industry that we can profit from a review of some of his work in this field.

Taylor came from a well-to-do Philadelphia family, was trained at Phillips Exeter Academy to enter Harvard, and after but a year and a half at Phillips Exeter passed the Harvard entrance examinations with honors but at the cost of seriously impaired eyesight. Forced to give up the idea of further study, at the age of eighteen he obtained a job in a machine shop where he served the apprenticeships of machinist and pattern-maker. In 1878, when he was twenty-two, he went to work at the Midvale Steel Works. As business conditions were bad at that time, he took a job as an ordinary laborer. He was rapidly promoted to time clerk, journeyman, lathe operator, gang boss, foreman of the machine shop, and at the age of thirty-one was made chief engineer of the works. During his early years at Midvale, Taylor studied at night and in 1883 obtained a degree in mechanical engineering from Stevens Institute.

Taylor's Principles of Management. It was as gang boss and foreman that Taylor first came face to face with such problems as "Which is the best way to do this job?" "What should constitute a day's work?" and problems of a similar nature. Taylor, being very conscientious himself, expected the men under him to do a fair day's work. He set for himself the task of finding the proper method of doing a given piece of work, teaching the worker how to do it in this way, maintaining all conditions surrounding the work so that the worker could do the task properly, setting a definite time standard for accomplishing the work, and then paying the worker a premium in the form of extra wages for doing the task as specified. Many years later Taylor explained his objectives in the following way:

[3] Some maintain that Taylor merely tried to squeeze more work from the employees and that his methods were not scientific. For objections to Taylor's methods, see:

(a) R. F. Hoxie, "Scientific Management and Labor," D. Appleton & Co., New York, 1915.

(b) Symposium—"Stop-Watch Time Study, an Indictment and a Defense," *Bul. Taylor Soc.*, Vol. 6, No. 3, pp. 99-135, June, 1921.

(c) E. Farmer, "Time and Motion Study," *Ind. Fatigue Research Bd.*, Report 14, H. M. Stationery Office, London, 1921.

First.   The development of a science for each element of a man's work, thereby replacing the old rule-of-thumb methods.

Second.   The selection of the best worker for each particular task and then training, teaching, and developing the workman; in place of the former practice of allowing the worker to select his own task and train himself as best he could.

Third.   The development of a spirit of hearty cooperation between the management and the men in the carrying on of the activities in accordance with the principles of the developed science.

Fourth.   The division of the work into almost equal shares between the management and the workers, each department taking over the work for which it is the better fitted; instead of the former condition, in which almost all of the work and the greater part of the responsibility were thrown on the men.[4]

Taylor stated many times that scientific management required "a complete mental revolution on the part of the workman—and on the part of those on management's side."[5]   "Both sides must recognize as essential the substitution of exact scientific investigation and knowledge for the old individual judgment or opinion."[6]

Although Taylor realized that there was more to the management of an industrial enterprise than conducting investigations on methods of doing work, he stated in no uncertain terms that one of the first duties of management was "to develop a science for each element of a man's work" and he used and advocated the scientific approach in the solution of every problem that arose in this connection.

Mr. Eric Farmer of Great Britain, in a most critical analysis of Taylor's work, states, "Taylor's greatest and lasting contribution to the science of industry is the method he adopted.   He approached problems which had been thought either not to exist or to be easily solved by common sense, in the spirit of scientific enquiry."[7]

During his many years in industry Taylor carried on extended investigations in order to determine the best way to do work and to obtain specific data for standardizing the task.   In order to illustrate his approach, one of his well-known studies will be briefly described here.

[4] F. W. Taylor, "The Principles of Scientific Management," p. 36, Harper & Bros., New York, 1929.

[5] F. B. Copley, "Frederick W. Taylor," Vol. I, p. 10, Harper & Bros., New York, 1923.

[6] *Ibid.*, p. 12.

[7] E. Farmer, "Time and Motion Study," *Ind. Fatigue Research Bd.*, Report 14, H. M. Stationery Office, London, 1921.

Taylor's Investigation of Shoveling. In 1898, when Taylor went to the Bethlehem Steel Works, he undertook to improve methods in various parts of the plant. One task that came to his attention was shoveling. Four hundred to 600 men were employed in the yard, and much of their work was shoveling. More iron ore was shoveled than any other material, and rice coal came next in tonnage. Taylor found that each good shoveler in that yard owned his own shovel; he preferred to do this rather than to have the company furnish it. A foreman supervised 50 to 60 men, and they shoveled a variety of material in the course of a day. The yard was approximately two miles long and a quarter of a mile wide, so that the gang moved about over a large area.

With little investigation Taylor found that shovelers were lifting loads of 3½ pounds when handling rice coal and up to 38 pounds to the shovel when moving ore. He immediately set about to determine what shovel load permitted a first-class shoveler to move the most material in a day. Taylor took two good shovelers and set them to work in different parts of the yard and set two time study men with stop watches to study the work of these men. At first large shovels were used so that heavy loads were taken. Then the end of the shovel was cut off to permit a smaller shovel load and again the tonnage handled was noted. This procedure was continued—from very heavy shovel loads to very light ones. The results of this study showed that, with a load of 21½ pounds on the shovel, a man could handle a maximum tonnage of material in a day. Thus, a small spade-shovel that would just hold 21½ pounds was provided for the worker when he handled ore and a large scoop was provided for light material, such as ashes.

A tool room was established and special shovels were purchased and issued to the workers as needed. In addition Taylor inaugurated a planning department to determine in advance the work to be done in the yard. This department issued orders to the foremen and the workers each morning, stating the nature of the work to be done, the tools needed, and the location of the work in the yard. Instead of the men working together in large gangs the material handled by each man was measured or weighed at the end of the day and each man was paid a bonus (60 per cent above day wages) when he did the specified amount of work. If a man failed to earn the bonus, an instructor was sent out to show the worker how to do his job in the proper way and so earn his bonus.

After three and one-half years at the Bethlehem plant Taylor was

doing the same amount of work in the yards with 140 men as was
formerly done by 400 to 600. He reduced the cost of handling material
from 7 to 8 cents to 3 to 4 cents per ton. After paying for all added
expenses, such as planning the work, measuring the output of the
workers, determining and paying bonuses each day, and maintaining
the tool room, Taylor still showed a saving during the last six-month
period at the rate of $78,000 per year.[8]

One cannot read Taylor's experiments on the art of cutting metals,[9]
his study of rest pauses in handling pig iron,[10] or his investigations in
shoveling without at once realizing that he was a scientist of high
order. With Taylor, as with the factory manager today, time study
was a tool to be used in increasing the overall efficiency of the plant,
making possible higher wages for labor, and lower prices of the finished products to the consumer.

MOTION STUDY AS IT WAS DEVELOPED BY THE GILBRETHS

Motion study cannot be discussed without constant reference to the
work of Frank B. Gilbreth and his wife, Lillian M. Gilbreth. Industry
owes a great debt to them for their pioneering work in this field. The
fundamental character of their work is indicated by the fact that the
principles and techniques which they developed many years ago are
being adopted by industry today at an increasingly rapid rate.

The story of the work of the Gilbreths is a long and fascinating
one. Mrs. Gilbreth's training as a psychologist and Mr. Gilbreth's
engineering background fitted them in a unique way to undertake work
involving an understanding of the human factor as well as a knowledge
of materials, tools, and equipment. Their activities cover a wide
range including noteworthy inventions and improvements in building
and construction work,[11] study of fatigue,[12] monotony,[13] transfer of
skill, and work for the handicapped,[14] and the development of such

[8] F. B. Copley, "Frederick W. Taylor," Vol. II, p. 56, Harper & Bros., New
York, 1923.
[9] F. W. Taylor, "On the Art of Cutting Metals," *Trans. A.S.M.E.*, Vol. 28,
Paper 1119, pp. 31-350, 1907.
[10] Copley, *Op. cit.*, p. 37.
[11] F. B. Gilbreth, "Motion Study," D. Van Nostrand Co., New York, 1911.
[12] F. B. and L. M. Gilbreth, "Fatigue Study," Macmillan Co., New York, 1919.
[13] L. M. Gilbreth, "Monotony in Repetitive Operations," *Iron Age*, Vol. 118,
No. 19, p. 1344, Nov. 4, 1926.
[14] F. B. and L. M. Gilbreth, "Motion Study for the Handicapped," George
Routledge Sons, London, 1920.

techniques as the process chart, micromotion study, and the chrono-cyclegraph.

In this volume particular attention is given to their work dealing with the process chart, motion study, and micromotion study.

The Beginning of Motion Study. In 1885, Gilbreth, as a young man of seventeen, entered the employ of a building contractor. In those days brick construction constituted an important part of most structures, so Gilbreth began by learning the bricklayer's trade. Promotions came rapidly and by the beginning of the century Gilbreth was in the contracting business for himself. From the very beginning of his connection with the building trades Gilbreth noted that each craftsman used his own peculiar methods in doing his work, and that no two men did their work in exactly the same way. Furthermore, he observed that the worker did not always use the same set of motions. The bricklayer, for example, used one set of motions when he worked rapidly, another set of motions when he worked slowly, and still a third set when he taught someone else how to lay brick.[15] These observations led Gilbreth to begin investigations to find the one best way of performing a given task. His efforts were so fruitful and his enthusiasm for this sort of thing became so great that in later years he gave up his contracting business entirely in order to devote his entire time to motion study investigations and applications.[16]

It was apparent from the beginning that Gilbreth had a knack for analyzing the motions used by his workmen. He readily saw how to make improvements in methods, substituting shorter and less fatiguing motions for longer and more tiring ones. He made photographs of bricklayers at work, and from a study of these photographs he continued to make progress in bringing about increased output among his workers. For example, Gilbreth invented a scaffold which could quickly and easily be raised, a short distance at a time, thus permitting it to be kept near the most convenient working level at all times. This scaffold was also equipped with a bench or shelf for holding the brick and mortar at a convenient height for the workmen. This saved the bricklayer the tiring and unnecessary task of bending over to pick up a brick from the floor of the scaffold each time he laid one on the wall.

[15] L. M. Gilbreth, "The Quest of the One Best Way," p. 16, a sketch of the life of F. B. Gilbreth published by Mrs. Gilbreth, 1925.

[16] John G. Aldrich. See discussion of Gilbreth's work at the New England Butt Company. "The Present State of the Art of Industrial Management," *Trans. A.S.M.E.*, Vol. 34, Paper 1378, pp. 1182-1187, 1912.

Formerly, brick were dumped in a heap on the scaffold and the bricklayer selected the brick as he used them. He turned or flipped the brick over in his hand in order to find the best side to place on the face of the wall. Gilbreth improved this procedure. As the brick were unloaded from the freight car, Gilbreth had low-priced laborers sort them and place them on wooden frames or "packets" three feet long. Each packet held ninety pounds of brick. The brick were inspected by these men as they unloaded them. They were then placed on the packet, side by side, so the best face and end were uniformly turned in a given direction. The packets were then placed on the scaffolds in such a way that the bricklayer could pick up the brick quickly without having to disentangle them from a heap. Gilbreth had the mortar box and the packets of brick arranged on the scaffold in such relative positions that the bricklayer could pick up a brick with one hand and a trowel full of mortar with the other at the same time. Formerly, the bricklayer in reaching down to the floor to pick up a brick with one hand permitted the other hand to remain idle.

In addition, Gilbreth arranged for the mortar to be kept of the proper consistency so that the brick could be shoved into place on the wall with the hand. This eliminated the motion of tapping the brick into place with the trowel. These changes, along with others which Gilbreth developed, greatly increased the amount of work which a bricklayer could do in a day. For example, in exterior brick work, using the "pick and dip" method, the number of motions required to lay a brick were reduced from 18 in the old method to 4½ in the new method.[17]

On a particular building near Boston, on a twelve-inch brick wall with drawn joints on both sides and of two kinds of brick, which is a rather difficult wall to lay, bricklayers were trained in the new method. By the time the building was a quarter to a half of the way up, the average production was 350 bricks per man per hour. The record for this type of work previous to the adoption of the new system had been but 120 bricks per man per hour.[18]

Definition of Micromotion Study. Although Gilbreth was aided greatly in his motion study investigations by the use of photographs which he made of his workers in motion, it was not until he adapted the motion-picture camera to his work that he made his greatest con-

[17] F. B. Gilbreth, "Motion Study," p. 88, D. Van Nostrand Co., New York, 1911.

[18] "Taylor's Famous Testimony Before the Special House Committee," *Bul. Taylor Soc.*, Vol. 11, Nos. 3 and 4, p. 120, June-August, 1926.

tribution to the art. In fact, the technique of micromotion study as he and Mrs. Gilbreth developed it was made possible only through the use of motion pictures.

The term micromotion study was originated by the Gilbreths and the technique was first made public [19] at a meeting of the American Society of Mechanical Engineers in 1912. A brief explanation of micromotion study might be given as follows: Micromotion study is the study of the fundamental elements or subdivisions of an operation by means of a motion-picture camera and a timing device which accurately indicates the time intervals on the motion-picture film. This, in turn, makes possible the analysis of the elementary motions recorded on the film and the assignment of time values to each.

The Gilbreths made little use of stop-watch study. In fact, concentrating on finding the very best way for doing work, they wished to determine the shortest possible time in which the work could be performed. They used timing devices of great precision and selected the best operators obtainable as the subjects for their studies.

The Chronocyclegraph. Gilbreth developed still another technique, which he called the chronocyclegraph, for the study of motions. A description of this will be given here.

It is possible to record the path of motion of an operator in three dimensions by attaching a small electric light bulb to the finger, hand, or other part of the body and photographing, with a stereoscopic camera, the path of light as it moves through space. Such a record is called a cyclegraph.[20]

If an interrupter is placed in the electric circuit with the bulb, and if the light is flashed on quickly and off slowly, the path of the bulb will appear as a dotted line with pear-shaped dots indicating the direction of the motion. The spots of light will be spaced according to the speed of the movement, being widely separated when the operator moves fast and close together when the movement is slow. From this graph it is possible to measure accurately time, speed, acceleration, and retardation; and to show direction and the path of motion in three dimensions. Such a record is called a chronocyclegraph. From the chronocyclegraph it is possible to construct accurate wire models of the motion paths. Gilbreth used these to aid in improving methods, to demonstrate correct motions, and to assist in teaching new operators.

[19] F. B. Gilbreth. See his discussion in "The Present State of the Art of Industrial Management," *Trans. A.S.M.E.*, Vol. 34, pp. 1224-26, 1912.

[20] F. B. and L. M. Gilbreth, "Applied Motion Study," p. 73, Sturgis and Walton Co., New York, 1917.

The Narrower Interpretation of Time Study Is Rapidly Passing.
If the development of time study and of motion study is followed
carefully and in some detail, it is not difficult to understand how these
two terms came to be interpreted by some as having widely different
objectives. One group saw time study only as a means of setting
rates, using the stop watch as the timing device.[21] Another group
saw motion study only as an expensive and elaborate technique, requiring a motion-picture camera and laboratory procedure for determining a good method of doing work. At the same time, still others
more readily took the best from the work of both Taylor and Gilbreth
and, with a proper sense of proportion, they used the methods and the
devices that seemed to be most applicable for the solution of the
particular problem at hand.

Today the controversy between the value of using either the one
or the other of the two techniques has largely passed and industry
has found that time study and motion study are inseparable, as their
combined use in many factories and offices now demonstrates. With
the increasing use of both time study and motion study, and with the
growing belief that the two are dependent upon each other, there
has come a desire on the part of many for a single term with which
to designate the whole subject. Some have suggested "operation
study," "job standardization," "time and motion study," "methods
study," "job study," and "motion and time study." Of these terms
the last seems to be the most logical, the most accurate, and the one
that most nearly interprets the present practice in this field. It also
has the desirable feature of lending itself to the broad meaning which
some of the other terms do not have.

In consideration of the developments in this field since the time
of Taylor and in consideration of the present trends, it seems best to
use motion and time study in the sense explained in the preceding
chapter.

---

[21] L. M. Gilbreth, "The Psychology of Management," p. 106, Sturgis & Walton Co., New York, 1914.

CHAPTER 3

EXTENT TO WHICH MOTION AND TIME STUDY
MAY BE PROFITABLY USED

Having outlined the scope of motion and time study and having indicated the several techniques that may be employed, the next step is to determine where and to what extent these several procedures may be used to best advantage.

The problem is parallel to that of selecting a device for measuring length. The carpenter framing a house would need no more accurate scale than his two-foot rule, whereas the machinist grinding a steel shaft would require an accurate micrometer, and the tool maker building a master gauge for the most accurate work in the manufacture of automobile motor parts would need precision gauge blocks as his measuring device. Each of these three devices has its place in the measurement of length, and in a similar manner each of the several techniques has its place in motion and time study work.

Every job investigated will not require all the refinements that motion and time study has to offer. Some classes of work will justify a thorough analysis; others will not warrant such an expenditure of time. The more extensive the study, the greater the amount of time required to make it. Only such expense should be incurred in investigating an operation or a process as will be economically justified. A long-time point of view should be taken in evaluating certain phases of motion and time study work. For example, it is not advisable to curtail a study to the extent that it is impossible to obtain accurate and dependable time standards and satisfactory standard practice records.

Motion and Time Study Techniques. The objects of motion and time study may be achieved in a number of different ways. There are many combinations of the various techniques that may be used and each of these will be fully described in succeeding chapters. It seems convenient to list in tabular form (see Table I) five combinations that are very frequently used in motion and time study applications. They range from the most complete, Type A, on the left, to the simplest, Types D and E, on the right.

TABLE I

Combinations of Motion and Time Study Techniques

Type	A	B	C	D	E
Finding the most economical way of performing the operation—considering a. Methods b. Materials c. Tools and equipment d. Working conditions	Process analysis; Full micromotion study of operation; Application of motion-economy principles	Process analysis; Motion study Detailed analysis by therbligs; Application of motion-economy principles	Process analysis; Motion study Detailed analysis of elements; Application of motion-economy principles	............; Motion study Cursory analysis; Application of motion-economy principles	............; Motion study Cursory analysis; Application of motion-economy principles
Standardizing the: a. Methods b. Materials c. Tools and equipment d. Working conditions	Standardization of the operation	Standardization of the operation	Standardization of the operation	Standardization of the operation	Standardization of the operation
Written standard practice	Written standard practice; Instruction sheet; Motion-picture record of improved method	Written standard practice; Instruction sheet	Written standard practice or; Instruction sheet	Written standard practice or; Instruction sheet	Written standard practice or; Instruction sheet (standardized for each class of work)
Setting the time standard	1. Stop-watch study 2. Micromotion study 3. Standard time data a. For certain therbligs b. For certain elements 4. Complete standard-time data 5. Formulas	1. Stop-watch study 2. Standard-time data 3. a. For certain therbligs b. For certain elements 4. Complete standard-time data 5. Formulas	1. Stop-watch study 2. .... 3. .... 4. .... 5.	1. Stop-watch study 2. .... 3. .... 4. .... 5.	1. .... 2. .... 3. .... 4. Complete standard-time data 5. Formulas
Training the operator	In separate training department or at work place	In separate training department or at work place	.... at work place	.... at work place	.... at work place
Applying the wage incentive	Motion pictures Instruction sheets	Instruction sheets	Instruction sheets	Instruction sheets	Instruction sheets (standardized for each class of work)

This is not a part of motion and time study but usually accompanies it.

There are four principal factors which determine the combination of motion and time study techniques to be used. These are:

1. The extensiveness of the job, that is, the average number of man-hours per day or per year used on the work.
2. The anticipated life of the job.
3. Labor considerations of the operation, such as:
    (a) The basic wage rate
    (b) The ratio of handling time to machine time
    (c) Special qualifications of the employee required, unusual working conditions, labor union requirements, etc.
4. The investment in the machines, tools, and equipment required for the job.

An Example of the Most Refined Use of Motion and Time Study. The Type A study would include an analysis of the process and the construction of a process chart of the entire manufacturing process of which the operation under consideration is a part. It would require a full micromotion study and the application of the principles of motion economy which would include a consideration of the most economical use of materials, tools, and equipment, and the provision for satisfactory working conditions. After the most economical way of doing the work has been found it would be standardized and a written standard practice prepared. It might also involve the making of motion pictures of the old and of the improved method. A time standard would then be set by means of stop-watch study, or from data taken from the micromotion study, or from standard data already available. The Type A study would also provide for the training of the operator, either in a separate training department or at the work place and with the aid of motion pictures and instruction sheets. The time study would more than likely be followed by the application of a wage incentive to the job.

An example will be given to show where a Type A study would be used. The job is a semi-automatic lathe operation. The data for this operation, tabulated under the four headings listed above, would appear as follows:

1. More than 100 girls are employed on this operation. They work an 8-hour day, 40-hour week, and 50-week year which gives 200,000 man-hours per year.
2. The job is a permanent one. This operation has been performed for many years and it is expected that it will be continued indefinitely.
3. Female labor is used.
    (a) The basic hourly wage is $0.45 per hour. A premium plan of

wage payment similar to the 75 per cent Halsey is used. Standards are set by stop-watch study and the base wage is guaranteed.

(b) Each cycle requires 0.25 minute of which approximately 60 per cent is handling time and 40 per cent is machine time.

(c) Because special skill is required to perform this operation, each new operator is given 6 weeks of special training in a separate training department. Working conditions are normal.

4. The semi-automatic lathe, fully equipped, costs approximately $1500.00 when new.

It is apparent that this operation has great potential savings. The fact that 100 girls are employed on this single operation and that more than 50 million units are produced annually would at once indicate a Type A study. In fact, for every hundredth of a minute saved per piece on this operation there would be a saving to the company in direct labor cost of over $3500.00 per year.

An Example of the Simplest Use of Motion and Time Study. On the other extreme are the Type D and the Type E motion and time studies. These are alike except that the Type E is used where an entire class of work has been previously standardized and where only sufficient analysis need be made to determine into what subdivision a given operation falls. The Type D study would be made on operations of short duration, and with little prospect for improvements. This study would involve but a cursory analysis and a very general application of the principles of motion economy, a written standard practice, rates set by a stop-watch study, and an instruction sheet prepared to aid in training the operator. A wage-incentive application would more than likely be used after the motion and time study.

A Type D study would be used on the following job. The operation is drilling and counterboring a small bracket on a sensitive drill press. The job requires the time of one man for 10 days per month. The operation is expected to last for 6 months when the model will be changed. The operator is paid $0.52 per hour. In this case a cursory analysis would include a check of the drill speeds, the arrangement of the tote boxes, location of the jig and air hose, and other similar factors. Only a few hours would be required for the analysis and for the execution of the recommended changes. For every hundredth of a minute saved per piece on this operation there would be a saving to the company in direct labor cost of less than $10.00 per year. A stop-watch study would be made and a wage incentive would probably be applied.

The time required for making the Type D study described above would be short and the cost would be small, whereas months would be required for study of the semi-automatic lathe operation and considerable expense would be involved.

Types A and B studies are used either for individual jobs or for classes of similar work; Types C and D studies are used primarily for individual jobs. In some plants there are many short operations of similar nature which in themselves would warrant only a Type D study, but when considered together as a class would justify the use of a Type A or B study.

The Type E study is used for individual jobs within classes or families, for jobs of a similar nature, and for work already standardized. This type would largely involve the selection of necessary information from standard data on file. Chapter 20 gives an example of such a class of work, i.e., hobbing teeth on straight spur gears. The methods, tools, equipment, and working conditions have been standardized. By means of standard-time data and the use of formulas it is possible to determine time standards synthetically for such work. Instruction sheets are prepared by filling in the necessary machine time (see italics in Fig. 191 on page 360) on standard forms.[1]

---

[1] For additional material on the extent to which motion and time study should be used, see: H. B. Maynard, "Methods Engineering Installation: Mapping out the Program," *Modern Machine Shop,* Vol. 9, pp. 62-70, July, 1936, and pp. 46-52, August, 1936; also H. B. Maynard and G. J. Stegemerten, "Operation Analysis," McGraw-Hill Book Co., New York.

CHAPTER 4

PROCESS AND OPERATION ANALYSIS

The entire process of making a part or of doing a piece of work should be studied before undertaking a thorough investigation of a specific operation. Such an overall study will ordinarily include a fairly minute analysis of each step in the manufacturing process. The data obtained may be arranged in graphical form by means of a process chart.

Process Charts. The process chart is a device for recording, in a compact manner, a process as a means of improving it. The chart usually begins with the raw material entering the factory and follows it through every step, such as transportation to storage, inspection, machining operations, assembly, until it either becomes a finished unit in itself or a part of a subassembly. The process chart might, of course, record the process through only one or a few departments.

A careful study of such a chart, giving a graphic picture of every step in the process through the factory, is almost certain to suggest improvements. It is frequently found that certain operations can be eliminated entirely or that a part of an operation can be eliminated, that one operation can be combined with another, that better routes for the parts can be found, more economical machines used, delays between operations eliminated, and other improvements made, all of which go to produce a better product at a lower cost. The process chart assists in showing the effects that changes in one part of the process will have on other parts or elements. Moreover, the chart may aid in discovering particular operations in the process which should be subjected to more careful analysis.

The process chart may profitably be made by almost any one in an organization. However, a person familiar with the construction and use of such charts and versed in the principles of motion and time study can profit most from them. A questioning attitude should be developed by the analyst and the following six questions might well be asked about every operation in the process.

1. *Why* should the work be done?
2. *What* is to be done?
3. *How* is the work to be done?
4. *Who* is to do the work?
5. *Where* is the work to be done?
6. *When* is the work to be done?

The Gilbreths originated a set of symbols shown in Fig. 2 which they used in the construction of process charts.[1] Some organizations

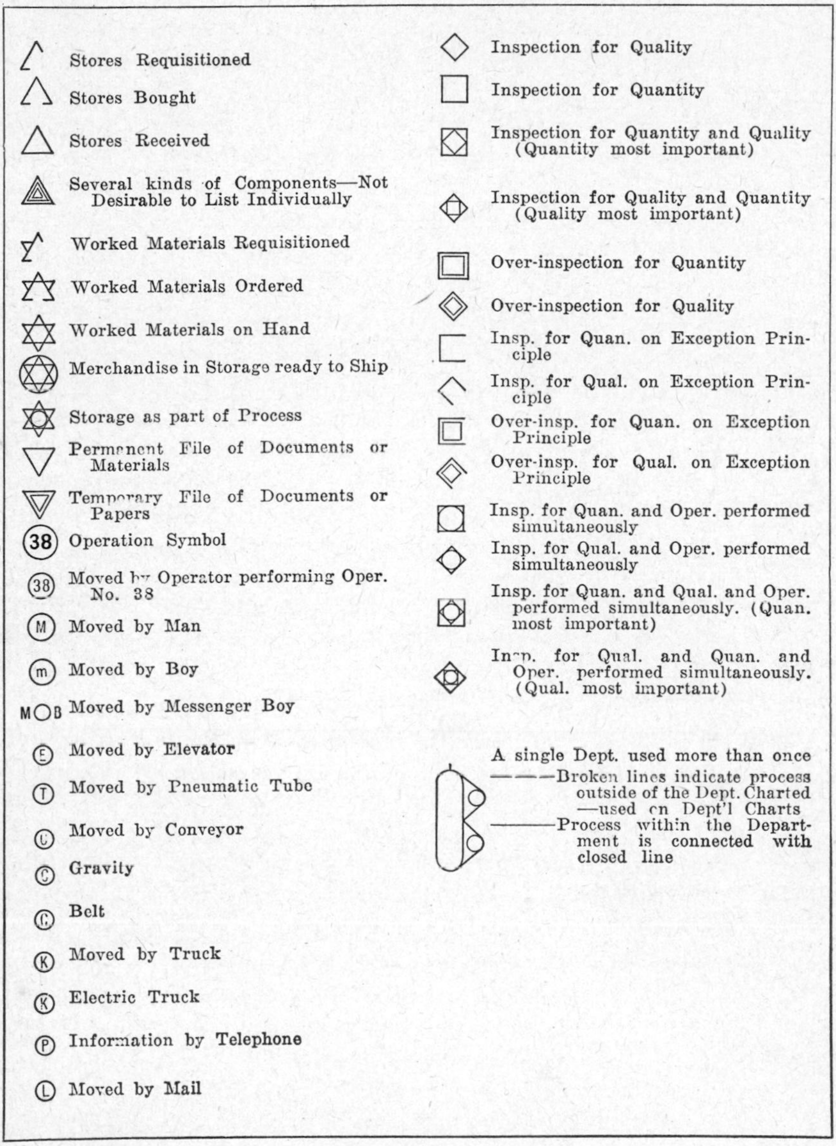

⟋	Stores Requisitioned	◇	Inspection for Quality
△	Stores Bought	□	Inspection for Quantity
△	Stores Received	◈	Inspection for Quantity and Quality (Quantity most important)
△	Several kinds of Components—Not Desirable to List Individually	◈	Inspection for Quality and Quantity (Quality most important)
⤳	Worked Materials Requisitioned	▱	Over-inspection for Quantity
✡	Worked Materials Ordered	◇	Over-inspection for Quality
✡	Worked Materials on Hand	⌐	Insp. for Quan. on Exception Principle
✡	Merchandise in Storage ready to Ship	⟨	Insp. for Qual. on Exception Principle
✡	Storage as part of Process	▱	Over-insp. for Quan. on Exception Principle
▽	Permanent File of Documents or Materials	◈	Over-insp. for Qual. on Exception Principle
▽	Temporary File of Documents or Papers	▭	Insp. for Quan. and Oper. performed simultaneously
(38)	Operation Symbol	◇	Insp. for Qual. and Oper. performed simultaneously
(38)	Moved by Operator performing Oper. No. 38	◙	Insp. for Quan. and Qual. and Oper. performed simultaneously. (Quan. most important)
(M)	Moved by Man	◈	Insp. for Qual. and Quan. and Oper. performed simultaneously. (Qual. most important)
(m)	Moved by Boy		
M○B	Moved by Messenger Boy		
(E)	Moved by Elevator		A single Dept. used more than once
(T)	Moved by Pneumatic Tube		— — —Broken lines indicate process outside of the Dept. Charted —used on Dept'l Charts
(U)	Moved by Conveyor		———Process within the Department is connected with closed line
(C)	Gravity		
(C)	Belt		
(K)	Moved by Truck		
(K)	Electric Truck		
(P)	Information by Telephone		
(L)	Moved by Mail		

Fig. 2—Process chart symbols.

[1] F. B. and L. M. Gilbreth, "Process Charts," *Trans. A.S.M.E.*, Vol. 43, Paper 1818, pp. 1029-50, 1921.

now find that the five symbols shown in Fig. 3 give very satisfactory results. The process charts shown in Figs. 4 and 5 were constructed by using this abbreviated set of symbols. The very simple chart in Fig. 4 shows the steps preceding and following the assembly of three washers on a machine bolt. This unit is a subassembly which goes into the final assembly of a metal cabinet. Because of its simplicity, this bolt and washer assembly will be used as an illustration in other parts of the book.[2]

The process chart in Fig. 4 shows the bolts, lock washers, and plain steel washers received in the stores department as purchased parts. They are inspected and stored there and when needed they are drawn out and moved to the assembly bench. The material for the special rubber washers for the assembly is received in sheets. This material is inspected and stored. When needed it is drawn out, moved to the punch press where it is made into washers, and then the washers are moved to the assembly bench in Department A37. There the two steel washers and the rubber washer are assembled onto the bolt. This unit forms a subassembly, which is moved to the final assembly floor where it goes into the assembly of a steel cabinet. The entire process, from receipt of the materials until the subassembly goes to the final assembly floor, is pictured on this process chart.

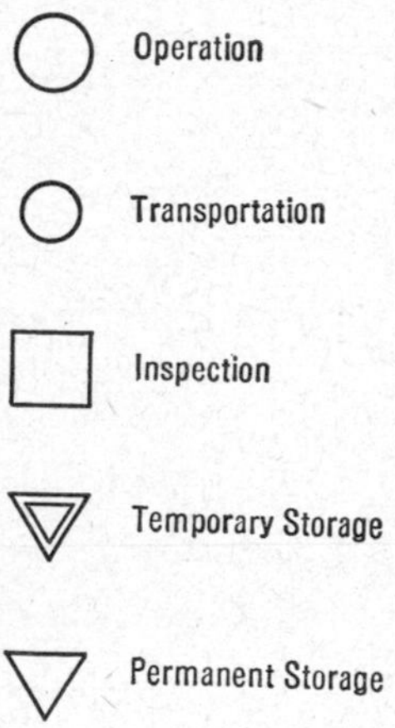

◯ Operation

◯ Transportation

▢ Inspection

▽ Temporary Storage

▽ Permanent Storage

FIG. 3—Process chart symbols most commonly used.

Figure 5 shows the flow chart of a longer and more complicated process, that of making, painting, filling, and closing a rectangular tin can for the export shipment of instruments. Part of this process is described on pages 311 to 314.

The raw material goes into stores and then through the various can-making operations. The two parts of the can are sprayed, the product inserted into the can, the can soldered shut, and the spraying completed.

A study of the process chart shows several long moves that should be eliminated. Also, from general observation of the spraying operations it is apparent that some improvement might be possible. The can cover is sprayed on the outside with the exception of a strip around the edge where it will be soldered to the bottom. In like manner the bottom of the can is sprayed on the outside with the exception of a strip around the edge for soldering it to

[2] See page 147.

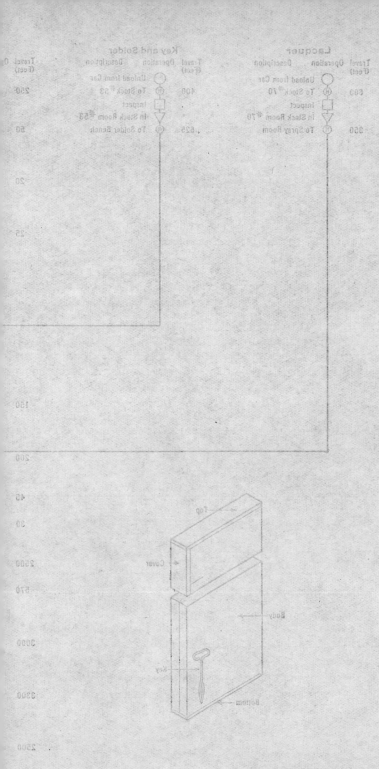

Fig. 5.—Process Chart for Making, Filling

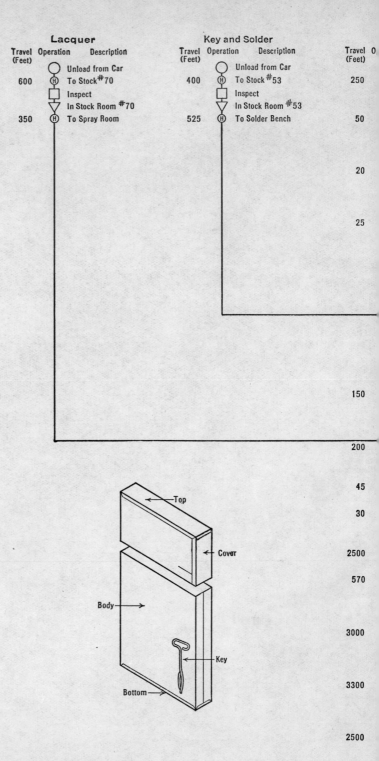

Travel (Feet)	Operation	Description	Travel (Feet)	Operation	Description	Travel (Feet)
		Lacquer			**Key and Solder**	
	○	Unload from Car		○	Unload from Car	
600	Ⓗ	To Stock #70	400	Ⓗ	To Stock #53	250
	☐	Inspect		☐	Inspect	
	▽	In Stock Room #70		▽	In Stock Room #53	
350	Ⓗ	To Spray Room	525	Ⓗ	To Solder Bench	50

20

25

150

200

45

30

Top

Cover — 2500

Body →

570

3000

Key

Bottom

3300

2500

Fig. 5.—Process Chart for Making, Filling,

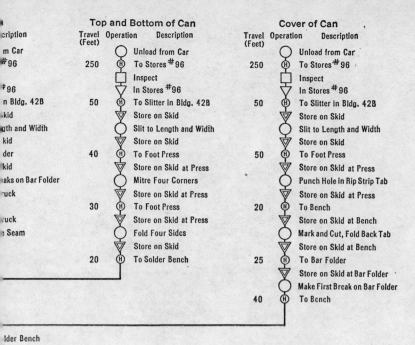

Top and Bottom of Can

Travel (Feet)	Operation	Description
	◯	Unload from Car
250	Ⓗ	To Stores #96
	▢	Inspect
	▽	In Stores #96
50	Ⓗ	To Slitter in Bldg. 42B
	▽	Store on Skid
	◯	Slit to Length and Width
	▽	Store on Skid
40	Ⓗ	To Foot Press
	▽	Store on Skid at Press
	◯	Mitre Four Corners
	▽	Store on Skid at Press
30	Ⓗ	To Foot Press
	▽	Store on Skid at Press
	◯	Fold Four Sides
	▽	Store on Skid
20	Ⓗ	To Solder Bench

Cover of Can

Travel (Feet)	Operation	Description
	◯	Unload from Car
250	Ⓗ	To Stores #96
	▢	Inspect
	▽	In Stores #96
50	Ⓗ	To Slitter in Bldg. 42B
	▽	Store on Skid
	◯	Slit to Length and Width
	▽	Store on Skid
50	Ⓗ	To Foot Press
	▽	Store on Skid at Press
	◯	Punch Hole in Rip Strip Tab
	▽	Store on Skid at Press
20	Ⓗ	To Bench
	▽	Store on Skid at Bench
	◯	Mark and Cut, Fold Back Tab
	▽	Store on Skid at Bench
25	Ⓗ	To Bar Folder
	▽	Store on Skid at Bar Folder
	◯	Make First Break on Bar Folder
40	Ⓗ	To Bench

lder Bench
arts and Solder
uck at Bench
or Cleaning
nch
ash and Dry
uck at Bench
oom
uck in Spray Room
e Cover from Body, Spray
utside of Cover and Body

uer

Assemble Cover and Body
uck at Bench
oom in Bldg. 10 B
Stores
Room
uck in Packing Room
Insert Product, Close Can
kid in Packing Room
n Bldg. 13 A
id at Bench
er to Body
kid at Bench
ooth in Bldg. 31 A
id at Booth
Soldered Seam
Lacquer Dries
Dept. in Bldg. 19 A

Improved Method for Lacquering Cans

Travel (Feet)	Operation	Description
	▽	Store at Solder Bench
	◯	Assemble Parts and Solder
	▽	Store in Truck at Bench
2500	Ⓚ	To Packing Room in Bldg. 10 B
	▽	Store on Truck in Packing Room
	◯▢	Open Can, Inspect Cover and Body, Insert Product, Close Can
	▽	Store on Skid in Packing Room
50	Ⓗ	To Bench
	▽	Store on Skid at Bench
	◯	Solder Can, Dip in Lacquer, Place on Rack to Dry
	▽	Store on Hangers while Lacquer Dries
2500	Ⓚ	To Shipping Dept. in Bldg. 19 A

Rectangular Can for Export Shipping of Instruments.

Top and Bottom of Can

Travel (feet)	Operation	Description
		Unload from Car
250		To Stores #98
		Inspect
		In Stores #98
50		To Slitter in Bldg. #28
		Store on Skid
		Slit to Length and Width
		Store on Skid
40		To Foot Press
		Store on Skid at Press
		Mitre Four Corners
		Store on Skid at Press
30		To Foot Press
		Store on Skid at Press
		Fold Four Sides
		Store on Skid
20		To Solder Bench

Cover of Can

Travel (feet)	Operation	Description
		Unload from Car
250		To Stores #98
		Inspect
		In Stores #98
50		To Slitter in Bldg. #28
		Store on Skid
		Slit to Length and Width
		Store on Skid
50		To Foot Press
		Store on Skid at Press
		Punch Hole in Flip Strip Tab
		Store on Skid at Press
20		To Bench
		Store on Skid at Bench
		Mark and Cut, Fold Back Tab
		Store on Skid at Bench
25		To Bar Folder
		Store on Skid at Bar Folder
		Make First Break on Bar Folder
40		To Bench

Improved Method for Lacquering Cans

Travel (feet)	Operation	Description
		Store at Solder Bench
		Assemble Parts and Solder
		Store in Truck at Bench
2500		To Packing Room in Bldg. 10 B
		Store on Truck in Packing Room
		Open Can, Inspect Cover and Body, Insert Product, Close Can
		Store on Skid in Packing Room
50		To Bench
		Store on Skid at Bench
		Solder Can, Dip in Lacquer, Place on Rack to Dry
		Store on Hangers while Lacquer Dries
2500		To Shipping Dept. in Bldg. 10 A

Rectangular Can for Export, Shipping of Instruments.

the cover. After these spraying operations, the two parts are assembled and moved 2500 feet to a store room, and then 570 feet to the

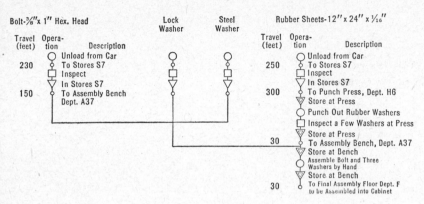

Fig. 4—Process chart of bolt and washer assembly.

packing department to be filled. The filled cans are moved 3000 feet to be soldered shut and then moved to still another building where the unpainted portion of the outside of the filled can is painted.

As a result of a careful study of this entire process the three spraying operations were eliminated entirely and one dipping operation substituted for them. Cleaning the cans before dipping them

TABLE II

SAVINGS RESULTING FROM IMPROVEMENT IN METHOD OF PAINTING RECTANGULAR CANS

Summary						
	Old		Improved		Saved	
Total number of operations..........	8		3		5	
Total distance traveled (ft.).........	12,295		5050		7245	
Total Moves:	No.	Dist.	No.	Dist.	No.	Dist.
By motor truck (K).................	4	11,300	2	5000	2	6300
By hand truck (H).................	5	995	1	50	4	945

PROCESS CHART

PRESENT METHOD				GEAR HUB-3786506-2	

Price $15.00 Operator-$9.80 for Helper
Rough bore flange and O.D. to 3/16" on side

OPERATOR		HELPER		MACHINE	
① Get long calipers 700')	36.0	① Assist operator	36.0		
② Put blocks in position) on mill					
③ Get drg. 700')					
▽ Personal)					
⑤ Lift to mill 12'	8.0	② Help with rigging	8.0		
⑥ Go after tools 700'	6.0	③ Sweep-up	1.0		
▽ Personal	2.0	▽ Wait for operator	7.0		
⑧ Get a driver	1.0	⑤ Look for driver	1.0		
⑨ Tighten driver	1.0	▽ Wait for operator	1½		
⑩ Look for wrench	½				
⑪ Tighten driver	½	⑦ Tighten driver	½		
⑫ Centrally locate hub on mill table by tightening driver	2.0	⑧ Tighten driver	2.0		
⑥① Grind tool 100'	3.0	▽⁵⁷ Wait for operator	3.0		
▽⁶² Wait for cut	12.0	▽⁵⁸ Wait for cut	12.0	⑪ Continue facing flange	12.0
⑥③ Grind tool 100'	3.0	▽⁵⁹ Wait for operator	3.0		
▽⁶⁴ Wait for cut	19.0	▽⁶⁰ Wait for cut	19.0	⑫ Continue facing flange	19.0
⑥⑤ Place a Carboloy tool in No.1 head (wrong use of tool) (did job however)	3.0	⑥① Assist operator	3.0	⑬ Continues both faces	12.0
▽⁶⁶ Wait for cut	18.0	▽⁶² Wait for cut	18.0	⑭ Cut under face of flange	6.0
⑥⑦ Check depth of hub rim from flange (cast ¼ too low)	3.0	▽⁶³ Wait for operator	3.0		
⑥⑧ Remove tool from head No.1 and replace it with another	4.0	⑥④ Assist operator	4.0	⑮ Face rim of O.D. 60'/min. ⅛" feed-¼" cut	11.0
▽⁶⁹ Wait for cut	11.0	▽⁶⁵ Wait for cut	11.0		
▽⁷⁰ Wait for cut	42.0	▽⁶⁶ Wait for cut	42.0	⑯ Face rim of O.D. (2 cuts) 70'/min. 3/32" feed-¼" cut	42.0
⑦① Setup turning tool for rim of flange	7.0	⑥⑦ Assist operator	7.0		
⑦② Check up caliper dim.	1.0	⑥⑧ Help check	1.0		
⑦③ Start cut and check O.D. with calipers	1.0	⑥⑨ Help check	1.0	⑰ Turn O.D. of rim of flange 70'/min. 3/32" feed-¼" cut	20.0
▽⁷⁴ Wait for cut	20.0	▽⁷⁰ Wait for cut	20.0		
⑦⑤ Check height of flange above spokes	4.0	⑦① Assist operator	8.0		
⑦⑥ Change to another Carboloy tool	2.0				
⑦⑦ Set tool	2.0			⑱ Rough face inside hub, speed 80'/min. feed 3/32"-cut 3/16"-¼"	17.0
▽⁷⁸ Wait for cut	17.0	⑦② Go for box 200'	1.0		
⑩③ Return drg. 700'	7.0	⑨⑧ Pick up blocks, etc.	4.0		
		⑨⑨ Carry scrap bolts etc. to scrap pile 80'	1.0		
		⑩⓪ Pick up blocks, etc.	2.0		

SUMMARY

OPERATOR		HELPER		MACHINE	
Total time	788	Total time	788		
Total foot travel	6,870 ft.	Total foot travel	3,700 ft.	Working time	397.5
Wait for cut	387.5	Wait for cut	307.0		
Wait for inspection	42.0	Wait for inspection	42.0		
Wait for crane	11.0	Wait for crane	11.0		
Handling	294.5	Wait for operator	66.0		
Machine repair	53.0	Handling	309.0		
		Machine repair	53.0		

Total time-13.15 hours
Total travel-both-10,570 ft.-2 miles

Waiting for cut $= \dfrac{387.5}{788} = 49.2\%$

Handling time $= \dfrac{294.5}{788} = 37.4\%$

Courtesy of Factory Management and Maintenance.

FIG. 6—Man-and-machine process chart.

in lacquer was also found to be unnecessary—a procedure required in the spraying operations.

The process chart of the improved method is shown in the lower right-hand corner of Fig. 5. A summary shown in Table II gives the savings resulting from the improved method.

The man-and-machine process chart in Fig. 6 shows graphically the work of the operator, the helper, and the machine. It is a record of the starts, stops, machine time, and idle time in relation to the work of the operator and his helper.

An overall investigation should be the first one made because entire operations or series of operations may be eliminated in this way. It would have been a waste of time to have made a minute

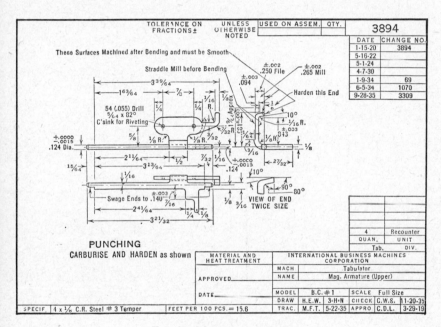

Fig. 7—Magnet armature.

study of the cleaning and of the spraying operations in the above case with the idea of improving them, only to find later that all of them could be eliminated.

No matter how complicated or intricate the manufacturing process may be, a process chart can be constructed in the same manner and serves the same purpose as those in the examples above. It is often

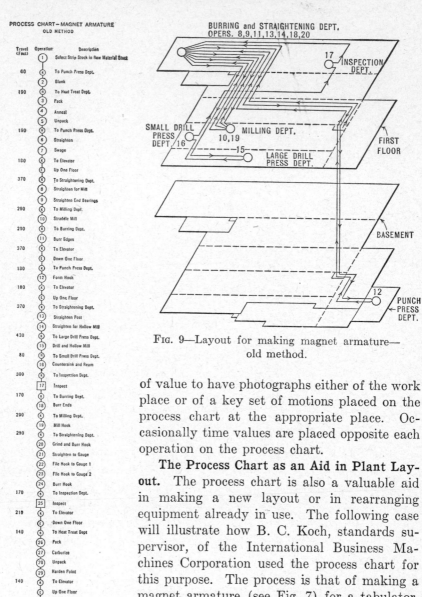

PROCESS CHART—MAGNET ARMATURE
OLD METHOD

Travel (Feet)	Operation	Description
	1	Select Strip Stock in Raw Material Stock
60		To Punch Press Dept.
	2	Blank
190		To Heat Treat Dept.
	3	Pack
	4	Anneal
	5	Unpack
190		To Punch Press Dept.
	6	Straighten
	7	Swage
100		To Elevator
		Up One Floor
370		To Straightening Dept.
	8	Straighten for Mill
	9	Straighten End Bearings
290		To Milling Dept.
	10	Straddle Mill
290		To Burring Dept.
	11	Burr Edges
370		To Elevator
		Down One Floor
180		To Punch Press Dept.
	12	Form Hook
180		To Elevator
		Up One Floor
370		To Straightening Dept.
	13	Straighten Post
	14	Straighten for Hollow Mill
430		To Large Drill Press Dept.
	15	Drill and Hollow Mill
80		To Small Drill Press Dept.
	16	Countersink and Ream
300		To Inspection Dept.
170	17	Inspect
		To Burring Dept.
	18	Burr Ends
290		To Milling Dept.
	19	Mill Hook
290		To Straightening Dept.
	20	Grind and Burr Hook
	21	Straighten to Gauge
	22	File Hook to Gauge 1
	23	File Hook to Gauge 2
	24	Burr Hook
170		To Inspection Dept.
	25	Inspect
210		To Elevator
		Down One Floor
140		To Heat Treat Dept
	26	Pack
	27	Carburize
	28	Unpack
	29	Harden Point
140		To Elevator
		Up One Floor
370		To Straightening Dept.
	30	Scrape off Lead
170		To Inspection Dept.
	31	Inspect
110		To Elevator
		Down One Floor
170		To Stock Room
	32	Store

BURRING and STRAIGHTENING DEPT.
OPERS. 8,9,11,13,14,18,20

17 INSPECTION DEPT.

SMALL DRILL PRESS DEPT. 16

MILLING DEPT.
10,19

—15—

LARGE DRILL PRESS DEPT.

FIRST FLOOR

BASEMENT

12 PUNCH PRESS DEPT.

FIG. 9—Layout for making magnet armature—
old method.

of value to have photographs either of the work place or of a key set of motions placed on the process chart at the appropriate place. Occasionally time values are placed opposite each operation on the process chart.

The Process Chart as an Aid in Plant Layout. The process chart is also a valuable aid in making a new layout or in rearranging equipment already in use. The following case will illustrate how B. C. Koch, standards supervisor, of the International Business Machines Corporation used the process chart for this purpose. The process is that of making a magnet armature (see Fig. 7) for a tabulator.

FIG. 8—Process chart of old method
of making magnet armature.

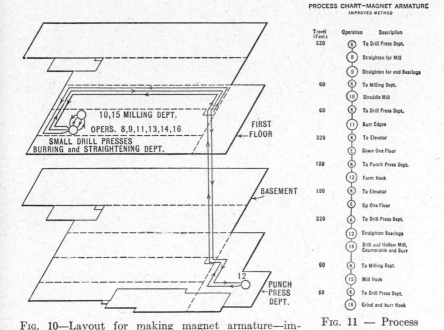

FIRST FLOOR

10,15 MILLING DEPT.
OPERS. 8,9,11,13,14,16
SMALL DRILL PRESSES
BURRING and STRAIGHTENING DEPT.

BASEMENT

12

PUNCH PRESS DEPT.

Fig. 10—Layout for making magnet armature—improved method.

PROCESS CHART—MAGNET ARMATURE
IMPROVED METHOD

Travel (Feet)	Operation	Description
320	K	To Drill Press Dept.
	8	Straighten for Mill
	9	Straighten for end Bearings
60	K	To Milling Dept.
	10	Straddle Mill
60	K	To Drill Press Dept.
	11	Burr Edges
320	K	To Elevator
	E	Down One Floor
180	K	To Punch Press Dept.
	12	Form Hook
180	K	To Elevator
	E	Up One Floor
320	K	To Drill Press Dept.
	13	Straighten Bearings
	14	Drill and Hollow Mill, Countersink and Burr
60	K	To Milling Dept.
	15	Mill Hook
60	K	To Drill Press Dept.
	16	Grind and burr Hook

Fig. 11 — Process chart of improved method of making magnet armature.

TABLE III
Savings Resulting from Improvement in Method of Making Magnet Armature

Summary					
	Old		Improved		Saved
Total number of operations...........	31		28		3
Total distance traveled (ft.)..........	5710		3750		1960

Total Moves:	No.	Dist.	No.	Dist.	No.	Dist.
By electric truck (K)................	22	5250	19	3370	3	1880
By hand truck (H).................	3	460	2	380	1	80
By elevator (E).....................	6	110	6	110	0	0

As Figs. 8 and 9 show, 31 operations were originally required and the part traveled 5710 feet during the course of manufacture. The process charts in Figs. 8 and 11 do not show the temporary storage symbols because it is understood that in all the manufacturing operations in this factory there is a temporary storage in the department immediately preceding and immediately following each operation.

FIG. 12—Location of turret lathes on either side of table permits machining the ends of casings with a minimum of handling.

A study of this process chart and of the flow lines on the floor plans in Fig. 9 led to a rearrangement of equipment. A small bench containing a disc grinder and some special filing fixtures was moved from the "bench-work department" to the drill-press department. This permitted an improvement in several operations. Figures 10 and 11 show those operations (numbers 8 to 16) affected by the change.

The improved layout resulted in the following:

1. All drilling operations were performed on one drill press.
2. Two inspection operations were combined.
3. Two straightening and two burring operations were combined.
4. Four moves were eliminated.
5. The total distance traveled was reduced from 5710 feet to 3750 feet, a reduction of 34 per cent.
6. The total manufacturing time was reduced from 16.0 to 11.5 hours per hundred pieces, a reduction of 28 per cent. (See also Table III.)

Arrangement of Lathes for Machining Ends of Casings.   Figure 12 shows an installation of twelve Gisholt heavy-duty turret lathes laid out to machine taper seals concentric with threads for leak-proof pressure joints on standard seamless line casings. Each pair of turret lathes is placed end to end with a roller table between. The lathes machine the two ends of casings 30 to 40 feet long with a minimum of handling.

Rearrangement of Departments in a Hotel. The process chart has had widest use in the factory as an aid in eliminating operations, improving the layout of equipment, and in reducing the amount of handling of materials. However, because of the opportunity for large savings, offices, banks, restaurants, and hotels are using this approach in studying many of their processes.

Fig. 13 — One container manufacturer placed scales in the floor of elevators to eliminate unnecessary movement of folded cartons ready for shipment.

Because of the success which Hotel Lowry in St. Paul has had in this field, it seems appropriate to cite some of the results of their work. H. E. Stats, under whose direction this work was carried on, states that, whereas the original objective was to study the plant layout for the purpose of improving space utilization and materials handling, they were so successful in doing this that they extended the scope of the work to include a well-rounded, small-scale application of scientific management in:

1. Plant layout and materials handling.
2. Personnel, including training and improvement on individual and group productivity.[3]
3. Service functions (including cost accounting, analysis of printed forms, maintenance policies, etc.).
4. Use of scientific administration in the overall organization setup.[4]

The hotel has approximately 250 employees and has been able to carry on all engineering activities at a cost of less than one-half of one per cent of the total sales of the company.

The following paragraphs summarize some of the changes that have been made up to the present time.

1. All stores were consolidated into one unit directly responsible to a newly created centralized purchasing department. Seven executives [5] who had spent part of their time buying under the old system, where each department did its own purchasing, were released from this responsibility and made available for additional supervisory duties.
2. The receiving department was combined with the central stores department, eliminating the receiving room entirely as a separate function.
3. A complete change in the location of the linen room, resulting in the consolidation of two other departments (the work dispatching department and the service bureau), made it possible for the functions of these departments to be handled easily by the service bureau alone. Control on supplies and personnel was increased by the move.
4. The woodworking, paint, and repair shops, originally located in three separate rooms on different floor levels, were consolidated in a works department room, formerly used as a rubbish catch-all.
5. Re-location of the bottling department resulted in a large reduction of labor and equipment expenditures.
6. Removal of the butcher department from the stores on the basement level to the kitchen on the main floor eliminated the last necessity for direct departmental issues of raw materials. Cut meats are now more quickly available for preparation and the butcher is now able to utilize his spare time on other kitchen work.
7. Perhaps the most revolutionary change in layout and materials handling was the centralization of all dishwashing in one department adjoining the main kitchen. This department is fed by an overhead chain conveyor which also runs to the Coffee Shop kitchen. The con-

[3] H. E. Stats, "Personnel Relations in Hotel Management," *Journal of Society for the Advancement of Management,* Vol. II, No. 4, p. 101, July, 1937.

[4] H. E. Stats, "Evolution of an Organization Plan," *Proceedings of the Minnesota Hotel Association,* 1938.

[5] Manager, Auditor, Catering Manager, Chef, Steward, Housekeeper, and Building Superintendent.

veyor is also used for transporting food orders and raw materials between the kitchens.

CONSOLIDATION OF LINEN ROOM, SERVICE BUREAU AND DISPATCHING DEPARTMENT

	Old Method	New Method
Labor..............................	64 man-hours an average day	28 man-hours an average day
Materials.............................	100*	64
(Includes reduction in working inventory)		
Space.................................	2700 square feet	700 square feet
Equipment............................	100*	106
Miscellaneous.........................	$400.00 a year	$225.00 a year
(Cost of change paid out in approximately 4 months)		

* In quoting changes in materials and equipment, the index "100" is used to indicate the original expense or volume. The index shown under the new method is, of course, comparative to that shown under the old method.

TYPICAL RESULTS—INDIVIDUAL OPERATIONS

A. COMBINING RECEIVING DEPARTMENT WITH CENTRAL STORES

Operation: Receiving potatoes
Material: Potatoes in sacks

	Ft. Traveled		Ft. U. Stairs		Ft. D. Stairs		Operations	
	Old	New	Old	New	Old	New	Old	New
Material..............	100	20	0	0	0	0	9	3
Machine..............	200	25	0	0	0	0	3	3
Operator (1)								
Vendor's driver......	200	25	5	5	5	5	15	3
Operator (2)								
Receiving clerk......	10	12	0	0	0	0	9	6

B. REMOVAL OF BUTCHER DEPARTMENT FROM STORES TO KITCHEN

Operation: Obtaining beefsteak for preparation
Material: One order of beefsteak

	Ft. Traveled		Ft. U. Stairs		Ft. D. Stairs		Operations	
	Old	New	Old	New	Old	New	Old	New
Material..............	166	8	28	0	0	0	4	3
Operator (1)								
Messenger...........	217	0	28	0	28	0	4	0
Operator (2)								
Butcher..............	25	14	0	0	0	0	4	3

Centralization of Dishwashing Department:

    A. Toweling of dishes and glasses is now completely automatic. New equipment dries dishes and glasses automatically.

    B. Use of conveyor for transferring food orders allows complete shutdown of one kitchen when production falls below a certain point. Large savings effected by this are not included in the table below. Orders are transmitted by intercommunicating loud speakers and delivered by conveyor.

    C. Rhythm of moving conveyor paces other kitchen operations.[6]

Fig. 14—Centralized dishwashing department, silver burnisher in foreground; two dishwashing machines and chain conveyor which carries dishes in background.

    D. The conveyor is used for storage of dirty dishes during production peaks, eliminating production bottleneck and breakage because of congestion in dishwashing department.

    E. The conveyor is used for temporary storage of clean dishes during production valleys, eliminating unnecessary handling and stacking.

    F. Dishwashing personnel concentrated in one location simplifies supervision.

    [6] Kitchen department heads have reported an unusual psychological influence on employees in the department as a result of the presence and constant, regular motion of the overhead chain conveyor, apparently assisting the employees in maintaining a steady and smooth work pace, even though not directly connected with the conveyor.

OLD METHOD OF DISHWASHING
(Does not include potwasher or silverman)

Coffee Shop
Chinaware   *Hours*
 One dishwasher (male)............   6:00 A.M.–4:00 P.M.
         (from 6:00 A.M. to 11:00 A.M. worked alone)
 One dishwasher (male)............   11:00 A.M.–8:00 P.M.
         (from 4:00 P.M. to 8:00 P.M. worked alone;
         mopped floors from 3:00 to 4:00 P.M.)
 One dishwasher (male)............   8:00 P.M.–5:00 A.M.

 Glassware (carried to main kitchen for washing)
 One bus boy.......................................   6:00 A.M.–4:00 P.M.
               (also bussed dishes)
 One bus boy, part time..........................   4:00 P.M.–8:00 P.M.
 Total Daily Wages—$11.93

Main Kitchen
Chinaware
 Two dishwashers (male)...........   11:00 A.M.–8:00 P.M.
        (both also did floor mopping odd hours)
 Two dishwashers (male)...........   7:00 P.M.–4:00 A.M.

 Glassware
 One glasswasher (female)..........   9:45 A.M.–6:45 P.M.
 One glasswasher (female)..........   6:45 P.M.–3:45 A.M.
 One bus boy (split shift)..........   1:00 P.M.–5:00 P.M.
          9:00 P.M.–2:00 A.M.
       (also stacked and helped with glass wiping)

 Total Daily Wages—$17.85

Total Monthly Costs
 Coffee shop labor... $357.90
 Main kitchen labor...   535.50
 Dish scouring (4 hours weekly—outside labor).....................   16.03
 Cleaning compound...   45.00
 Towel cost..   5.00
 Towel laundering..   10.50

 Total Costs, Old Method...................................... $969.63

NEW METHOD OF DISHWASHING
(Does not include potwasher or silverman)

Main Kitchen (combined with Coffee Shop)
Chinaware   *Hours*
 One dishwasher (male)................   8:00 A.M.–3:30 P.M.
         (seven-hour shift)
 One dishwasher (male)................   12:00 M.–8:00 P.M.
         (both men also wash glasses)
 One dishwasher (male)................   1:00 P.M.–9:00 P.M.
 One dishwasher (male)................   7:00 P.M.–3:00 A.M.
        (mops floors from 3:30 to 5:00 P.M.)

The above schedule always puts two men at a time on the combined dish and glass operation during rush hours of the daytime.   One man pulls racks off the conveyor, scrapes, and racks the dishes.   The other man pulls clean dishes from the racks at the other end of the machine and intermittently runs the glass machine.

Glassware

One glasswasher (male)............................ 8:00 P.M.–4:00 A.M.

Total Daily Wages—$13.35

No toweling except with silver—glasses not toweled—bussing of dishes and glasses now handled by conveyor.

Total Monthly Costs

Combined kitchen labor cost.....................................	$400.50
Dish scouring, none, except incidental...........................	
Cleaning compound...	32.30
Towel cost..	1.75
Towel laundering..	4.20
Total Costs, New Method.....................................	$438.75
Old Method, Monthly..	$969.63
New Method, Monthly..	438.75
Savings, Monthly...	$530 88
Yearly Savings...	$6370.56

Outline of Procedure for Making a Process Chart:

1. Obtain floor plans of the department, or plant, showing location of machines and equipment used in making the part. If these are not available, draw floor plans and mount at proper locations cardboard templets to represent machines and equipment.
2. Draw in pencil the path of the part through the plant, noting the direction by means of arrowheads. It is better actually to follow the part through the plant, plotting the path as you go along, rather than to try to do this from memory. If the product passes from one floor to another in a multistory building, it may be desirable to mount the floor plans on thin plyboard panels and place them one above the other in a rack.[7]
3. Record the steps in the process on a sheet of paper of sufficient size under the headings of *Travel* (*Distance in Feet That the Material Was Moved*), *Symbol, Description of Operation,* and possibly *Time for*

[7] In planning a new chemical plant one manufacturer mounted wood models of machines and equipment on plate glass and arranged these glass plates one above the other in order to show the location of certain equipment which extended through several floors.

Operation. Ordinarily the abbreviated set of symbols is satisfactory for process chart making.

4. Include at the bottom of the sheet a tabular summary with the number of operations, number of moves of each kind and distance the part was moved, number of inspections, and number of temporary storages and permanent storages. After improvements have been made, a combined summary may be compiled giving the above information for the old process, the new process, and the savings resulting.

Operation Analysis. After the analysis of the process of which the particular operation under consideration is a part, the next step is to analyze the operation itself. Although this analysis centers around the method of doing the work, it also involves a careful consideration of materials, tools, jigs, fixtures, handling equipment, working conditions, and other factors affecting the job.

One approach to the problem of finding a better way of doing the work is to subject the operation to specific and detailed questions. If the several persons interested in the job consider these questions together, a more satisfactory solution is likely to result. Finding the best way is not always easy and considerable imagination, ingenuity, and inventive ability are required. Therefore, the cooperation of such persons as the foreman, tool-designer, and the operator are often of decided value to the analyst.

After recording all that is known about the job, the various phases of the operation should be considered, such as:

I. Materials:
  1. Can cheaper material be substituted?
  2. Is the material uniform and in proper condition when brought to the operator?
  3. Is the material of proper size, weight, and finish for most economical use?

II. Materials Handling:
  1. Can the number of times the material is handled be reduced?
  2. Can the distance moved be shortened?
  3. Is the material received, moved, and stored in suitable containers? Are the containers kept clean?
  4. Are there delays in the delivery of material to the operator?
  5. Can the operator be relieved of handling materials by the use of conveyors?

III. Tools, Jigs, and Fixtures:
  1. Are the tools the best kind for this work?
  2. Are the tools in good condition?

3. If metal-cutting tools, are the cutting angles of the tools correct and are they ground in a centralized tool-grinding department?
4. Can tools or fixtures be changed so that less skill is required to perform the operation?
5. Are both hands occupied by productive work in using the tools or fixtures?

IV. Machine:

A. Setup:
1. Should the operator set up his own machine?
2. Can the number of setups be reduced by proper lot sizes?
3. Are drawings, tools, and gauges obtained without delay?
4. Are there delays in making inspection of first pieces produced?

B. Operation:
1. Can the operation be eliminated?
2. Can the work be done in multiple?
3. Can the machine speed or feed be increased?
4. Can an automatic feed be used?
5. Can the operation be divided into two or more short operations?
6. Can two or more operations be combined into one?
7. Can the sequence of the operation be changed?

V. Operator:
1. Is the operator qualified to perform this operation?
2. Can unnecessary fatigue be eliminated by a change in tools, fixtures, layout, or working conditions?
3. Is the base wage correct for this kind of work?
4. Is supervision satisfactory?
5. Can the operator's performance be improved by further instruction?

VI. Working Conditions:
1. Are the light, heat, and ventilation satisfactory on the job?
2. Are wash rooms, lockers, rest rooms, and dressing facilities adequate?
3. Are there any unnecessary hazards involved in the operation?
4. Is provision made for the operator to work in either a sitting or a standing position?
5. Is the length of the working day and the rest periods set for maximum economy?

The above list of questions, although by no means complete, shows some of the elements that enter into a thorough consideration of the problem of finding the best way of doing work.

Another approach to the problem is to divide the job into the three phases: (1) get ready; (2) do the work (or use); and (3) clean up. This classification may be illustrated by a drill-press operation.

The *get ready* refers to picking up the piece, placing it under the drill, and lowering the drill to the piece. The *do it* or *use* refers to drilling the hole in the piece. The *clean up* refers to raising the drill, removing the drilled piece, and disposing of it. The second phase is the primary object of the work and the first and the third phases are auxiliary to it. Often the get ready and the clean up can be shortened and simplified without impairing the do or use phase of the operation.

Motion Study. Motion study has for its purpose the analysis of the motions used by the worker in performing an operation in order to find the most economical way of doing it. A systematic attempt is made to eliminate all unnecessary motions and to arrange those that are necessary, in the best sequence. Motion study consists of both analysis and synthesis.

The extent to which motion study, as well as the other phases of motion and time study, should be carried will depend largely upon the anticipated savings in cost. As Table I on page 18 shows, motion study may vary in extent from a cursory analysis followed by a general application of motion-economy principles to a detailed study of individual motions of each hand followed by a careful and extensive application of motion-economy principles. The most elaborate analysis, of course, is possible only by means of full micromotion study, which will be explained in the chapters to follow.

Operation Charts. For those who are trained in the micromotion study technique, that is, those who are able to visualize work in terms of elemental motions of the hands, the operation chart is a very simple and effective aid for analyzing an operation. No timing device is needed and on most kinds of work the analyst is able to construct such a chart from observations of the operator at work. The principal purpose of such a chart is to assist in finding a better way of performing the task, although this chart also has definite value in training operators.

The operation charts in Figs. 15 and 16 show the old and the improved method of assembling the bolt and washer described on page 147. The charts give the motions of the two hands but do not include time values for these motions.

Fundamental motions of the right hand and of the left hand with therblig [8] symbols for each may be used, or several of these motions may be grouped together into longer elements. When this is done symbols such as those shown in Figs. 15 and 16 may be used.

[8] See definition and symbols on pages 62 to 66.

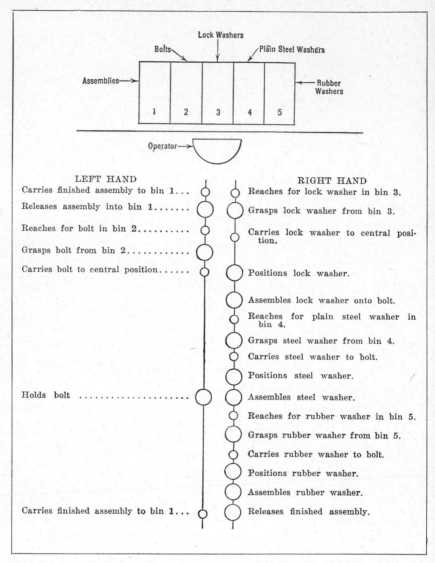

FIG. 15—Operation chart of bolt and washer assembly—old method.

Spray Inside and Outside of Metal Container Covers and Bottoms. This case shows the steps that were taken to improve the method of spraying the two parts of a small metal container. Of the questions listed on pages 37 and 38, the one that seemed to give the greatest promise in this case was IV-B-6—"Can two or more operations be

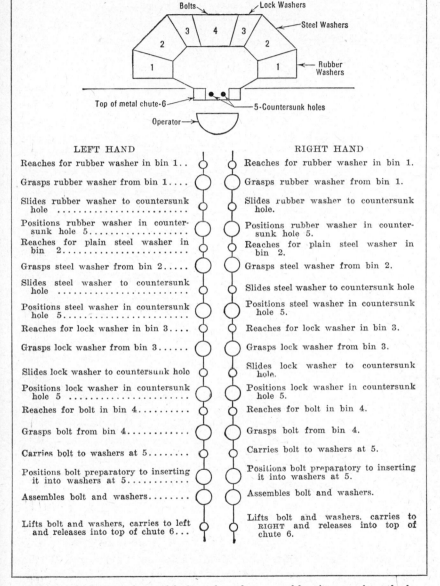

LEFT HAND | RIGHT HAND

Reaches for rubber washer in bin 1.. | Reaches for rubber washer in bin 1.

Grasps rubber washer from bin 1.... | Grasps rubber washer from bin 1.

Slides rubber washer to countersunk hole .... | Slides rubber washer to countersunk hole.

Positions rubber washer in counter-sunk hole 5.................... | Positions rubber washer in counter-sunk hole 5.

Reaches for plain steel washer in bin 2........................ | Reaches for plain steel washer in bin 2.

Grasps steel washer from bin 2..... | Grasps steel washer from bin 2.

Slides steel washer to countersunk hole .... | Slides steel washer to countersunk hole

Positions steel washer in countersunk hole 5....................... | Positions steel washer in countersunk hole 5.

Reaches for lock washer in bin 3.... | Reaches for lock washer in bin 3.

Grasps lock washer from bin 3...... | Grasps lock washer from bin 3.

Slides lock washer to countersunk hole | Slides lock washer to countersunk hole.

Positions lock washer in countersunk hole 5 .... | Positions lock washer in countersunk hole 5.

Reaches for bolt in bin 4.......... | Reaches for bolt in bin 4.

Grasps bolt from bin 4............ | Grasps bolt from bin 4.

Carries bolt to washers at 5........ | Carries bolt to washers at 5.

Positions bolt preparatory to inserting it into washers at 5............ | Positions bolt preparatory to inserting it into washers at 5.

Assembles bolt and washers........ | Assembles bolt and washers.

Lifts bolt and washers, carries to left and releases into top of chute 6... | Lifts bolt and washers. carries to RIGHT and releases into top of chute 6.

FIG. 16—Operation chart of bolt and washer assembly—improved method.

combined into one?"—referring to the possibility of spraying the inside and the outside of the container in a single operation.

When a systematic attempt is made to find a better method it is seldom that the first one tried proves to be the best one. Finding the most economical method for doing a given task is usually a process of development and invention. The following case illustrates this in an excellent manner.

The containers, made in slightly different sizes and shapes, are used for such products as surgical instruments, sewing machine attachments, etc. The container is composed of a cover and a bottom which fit together to form a box. The cover is shown in Figs. 17 and 18. The containers are manufactured in lots of 5000 to 10,000.

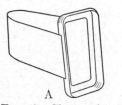 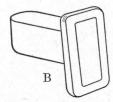

Fig. 17—Clamps for holding container covers and bottoms for spraying by the original method. *A*. For spraying inside; *B*. For spraying outside.

Original Method of Spraying. The operator, standing in front of the spray booth, procured an unsprayed container cover or bottom with the right hand from a tote box at her right and placed it on the metal fixture *A* shown in Fig. 17, which she held in her left hand. She then grasped the spray gun in her right hand and holding the cover or bottom inside the spray booth she sprayed the inside surface and disposed of it on a screen tray, taking care to prevent contact with others on the screen. When the screen tray was filled (35 covers or bottoms) it was placed on an oven rack and an empty screen was positioned at the left of the spray booth.

When an oven rack was full the oven man moved it into the baking oven on the other side of the room where it was baked for one and one-half hours. The rack was then removed, cooled, and the outside of the covers or bottoms were sprayed, using fixture *B* shown in Fig. 17. The sequence of motions used in spraying the outside was similar to that used for spraying the inside. The covers or bottoms were again baked in the oven for one and one-half hours and when removed and cooled were ready for the final inspection.

Improved Methods. The following methods were tried in the order indicated below:

1. Steel Spring Hooks. It was apparent that considerable savings could be made if a way could be devised that would permit the operator to spray both the inside and the outside of the container cover or bottom in a single operation.

Several designs of spring hooks, similar to those used for another type of container, which held the piece from the inside were tried.

Results: It was found that the blast from the air gun would blow the piece from the hook. Hooks made from stiffer spring made hooking too difficult for girl operators. This method was discarded as impractical.

2. Dipping in Japan. Since some products were being satisfactorily dipped in japan and baked in a continuous oven it was suggested that an attempt be made to dip the containers. Wire hangers, like *A* shown in Fig. 18, were made and dipping was tried.

Results: An air pocket formed in the upper corner of the covers and bottoms which prevented the japan from making contact with the metal. Also the japan failed to drain out of the lower corner properly. The device for dipping the containers was discarded.

3. Spray Outside on Turntable. The covers and bottoms were sprayed on the inside in the old manner and placed on a narrow tray *B* shown in Fig. 18. When seven covers or bottoms had been placed on

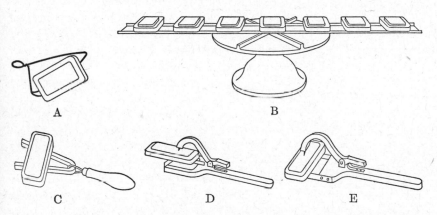

A   B

C   D   E

FIG. 18—Devices for use in japanning container covers and bottoms by "improved" methods. *A.* Steel spring hook for dipping; *B.* Rack and turntable; *C.* Magnetic fixture; *D.* Mechanical fixture; *E.* Improved mechanical fixture—the one finally adopted.

the tray the outsides of all of them were sprayed and the trayful then sent to the oven for baking.

Results: The air from the spray gun blew the containers off the rack. If heavy corrugations or teeth were cut in the edges of the tray, they disfigured the japan finish on the containers. This method was discarded.

4. Magnetic Fixture. A permanent magnet C shown in Fig. 18 was used to hold the cover or bottom while the operator sprayed both the inside and the outside in one operation.

Results: This proved to be a satisfactory method for holding the cover or bottom but it was difficult to get the sprayed pieces off the magnet to the screen tray. The suggestion was not used.

5. Mechanical Fixture. The fixture D shown in Fig. 18 was made so that the cover or bottom rested on three knife edges and was held mechanically in place with a needle point.

Results: This device was satisfactory in that it permitted the inside and outside of the cover or bottom to be sprayed at one operation, and it was easy to release the piece and dispose of it on the screen tray. However, the two knife edges tended to scrape the japan off the edges of the cover or bottom as it slid off the holder in disposing of it onto the screen tray.

6. Improved Mechanical Fixture. The holder E shown in Fig. 18 was built with two parallel knife edges so that they did not scrape off the japan in disposing of the sprayed cover or bottom.

Results: This fixture proved to be entirely satisfactory, and several were made of aluminum and immediately put into use on production work. Each operator is supplied with two fixtures, allowing one to soak in solvent while the other one is being used.

The improved method, using this fixture, proved to be superior to the old method in the following ways:

1. The operator now sprays both the inside and the outside of the cover or bottom at one operation. This effects a saving of approximately 25 per cent in direct labor.

2. The covers and bottoms are baked only once instead of twice. This reduces the use of the baking ovens 50 per cent and also reduces the indirect labor for handling racks and trays 50 per cent.

3. An additional saving results in that the investigation showed that the inside of the container covers and bottoms were being sprayed with a dull-finish japan and the outside with a glossy-finish japan. As there is no need for the dull finish on the inside and since dull-finish japan is more expensive than glossy, use of the dull has been discontinued and the entire container sprayed with glossy japan. This alone has saved in one year more than enough to pay for all the experimental fixtures that were used in the development work.

Design of Machines and Equipment. Manufacturers of machines and equipment are confronted with the problem of designing machines that will do better work at a lower cost. In approaching this problem they should study the process and the individual operations from the point of view of the person who is doing the work and design the machine or equipment to save his time and energy.

The fact that new equipment saves time by eliminating some operations is often used in advertising the equipment. Figure 19 is a reproduction of part of an advertisement used by a commercial laundry machinery manufacturer to show that an extractor of improved design eliminates several hand operations and does, in 8 minutes, work that formerly took 29½ minutes. A more complete description of this work is given here.

Extracting Water from Clothes in a Commercial Laundry— Ordinary Method. After clothes are washed in a commercial laundry, they are removed from the washing machine by hand, placed in a truck, moved to an extractor, and unloaded by hand from the truck into the extractor. The extractor lid is then closed and the extractor is run at high speed 10 to 15 minutes, during which time the water is thrown out of the clothes by centrifugal force.

The extractor is then stopped, the lid opened, and the clothes removed from the extractor by hand and placed in a truck. The truck is then moved to a "shake-out" table and the clothes are removed from the truck by hand and placed on the table.

Extractor with Removable Containers. An extractor (see Fig. 20) is now being manufactured with a removable container or spinner basket made in two parts or halves. Each of the two parts of the container is fitted with casters, and the bottom is hinged on one side and opens downward.

With this new extractor the operation of extracting water from clothes is as follows. The halves of the container are moved to the washing machine, and the clothes are removed from the washing machine by hand and placed in them. The container halves are then shoved together to form a cylinder (see Fig. 20) and, by means of a power hoist mounted on a monorail, the container is lifted up and moved over the extractor, balanced, and lowered in place. The extractor is run for 15 minutes. After the water is removed from the clothes, the extractor is stopped, the lid opened, and the container is lifted out of the extractor with the hoist, moved over the "shake-out" table, the hinged bottom of each half of the container opened downward, and the clothes allowed to drop on to the "shake-out"

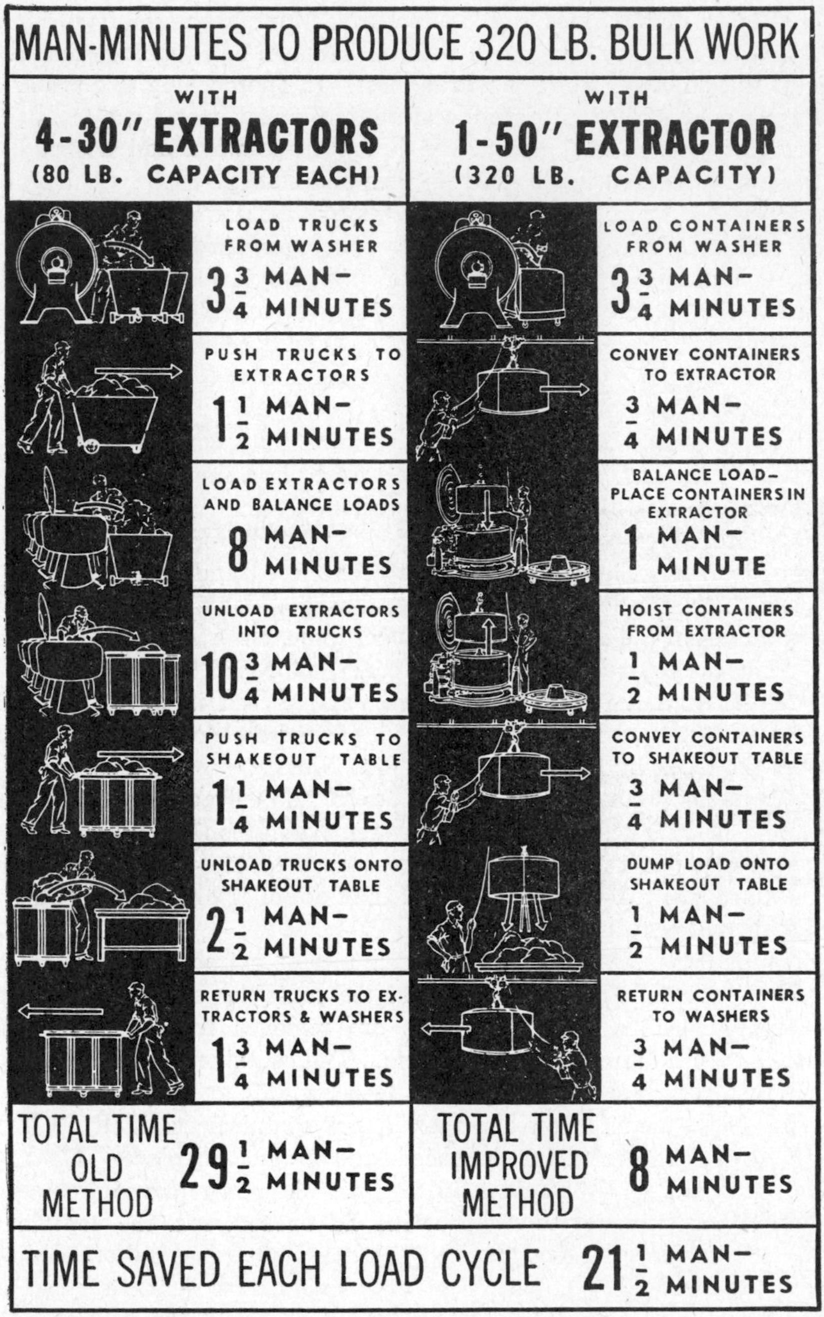

MAN-MINUTES TO PRODUCE 320 LB. BULK WORK

WITH 4-30" EXTRACTORS (80 LB. CAPACITY EACH)	WITH 1-50" EXTRACTOR (320 LB. CAPACITY)
LOAD TRUCKS FROM WASHER — $3\frac{3}{4}$ MAN-MINUTES	LOAD CONTAINERS FROM WASHER — $3\frac{3}{4}$ MAN-MINUTES
PUSH TRUCKS TO EXTRACTORS — $1\frac{1}{2}$ MAN-MINUTES	CONVEY CONTAINERS TO EXTRACTOR — $\frac{3}{4}$ MAN-MINUTES
LOAD EXTRACTORS AND BALANCE LOADS — 8 MAN-MINUTES	BALANCE LOAD—PLACE CONTAINERS IN EXTRACTOR — 1 MAN-MINUTE
UNLOAD EXTRACTORS INTO TRUCKS — $10\frac{3}{4}$ MAN-MINUTES	HOIST CONTAINERS FROM EXTRACTOR — $1\frac{1}{2}$ MAN-MINUTES
PUSH TRUCKS TO SHAKEOUT TABLE — $1\frac{1}{4}$ MAN-MINUTES	CONVEY CONTAINERS TO SHAKEOUT TABLE — $\frac{3}{4}$ MAN-MINUTES
UNLOAD TRUCKS ONTO SHAKEOUT TABLE — $2\frac{1}{2}$ MAN-MINUTES	DUMP LOAD ONTO SHAKEOUT TABLE — $\frac{1}{2}$ MAN-MINUTES
RETURN TRUCKS TO EXTRACTORS & WASHERS — $1\frac{3}{4}$ MAN-MINUTES	RETURN CONTAINERS TO WASHERS — $\frac{3}{4}$ MAN-MINUTES
TOTAL TIME OLD METHOD — $29\frac{1}{2}$ MAN-MINUTES	TOTAL TIME IMPROVED METHOD — 8 MAN-MINUTES

TIME SAVED EACH LOAD CYCLE $21\frac{1}{2}$ MAN-MINUTES

Fig. 19—Chart used by a laundry machinery manufacturer to show how his extractor has been designed to eliminate hand operations and save time.

FIG. 20—Extractor used in commercial laundry to remove water from clothes by centrifugal force. The removable extractor container is made in halves, each of which is fitted with casters and a hinged bottom.

table by gravity. The bottom of each container is then closed, and the extractor is returned to the washing machine for another load of clothes.

Clean-up Work. Janitor or clean-up work represents a sizable part of the office and factory pay roll. For example, the wages paid for clean-up work in the Ford Motor Company run into millions of dollars per year with more than 5000 men employed on this kind of work. In some organizations such work accounts for as much as 10 to 15 per cent of the total wages.

In discussing this subject Lawrence A. Flagler of the Proctor and Gamble Company states, "A survey of our factory clean-up costs revealed the fact that clean-up represented one of the largest single classifications of wage expense. It showed that there were more than 700 people in the Company engaged in this kind of work. . . . It is my estimate that there are at least 150,000 full-time factory clean-up men employed in this country." [9]

Some of the results of a careful study of cleaning tools and equipment and of clean-up methods made by one organization are given here. These show what may be accomplished by setting out to answer such a single question as (see III-1, page 37) "Are the tools the best kind for this work?" Although these findings apply to conditions in this particular concern, many of the results of this investigation are basic and have wide application.

The first step was to find the best equipment. Since the tools that the janitor uses cost but a few dollars per year and since they represent less than two-tenths of one per cent of the total clean-up costs, it is false economy to purchase any but the most efficient tools.

Cleaning with Mop. Mopping of floors is one of the important classes of janitor work. Of the 700 people on clean-up work at Proctor and Gamble's, for example, the equivalent of 215 of these people spend their full time mopping floors.

An analysis of the operations used in mopping floors indicated that the following factors were most important in the selection of a mop:

1. High ratio of water absorption to give maximum transfer of water to and from the floor for each stroke of the mop.
2. Minimum retention of water in the mop after wringing in order to reduce the dead weight and its corresponding higher fatigue allowances.

[9] Lawrence A. Flagler, "Motion Study Applied to Factory Clean-Up." *Abstract of Papers Presented at the Management Conference,* University of Iowa, March 31, 1939, Extension Bul. 458, p. 9, 1939.

3. The shape of the mop to provide maximum surface contact between the mop and the floor.
4. Minimum weight of handle, hardware, or fixtures.
5. The wearing qualities of the mop.

Specifications for a Mop. Factory tests made of more than 40 different styles and kinds of mops resulted in the following specifications for a good mop:

1. Mops should be of wide tape type to be used with detachable handles.
2. The mop should be made of a good grade of 4-ply, soft roving, long staple yarn free from linters and foreign material.
3. The length of the mop strands should be 38 to 42 inches, taped in the middle with good cotton duck at least 5 inches wide. The completed mop should be 6¼ to 6¾ inches in width after sewing on the tape with at least three rows of double stitching. The mop is not to be sewed in the folded shape in order that both sides may be used to equalize wear.
4. The average dry weight of the cotton should be 23½ to 24½ ounces for wet mopping and 31½ to 32½ ounces for dry mopping.
5. The mop handle should be 60 inches long, 1¼ inches in diameter, and have an aluminum knob at the end.[10]
6. The mop attachment device should be of the claw or clamp type, wherein the mop is folded, placed in the open clamp, and the wing nut tightened. The hardware on the mop should be light in weight and made of rust-resisting material.

Figure 21 shows a good mop and a poor one. The "ferrule" mop on the right is unsatisfactory for factory work. The mop is too small, the handle is too short, and the ferrule where the mop is attached to the handle prevents the mop from lying flat on the floor.

The "head" mop on the left is well designed. The handle is long with a knob on the end. Because the head mop lies flat on the floor there is 30 per cent more cotton in contact with the floor than with a ferrule mop of equal weight. In addition the head mop fits the wringer better and 10 per cent more water can be removed, making for faster pick-up of dirty water from the floor, less dead weight for the janitor to handle, and fewer wringing operations.

Recommended Method of Mopping. The recommended method for mopping is the use of the "side to side" stroke rather than the "push or pull" stroke. The janitor positions himself in the middle of the

---

[10] When mopping in open unobstructed areas the mop stroke can be lengthened from 12 feet, 1½ inches, to 12 feet, 10½ inches, an increase of 6.9 per cent, by the use of a knob on the end of the regular handle.

stroke length with the feet spread well apart and at right angles to the direction of the stroke (see Fig. 23). The mop handle is grasped over the end with one hand and approximately 15 inches down the handle with the other hand. The mop is placed flat on the floor and passed from side to side in front of the janitor in the form of an arc. The arc should be slight, as too wide an arc will greatly increase the effort required in that the arms are extended in front of the body at a lower muscular efficiency. The mop should pass in front of the janitor and within about three inches of his feet. At the ends of the stroke the mop is slightly looped to reverse the direction. Centrifugal force in describing the arc spreads the mop strands to increase the area covered in the stroke. Periodically, depending on the floor condition, the mop is flopped over to give an equal distribution of water and to use both sides of the mop effectively. As the boundary is approached, the janitor reverses his position 180 degrees at the end of the stroke, and with proper timing this motion can be accomplished with only a momentary loss of time. The optimum length of stroke for a janitor of average height is 12 feet, which with an effective width of 0.70 foot will result in a coverage of 8.4 square feet per stroke.

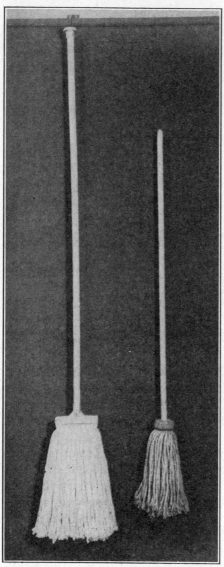

Fig. 21—Two common types of mops. *A.* "Head" mop; *B.* "Ferrule" mop.

In planning the work, the direction of mopping should be arranged so that a full stroke can be used. For example, an 11½- by 16-foot storage bay should be mopped with an 11½-foot stroke perpendicular to the 16-foot dimension. As most factories have a uniform size of storage bay, it is possible for the janitor to standardize his starting position so as to use the optimum length of stroke. In mopping aisles the direction of the stroke should parallel the aisle. For example, a 32 per cent saving in time is possible when a 5-foot by 120-foot aisle is mopped with lengthwise instead of crosswise strokes. Another reason for parallel mopping of aisles is that splashing of the mop against the mop boards or materials in storage is minimized.

Much time is lost in transporting water in small buckets. A specially designed mop-truck has been developed with three large water compartments having a 42-gallon capacity for clean water and a 37-gallon capacity for dirty water. The temperature of the clean water should not get below 130° F. for effective use.

By wearing non-skid sandals similar to those shown in Fig. 22 the janitor is able to keep his feet dry, and there is less danger of slipping, which brings an increase in output of 5 per cent.

Considering all of the improvements of mopping methods and equipment made, the hourly cover-

Fig. 22—Belting sandals.
This simple device keeps the janitor's feet dry, helps prevent slipping, and increases output 5 per cent.

age is now 2000 square feet per man in comparison with slightly less than 1000 square feet per man previous to the installation of the improvements.

Although space does not permit detailed analysis and recommendations for each of the other tools that the janitor uses, brief reference will be made to a few of them.

Cleaning with Push Brush. The most effective tools and methods for sweeping floors will depend upon such factors as kind and amount of dirt, kind of floor, kind and amount of obstructions, and the desired cleanliness of the floor. In general the following conclusions have been reached:

1. Push brushes made of Russian bristles are recommended for dry and light dirt.

2. Push brushes made of fiber are recommended for wet and heavy dirt.
3. Depending on the amount of obstruction, widths of brushes should vary from 18 to 36 inches.
4. Brush handles should be at least 68 inches long.
5. Corn brooms should never be used except for very special cases.

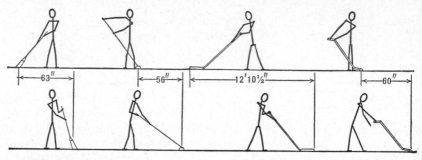

CLEANING WITH SWEEP BROOM

Length of Broom Handle 54 Inches

At start of stroke: Shoulder is normal, feet normal, and in a position for a forward step. Right arm is straight.

At end of stroke: Shoulder is turned 45 degrees, broom is just past vertical.

CLEANING WITH MOP

Length of Mop Handle 60 Inches

At start of stroke: Shoulder is turned 90 degrees to right with right arm at 45 degrees and down 14 inches on the handle. Weight is shifted to right foot with back inclined 4 inches to right. Left hand is grasping end of handle.

At end of stroke: Shoulder is turned 90 degrees to left with right arm at 45 degrees and down 14 inches on the handle. Weight is shifted to left foot with back inclined 4 inches to left. Left hand is grasping end of handle.

CLEANING WITH PUSH BRUSH

Length of Brush Handle 68 Inches

At start of stroke: Shoulder is turned 45 degrees and right arm is horizontal.

At end of stroke: Shoulder is normal, feet positioned for normal step forward on return stroke. Left arm is straight at 45 degrees with vertical. Back is turned 45 degrees at hip.

CLEANING WITH VACUUM TOOL

Height of Tool above Floor 29 Inches
Length of Tool 56 Inches

At start of stroke: Shoulder is turned 90 degrees, right arm is at 45 degrees to back, and feet are together.

At end of stroke: Shoulder is normal, right arm is 45 degrees to front, and a forward step is taken.

Fig. 23—Description of recommended methods for using a broom, brush, mop, and vacuum cleaner.

Cleaning with Vacuum Tool.

One concern found that for its particular conditions a vacuum cleaner with a high-speed motor mounted over a dust-collecting can on casters and with the filter exposed on the discharge side of the pump was most efficient. Studies showed that a cleaner tool 12 inches wide is most effective for areas with an average degree of obstruction. An aluminum handle with a double bend and a swivel at the point where the hose is fastened on to the vacuum cleaner is the best. The most efficient stroke was found to be looping the tool across the floor at the end of the stroke (see Fig. 24) rather than making an abrupt change in direction.

Type A	Type B	Type C
Length of stroke .. 60 in.	Length of stroke .. 60 in.	Length of stroke .. 60 in.
Width of stroke .. 12 in.	Width of stroke .. 12 in.	Width of stroke .. 12 in.
Coverage 200%	Coverage 100%	Coverage 103%
Area per stroke .. 5 sq. ft.	Area per stroke.. 10 sq. ft.	Area per stroke.. 8 sq. ft.
Std. time per stroke	Std. time per stroke	Std. time per stroke
0.03198 min.	0.05880 min.	0.04362 min.
Std. time per 100 sq ft.	Std. time per 100 sq. ft.	Std. time per 100 sq. ft.
0.639 min.	0.588 min.	0.545 min.

Fig. 24—Three types of vacuum-cleaner strokes. From the theoretical calculations shown above and from factory practice Type C was found to be most effective.

Washing Windows. In one plant windows were washed with wet rags, dried with chamois, and polished with a dry cloth. The method was changed to washing the windows with a wet sponge, drying with a squeegee, and cleaning the edges at the sash with a dry rag. The increase in production was from 316 13- by 10-inch panes to 910 panes of the same size in a given length of time.

CHAPTER 5

THE USE OF MICROMOTION STUDY

Two Purposes of Micromotion Study. Micromotion study may be used for two [1] purposes: (1) to assist in finding the most efficient method of doing work; and (2) to assist in training individuals to understand the meaning of motion study and, when the training is carried out with sufficient thoroughness, to enable them to become proficient in applying motion-economy principles.

It is essential that these two purposes of micromotion study be kept clearly in mind. Micromotion study might be of little value in many plants if it were used only as a means of determining methods for doing work. On the other hand, it might be highly profitable when used to train the factory or office organization in the use and value of motion study.

Micromotion Study as an Aid in Improving Methods. Micromotion study provides a technique that is unequaled for making a minute analysis of an operation. As will be explained in detail later, the motion-picture film records the motions made and permits an examination of these motions. The film is projected on the screen and the pictures are enlarged many times to facilitate the analysis of the motions. The timing of each movement of the worker can be made to any degree of accuracy desired. With such a tool available it might be expected that its use would be universal. This, however, is not true, for a number of very good reasons.

First, micromotion study is not necessary in a large majority of the operations in the factory. One who understands the technique and the principles of motion study can, in most cases, visualize the operation completely and, by applying the principles that go to make good motion economy, determine methods that should be used. Motion study may be carried out in most cases without taking a motion picture and making the full analysis that micromotion study requires.

---

[1] Micromotion study is occasionally used for pure research in this field, and for establishing time values for fundamental motions.

Moreover, a micromotion study, although not prohibitive in cost, does require special motion-picture equipment, film, and considerable time for the analysis. Other reasons why the full micromotion study technique is not more extensively used might be named but they are not necessary here. Micromotion study for determining methods of doing work has a place in industry, although not so large a place as some maintain. This is the less valuable of the two purposes of micromotion study.

Micromotion study should be treated as any tool—something to be used when it is profitable to do so. It might, for example, profitably be used in the investigation of such work as is highly repetitive or largely manual in character, or of work produced in large volume or of operations performed by large numbers of workers. These factors alone do not determine whether a micromotion study should be made or not. In fact, a micromotion study is often the last resort, the procedure that is used when the application of the principles of motion economy to the job does not seem to produce the desired results. Sometimes in a complex operation it is difficult to get the motions of the two hands balanced without the aid of the simo chart, which is the graphic picture of the motions on paper.

Micromotion Study as an Aid in Teaching. Industry has but recently realized the fact that micromotion study is of greatest value in aiding one to understand motion study. From its definition motion study would appear to be very simple and easily understood. However, there is a knack to getting at the real meaning of it, and in being able to understand it in its entirety.

It is essential for the individual to become proficient in detecting and following the motions used by the worker in performing his task. He must *see* the motions made by the operator's right hand, by his left hand, even noting what the fingers of each hand do. It is necessary to be able to detect where one motion ends and another begins. As the Gilbreths state, ". . . . one must have studied motions and measured them until his eye can follow paths of motions and judge lengths of motions, and his timing sense, aided by silent rhythmic counting, can estimate times of motion with surprising accuracy. Sight, hearing, touch, and kinesthetic sensations must all be keenly developed." [2]

The term "motion-minded" has been used to describe this ability

[2] F. B. and L. M. Gilbreth, "Applied Motion Study," p. 61, Sturgis & Walton, New York, 1917.

of the person who has trained himself to follow unconsciously the motions of the worker and check them against the principles of motion economy with which he is familar. Micromotion study is of great assistance in training individuals to become motion-minded.

A person may have made stop-watch studies for years and yet not understand the real meaning of motion study. To have set rates with a stop watch is no handicap in learning to apply motion-economy principles; it may be an asset. However, unless one understands the meaning of motion study he will be unable to practice time study in its fullest sense.

R. M. Blakelock once said, ". . . . the greatest value of micromotion training comes through the ability to visualize industrial operations in terms of motions . . . the ability to visualize the motions that are necessary to perform each step of an operation, and to recognize which are and which are not good motion practice, rather than think in such terms as describe steps in the operation itself.

"Most time study observers, as they record steps in the operation, think in terms of elemental operations, such as 'drills one hole,' 'faces off side,' 'rivets end,' or 'assembles part 2 to part 3,' making no analysis of the motions of the operator, and giving little thought to them unless there is a glaring case of bad motions that is quite obvious." [3]

R. M. Blakelock, while in charge of the micromotion study division at the Schenectady plant of the General Electric Company, said that he seldom found it necessary to make a micromotion study to determine proper methods for doing work. He applied the principles of motion study without needing to resort to the use of the motion-picture camera. However, he did make extensive use of this technique for training members of the organization.

The following information shows more specifically the use that this company has made of micromotion study for training. A few years ago representatives from the various plants of the General Electric Company were sent to Schenectady where training in micromotion study technique was given. This included both classroom instruction and practice in the shop. These representatives, after thorough training, returned to their respective plants and proceeded to carry out training programs of their own. The following is an ex-

[3] R. M. Blakelock, "Micromotion Study Applied to the Manufacture of Small Parts," *Factory and Ind. Management*, Vol. 80, No. 4, pp. 730-32, October, 1930.

ample of the extent to which this training has been carried out in one plant.

At the Fort Wayne works, classes in micromotion study have been carried on since January, 1929, when one class of planning and time study engineers was started. During a three-year period the following classes were conducted: [4]

3 Classes of planning and time study engineers (beginners) 27
4 Classes of planning and time study engineers (advanced) 61
16 Classes of general foremen, foremen, assistant foremen, leading operators 268
2 Classes of special tool and machine designers 27
3 Classes of leading operators, expert workers, and personnel workers
(women) 42
1 Class of plant-construction engineers 22
1 Class of expert workers (assemblers) 16

30 Total number of classes. Total number of persons trained 463

During the period in which the training was being carried on, new methods were devised by the application of motion study principles— in all, 96 jobs were studied and the methods revised. The new methods brought about an average reduction in time of 40.5 per cent; and the tools and equipment necessary to put the improved methods into effect cost 7.4 per cent of the total savings.

At the Metropolitan-Vickers Electrical Company in Manchester, England, training in the principles of micromotion study has been given over a period of the past eight years to groups of time study men, foremen, draftsmen, tool designers, production men, and employee representatives. During a period of two years alone ". . . for those investigations actually completed by the Motion Study Section, the average increase in the daily production per operator in 70 investigations has been 173 per cent." [5] In addition to this, many valuable suggestions were made by the other groups who received this training.

To cite another case, a midwestern manufacturing company with approximately 7000 employees conducted the following training program in micromotion study principles during one year.

[4] L. P. Persing, "Motion Study—The Teacher," *Factory and Ind. Management*, Vol. 83, No. 9, pp. 337-340, September, 1932.
[5] A. G. Shaw, "Motion Study Applied to Engineering," *J. Institution of Production Engineers*, Vol. 13, No. 7, p. 383, London, July, 1934.

13 Periods of 1¼ hours each (weekly)
    1 class of general foremen 28
    15 classes of foremen, assistant foremen, and group leaders (men) .. 206
    2 classes of group leaders (women) 30
20 Periods of 1¼ hours each (weekly)
    8 classes of time study men and planning engineers 100
8 Periods of 1¼ hours each (biweekly)
    1 class of executives—works manager, assistant managers, superin-
        tendent of costs, planning, engineering, etc. 24

        Total number receiving training 388

Training New Employees and Apprentices. The several training programs described above included a rather detailed presentation of the technique of micromotion study as well as a study of the principles of motion economy. A less comprehensive program was developed at Metropolitan-Vickers for training all new girls and a special school was established five years ago to give instruction in the basic principles of motion economy. This training program is described on page 366.

Miss A. G. Shaw, who has charge of this work, explains their apprentice training program as follows: "Until recently, boys had motion economy lectures during their apprentice course. Now all trade apprentices coming into the factory go through the Motion Study School, therefore, they too have a practical grounding in motion economy. Their training is, of course, different from that of the girls as they have to use different tools and are not engaged on such routine jobs. They are taught to plan how to tackle a job themselves. For instance, they may be given a job and told to make small fixtures themselves which will enable them to use their left hand for assembling instead of merely using it as a vise. They are also taught to pre-position their tools and material to the best advantage. This encourages them to apply the principles of motion economy on any job they tackle whether it has previously been investigated or not. It stimulates them to plan their work which will be useful in the workmen of the future, particularly in a factory where the production is not all standard. They have lectures directly connected with the jobs they are doing and before they are transferred to the shops they must attain a certain standard in a test based on the principles they had been taught in the school." [6]

[6] A. G. Shaw, "Motion Study and Its Applications," *The Woman Engineer*, Vol. 4, No. 4, p. 59, London, September-October, 1935.

The middle-western manufacturing concern referred to on page 57 has also developed a program of training in micromotion study for their apprentices. At the present time they have 25 boys, all with a high school education or better, spending 60 clock-hours in a micromotion study training school during the period of their apprenticeship.

Motion Study Training in Colleges and Universities. Since motion and time study occupies such an important place in American industry, universities, colleges, and technical schools have, for some years, incorporated work in this field in their curricula. During the past five or ten years there has been so much interest in motion study that many schools now have both staff and physical facilities for presenting this phase of the subject in a very satisfactory manner.[7] Professor David B. Porter at New York University was among the first to give such training and he has been notably successful in it.

Micromotion study as a means of teaching members of an organization to become motion-minded is, then, a separate function. Its purpose is wholly different from that of determining better methods. Many who in the past have found little use for micromotion study for the purpose of determining better methods are profiting enormously by its use in teaching. There is, of course, no reason why micromotion study cannot be used for both purposes as the needs arise.

Motion Study Applied by Every Member of the Organization. If the foremen, supervisors, setup men, maintenance men, tool designers, cost accountants, time study men, production-control men, and gang leaders have been trained in motion study fundamentals, they are able to apply them not only to their own particular work, but pass them along to the workers in the plant. And what is still more valuable, every member of the organization is available for consultation. From this large group of trained men valuable suggestions are constantly being received.

Although there are certain principles or rules of motion economy that may be applied in determining proper methods for doing a piece of work, yet there is no definite way of getting the most satisfactory results. Finding the best method is much like inventing or discovering something unknown. Suggestions, questions, discussions, and criticisms are all helpful. With several interested persons working on the problem, results are likely to come more quickly. Such cooperative

[7] Ralph M. Barnes, "The New Emphasis in Time and Motion Study," *J. Engg. Ed.*, Vol. 26, No. 3, pp. 239-248, November, 1935; also, "Motion Minds in the Making," *Factory Management and Maintenance,* Vol. 94, No. 1, pp. 19-20, January, 1936.

work produces an entirely different atmosphere from the one present where the "expert" works out the method himself and puts it into effect, consulting no one and taking the full credit.

The General Electric Company was among the first organizations in this country to give motion study training to large numbers of its staff, and A. M. Mogensen was one of the first consultants in this field to advocate this practice.

Cooperation. The training of all members of an organization in motion and time study principles and methods tends to bring about greater cooperation between the members of the motion and time study department and the rest of the organization. In those plants where all are not familiar with the work of this department, and particularly where motion-economy principles are not understood, there is often a resentment on the part of some foremen, supervisors, tool designers, and others when new methods are put into effect. This opposition is largely due to a lack of understanding of just what is being done and perhaps also, to the failure of those installing the new methods to consult others associated with the work in order to get their suggestions.

It is generally admitted that scarcely more than one person can be profitably used to set rates on a specified job at a given time. However, there is no reason why every member of the organization might not be constantly on the lookout for better methods of doing work. And when a particular job is under consideration for improvement, all those connected with it in any way are able to contribute, or at least understand fully what is being undertaken. The fine cooperation that usually results when all members of an organization have been trained in the use of motion study is an important and valuable by-product of such a training program.

Motion Pictures Not Micromotion Study. As will be shown later, making a motion picture of an operation is not identical with making a micromotion study of it. The motion picture does, however, have some very interesting and valuable uses apart from micromotion study. This value comes through the ability to picture motions on the screen. One of the most recent uses of the camera has been to make pictures of the old method, and then of the method after it has been improved. Such "before" and "after" pictures provide an excellent means of selling an organization on the value of motion study. Then since motion pictures may be slowed down, speeded up, reversed, or stopped on the screen, they offer possibilities for familiarizing any group with work that might be difficult to describe. The motion picture furnishes a permanent record of work that is impossible to obtain ir any other way.   These several uses of the motion-picture camera have been discussed here to emphasize the fact that a motion picture, although valuable in itself, should not be confused with a micromotion study. The latter requires, in addition to the picture of the operation, a very accurate timing device and a full analysis of the motions used.

CHAPTER 6

DEFINITION OF THERBLIGS

Frank B. Gilbreth, in his early work in motion study, developed certain subdivisions [1] or events which he thought common to all kinds of work. He coined the word "therblig" (Gilbreth spelled backwards) in order to have a short word with which to refer to any of these eighteen [2] elementary subdivisions of a cycle of motions.[3] Although these eighteen therbligs are not all pure or fundamental elements in the sense that they cannot be further subdivided, they are by far the best classification of hand motions that we have. The experienced analyst has no difficulty in using the therbligs in industrial applications.

The therbligs mentioned above together with their mnemonic symbols, letter symbols, and color designations [4] are shown in Fig. 25. The definitions of these therbligs are given below.

Definition of Therbligs

1. Search (Sh.)

Search refers to that part of the cycle during which the eyes or the hands are groping or feeling for the object. *Search* may be performed with either the eyes or the hands.

2. Find (F.)

Find occurs at the end of the therblig *search* and represents more of a mental reaction than a physical movement.

---

[1] Certain European investigators have used other subdivisions of work. See: R. Thun, "Work Studies with the Help of the Cinematograph," *International Rev. of Educational Cinematography,* Vol. 2, No. 7-8, pp. 849-885, July-August, 1930. For the therbligs used by A. B. Segar see: "Cost and Production Handbook," L. P. Alford, Ed., p. 580, Ronald Press Co., New York, 1934. Also see W. G. Holmes, "Applied Time and Motion Study," p. 217, Ronald Press Co., New York, 1938.

[2] Gilbreth used only seventeen therbligs.

[3] F. B. and L. M. Gilbreth, "Classifying the Elements of Work," *Management and Administration,* Vol. 8, No. 2, p. 151, August, 1924.

[4] The color symbols are included in order to indicate color on the printed simo charts in this book. These color symbols should *not* be used in the actual construction of simo charts. Colored pencils should be used instead.

3. Select (St.)

Select refers to the choice of one object from among several. In many cases it is difficult if not impossible to determine where the boundaries lie between these first three therbligs. For this reason it

Name of Symbol	Therblig Symbol		Explanation—suggested by	Color	Color Symbol	Dixon Pencil Number	Eagle Pencil Number
Search	Sh.	⊂⊃	Eye turned as if searching	Black		331	747
Find	F.	⬳	Eye straight as if fixed on object	Gray		399	747½
Select	St.	→	Reaching for object	Gray, light		399	734½
Grasp	G.	∩	Hand open for grasping object	Lake red		369	745
Transport loaded	T.L.	‿	A hand with something in it	Green		375	738
Position	P.	9	Object being placed by hand	Blue		376	741
Assemble	A.	#	Several things put together	Violet, heavy		377	742
Use	U.	U	Word "Use"	Purple		396	742½
Disassemble	D.A.	++	One part of an assembly removed	Violet, light		377	742
Inspect	I.	0	Magnifying lens	Burnt ochre		398	745½
Pre-position	P.P.	8	A nine-pin which is set up in a bowling alley	Sky-blue		394	740½
Release load	R.L.	⌢	Dropping content out of hand	Carmine red		370	744
Transport empty	T.E.	‿	Empty hand	Olive green		391	739½
Rest for over-coming fatigue	R.	⎰	Man seated as if resting	Orange		372	737
Unavoidable delay	U.D.	⌒ₒ	Man bumping his nose, unintentionally	Yellow ochre		373	736
Avoidable delay	A.D.	⌣ₒ	Man lying down on job voluntarily	Lemon yellow		374	735
Plan	Pn.	β	Man with his fingers at his brow thinking	Brown		378	746
Hold	H.	⌂	Magnet holding iron bar	Gold ochre		388	736½

FIG. 25—Standard symbols and colors for therbligs.

is usually the practice to combine them, referring to the group as the one therblig *select*.

Using the broader definition, *select* then refers to the searching, finding, and selecting of an object. *Select* usually occurs between the therblig *transport empty* and the therblig *grasp*. However, there is no therblig *select* when parts are *pre-positioned* for in such cases *transport empty* is followed directly by *grasp*.

4. Grasp (G.)

Grasp refers to taking hold of an object, closing the fingers around it preparatory to manipulating it, picking it up, or holding it. This therblig begins when the hand or fingers first make contact with the object being grasped and ends when the hand or fingers have reached the position necessary for the performance of the next therblig.

5. Transport Loaded (T.L.)

Transport loaded requires that a change in the location of an object be made. It is the moving of an object from one place to another. The object may be carried in the hands or fingers or it may be moved from one place to another by sliding, dragging, or pushing it along.

6. Position (P.)

Position consists of turning or locating an object in such a way that it will be properly oriented to fit into the location for which it is intended. It is possible to position an object during the therblig *transport loaded.* The carpenter, for example, may turn the nail into position for using while he is carrying it to the board into which it will be driven. *Position* usually follows the therblig *transport loaded* and precedes the therblig *use.*

7. Assemble (A.)

Assemble consists of placing one object into or on another object with which it becomes an integral part. The therblig begins as the hand starts to move the part into its place in the assembly. The motion ends when the hand has completed the assembly and just begins to release the part.

8. Use (U.)

Use may refer to an almost infinite number of particular cases. It always consists of manipulating a tool, device, or piece of apparatus for the purpose for which it was intended. *Use* is the most important of all therbligs. It represents the therblig for which the preceding therbligs have been more or less preparatory and for which the ones that follow are supplementary. *Use* begins the instant the hand applies itself in manipulating a device in such a way that the device functions for the purpose it was intended and ends the instant the hand ceases the application and begins the next therblig.

9. Disassemble (D.A.)

Disassemble consists of separating one object from another object of which it is an integral part. The therblig begins when the hand starts to remove one part from the assembly. The motion ends when the hand has separated the part completely from the remainder of the assembly and begins the next therblig.

10. Inspect (I.)

Inspect consists of testing a piece to determine whether or not it complies with standard size, shape, color, or other qualities previously determined. The inspection may employ sight, hearing, touch, odor, or taste. *Inspect* is predominantly a mental reaction and may occur simultaneously with other therbligs.

11. Pre-position (P.P.)

This therblig is the same as *position* with the added qualification that pre-position refers to positioning an object in a predetermined place in such a way that it may be grasped in the position in which it is to be held when it is needed. This eliminates the therblig *position* which would otherwise be necessary after the object was grasped. Usually a holder, bracket, or special container of some kind is used for holding the object in a way that permits it to be grasped easily in the position in which it will be used. *Pre-position* is the abbreviated term used for *pre-position for the next operation*.

12. Release Load (R.L.)

Release load refers to that part of the cycle during which the hand is letting go of the object grasped—letting it slip out of the hand. This therblig begins when the object starts to leave the hand and ends as the object has been completely separated from the hand or fingers.

13. Transport Empty (T.E.)

Transport empty consists of moving the empty hand in reaching for an object. This therblig usually begins the instant the hand begins to reach for an object and ends the instant a part of the hand comes in contact with the object to be grasped.

14. Rest for Overcoming Fatigue (R.)

Rest for overcoming fatigue is a fatigue or delay factor or allowance provided to permit the worker to recover from the fatigue incurred by his work.

15. Unavoidable Delay (U.D.)

Unavoidable delay may result from either of the following causes:

(*A*) A failure or interruption in the process.

(*B*) A delay caused by an arrangement of the operation which prevents one part of the body from working while other members are busy.

16. Avoidable Delay (A.D.)

Avoidable delay refers to any delay of the operator for which he is responsible and over which he has control. It refers to delays which the operator may avoid if he wishes.

(A) This therblig is assigned in most cases where there is an avoidable stopping of all motions of the hand.

(B) A delay is avoidable when it occurs in work that requires no delay.

17. Plan (Pn.)

Plan refers to a mental reaction which precedes the physical movement, that is, deciding how to proceed with the work.

18. Hold (H.)

The therblig *hold* has been used by some as a separate and distinct element. Strictly speaking, it is a form of grasp and was considered as such by Gilbreth. *Hold* denotes the retention of the object after it has been grasped, no movement of the object taking place.

CHAPTER 7

MICROMOTION STUDY EQUIPMENT

The motion-picture camera is the most important piece of equipment used in micromotion study work.[1] The first cameras were of the hand-cranked type, using 35-mm. width film. The camera was mounted on a tripod and fitted to take either single exposures or pictures at varying speeds up to 100 frames per second or faster.

Today the professional camera using 35-mm. film has entirely given way to the amateur motion-picture camera using 16-mm. or 8-mm. film for micromotion study work. This narrow film and the cameras which use it have been developed within the past ten or fifteen years. The greatly improved quality of amateur film now available makes the pictures entirely satisfactory.

Spring-Driven Camera. The typical amateur motion-picture camera is very compact and light in weight. It is operated by a spring-driven motor which runs less than a half minute with one winding. The speed with which the film passes through the camera is regulated by a governor which maintains a constant speed (within 5 per cent) until the spring motor runs down and stops. Some camera motors slow down sharply near the end of their "run" and need more frequent windings if an approach to a uniform speed is to be maintained.

The typical camera can be loaded or unloaded in the daylight, and takes either a 50-foot or a 100-foot roll of film. The normal speed is sixteen exposures per second. A 100-foot roll of film, exposed at normal speed, will last approximately four minutes. The amateur spring-driven camera may be operated satisfactorily for most kinds of out-of-door work without the use of a tripod. For micromotion study work, where pictures are made at close range, a tripod is necessary. A motion-picture camera which gives satisfactory results for general out-of-door subjects may be of no value when used inside the factory.

Since there are so many excellent cameras on the market suitable for micromotion study work, no attempt will be made to describe them here. However, a motion-picture camera should have at least

[1] The cyclegraph and the kymograph are used for research work in this field.

the following features if it is to be used satisfactorily for micromotion study work:

1. Lens—f.1.9 or faster
2. Focus—adjustable—from 4 feet or closer to infinity (a camera with a fixed focus lens is not satisfactory)
3. Film capacity—100 feet
4. Accurate film meter

The following additional features are desirable but not absolutely necessary:

5. Variable-speed spring motor which operates from one-half normal speed (8 frames per second) to six times normal speed (96 frames per second)
6. Interchangeable lenses
7. Electric motor drive attachment

Hand-Cranked Camera. The hand-cranked camera using 16-mm. film is more flexible in many ways than the spring-driven camera. It is, however, more cumbersome and bulky to use and must always be placed on a tripod while in use. With this camera it is possible to vary the speed to suit the operation. Furthermore, it is possible to expose an entire 100-foot roll of film without stopping the camera— a valuable asset when making pictures of a long operation.

Electric Motor-Driven Camera. Some use is being made of motion-picture cameras driven by a constant-speed electric motor.[2] The most common speed for an electric motor-driven camera is 1000 frames per minute. This speed is slightly faster than normal speed, which is 16 frames per second or 960 per minute. Camera speeds other than 1000 frames per minute may be obtained by changing the gear ratio between the motor and the camera.

An enlarged print from a strip of film made at a speed of 1000 frames per minute is shown in Fig. 26. The time interval that elapsed from one frame to the next on this film was exactly 1/1000 of a minute. The motions of the hand shown as taking place during the exposure of the 10 frames reproduced in Fig. 26 required 10/1000 of a minute (0.010).

---

[2] For use of 16-mm. motor-driven motion-picture camera for research work in micromotion study see: Ralph M. Barnes, "An Investigation of Some Hand Motions Used in Factory Work," *Univ. Iowa Studies in Engg.*, Bul. 6, p. 9, 1936. For use of 8-mm. motor-driven motion-picture camera for motion and time study work see: C. E. Bedaux, "8-mm. Measures Labor," *Movie Makers*, Vol. 10, No. 3, p. 120, March, 1935. For European practice see: S. Grillo, "The Contribution of the Cinema to Time Study," *International Rev. Educ. Cinematography*, Vol. 2, No. 7-8, p. 896, July-August, 1930.

Since the camera operates at a constant and known speed, the microchronometer (see Fig. 27) is not needed to indicate time on the film. Furthermore, it does not occupy valuable space in the picture nor shut out motions of the operator being studied. It is easy to assign time values to the motions since no study need be made of the position of the clock's hands. If the film is projected on a screen it is possible to know the exact projection speed by means of a tachometer attached to the projector. In other words, one can project the film on the screen at exactly the same speed at which it was made, or at a faster or slower speed of known value.

Although the hand-cranked cameras and the electric motor-driven cameras have certain advantages, a good amateur motion-picture camera of the regular spring-driven type is perfectly satisfactory for all ordinary micromotion study work.

Camera Speeds. The amateur motion-picture camera operates in such a way that one frame, or the film for one exposure, is suddenly "pulled down" or jerked in front of the lens of the camera during an instant when the camera shutter has closed the lens. After the film is in place, the rotating shutter opens and permits the subject to be photographed. The shutter then closes and the next frame is pulled down for the next exposure, and so on. The shutter is closed one-third to one-half of the time (depending on the design of the shutter) that the camera is in action. The ratio of the size of the open segment in the shutter to the closed segment determines the exposure time for one rotation of the shutter. The shutter makes one complete revolution each time an exposure is made. Therefore, if the camera is operating at the normal speed of 16 exposures per second, and the camera has a shutter with an open segment of 180 degrees, then

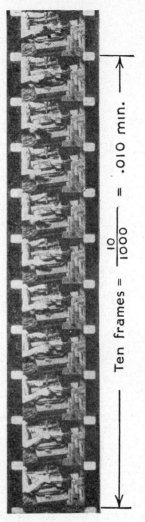

Ten frames = $\dfrac{10}{1000} = .010$ min.

(Film 16-mm. in width, enlarged ½.)

Fig. 26—Motion-picture film made with constant-speed motor-driven camera. This strip of film shows part of a counter-boring operation on a drill press.

the time that the lens will be open during one revolution is 1/16 ×
180/360 or 1/32 of a second.

The motion-picture camera photographs intermittent scenes. In
photographing moving subjects there is an instant (1/32 of a second
in the above case) between successive exposures during which no record
of action that has been taking place is made on the film. It is for
this reason that successive frames on the film show the moving object
at different points along its line of motion (see enlarged print in
Fig. 36). The hand reaching for an object is shown first a foot away
from the object, then 10 inches, then 8 inches, etc. Where the movement of the subject is relatively rapid, the moving object appears to
be blurred. The right hand in Fig. 42 appears blurred in exposures
2, 7, and 8. This blur is due to the fact that during the short instant
when the shutter was open the hand moved a sufficient distance to
cause the blur. These blurs are eliminated by exposing the film at a
more rapid rate. Had the picture been made at 32 instead of 16
exposures per second, the time during which the shutter remained open
would have been but 1/64 of a second, and the hand would have
moved but one-half the distance. This would have reduced or entirely
eliminated the blur.

With the camera operating at normal speed, it frequently happens
that the hand, for example, changes direction entirely, while the
shutter is closed. If an operator should reach for an object, the hand
might be shown moving to the right on one frame of the film. On
the next frame it might be shown moving to the left. During the
instant that the shutter was closed the hand had actually continued
to move to the right, grasped a piece of material, and was on its
return movement when the next exposure was made. For very accurate studies such hidden motions are undesirable. To prevent this
it is necessary to operate the camera at higher speeds.

Although the camera normally operates at a speed of 16 exposures
per second, amateur spring-driven cameras are available which operate at speeds as high as six to eight times normal. The hand-cranked
camera with a "slow motion" attachment will also function properly
at such high speeds.[3]

[3] Baron C. Shiba of the Tokyo Imperial University has made exposures at the
rate of 20,000 per second for aerodynamic investigations. See A. Klemin, "Kin-
ematographic Studies in Aerodynamics," *Mech. Engg.*, Vol. 50, No. 3, p. 217,
March, 1928. Professor Edgerton has taken still photographs with an exposure
of a millionth of a second and has taken motion pictures at 6000 exposures a
second. See H. E. Edgerton, J. K. Germeshausen, and H. E. Grier, "High Speed

For ordinary micromotion study work the normal camera speed is satisfactory. For studying rapid hand motions it may become necessary to use twice normal speed, and in evaluating very short and fast motions such as a "sliding grasp," under laboratory conditions, speeds of 5000 exposures per minute or higher may be required.

Motion Pictures Are Easy to Make. The amateur motion-picture camera is designed so that the average person is able to make satisfactory pictures without practice. However, pictures inside the factory for micromotion study work are more difficult to make than out-of-door pictures. Most people are able to make very satisfactory pictures by following the directions which come with the camera. Even though a person may be able to make successful pictures of the ordinary factory operations, it will be to his advantage to learn as much about photography as he can.[4]

A motion-picture data sheet similar to the one shown on page 83 is of real assistance in improving one's ability to take good pictures under widely varying conditions. This data sheet provides a permanent record of all important factors connected with the taking of the pictures. The information on this sheet may be used as a check if pictures do not turn out satisfactorily, or as a reference if pictures are to be made under new conditions. The mere necessity of recording the various items on the data sheet, such as diaphragm opening, focus, distance of the subject from the camera, number of spotlights used, automatically prevents the beginner from making the picture before he has adjusted his camera and completed his setup. The greatest value of using such a data sheet, as will be explained more fully in the next chapter, is that it together with the film number forms a permanent record for completely identifying any piece of film.

Microchronometer. Since the number of exposures made on the film in any given time interval will depend upon the speed of the camera, and since the speed of a spring-driven or a hand-cranked

Photographic Methods of Measurement," *J. of Applied Physics*, Vol. 8, No. 1, p. 1, January, 1937.

[4] For a very full and authoritative discussion of amateur motion-picture photography see C. E. K. Mees, "Photography," Macmillan Co., New York, 1937; A. L. Gale and R. C. Holslag, "Making Better Movies," Amateur Cinema League, Inc., New York; H. C. McKay, "Amateur Movie Making," Falk Publishing Co., New York; "How to Make Good Movies," Eastman Kodak Co., Rochester, N. Y., 1939; also, R. C. Holslag, "Knowing Your Camera's Eye," *Movie Makers*, Vol. 4, No. 11, p. 703, November, 1929; p. 805, December, 1929; and p. 42, January, 1930.

camera is neither known nor constant, it is necessary to place some very accurate timing device in the picture so that the time interval from the exposure of one frame to the exposure of the next will be indicated on the film.

Gilbreth developed a spring-driven, fast-moving clock, called a microchronometer, capable of indicating time to 1/2000 of a minute. The dial of the clock was divided into 100 equal spaces and the hand made 20 revolutions per minute.

Synchronous motor-driven clocks have recently come into use. Such clocks are very accurate and the hands may be geared to indicate time intervals of any desired length. The clock shown in Fig. 27 is driven by a small synchronous motor. It has 100 equal divisions on the dial, the large hand makes 20 revolutions per minute, and the small hand 2 revolutions per minute.

Fig. 27—Electric motor-driven microchronometer. The large hand makes 20 revolutions per minute and the small hand makes 2.

Each division on the dial indicates 1/2000 of a minute. By changing the gear ratio inside the clock, the large hand will make 50 revolutions per minute and the small hand 5. By using this latter arrangement it is possible to read time intervals of 1/5000 of a minute without interpolation. The clock is operated at this fast speed only when the film is exposed at 2000 frames per minute or faster.

When the electric motor-driven camera is used the microchronometer is not needed unless it is wanted for the purpose of quickly identifying particular motions or places in a cycle. It is often used for this purpose.

Illumination. Daylight should be used in so far as possible for making motion pictures. Frequently some additional illumination is required. Such illumination is easily provided by portable spotlights. The common type consists of a 500-watt incandescent electric light bulb fitted with a suitable reflector and supported by a tripod. Recently, inexpensive "photoflood" lamps have been placed on the market. Although this bulb gives but a few hours of constant burning it is economical because of its low original cost. With either the standard spotlight or the new photoflood lamp, the problem of lighting the subject to be photographed is easily solved. Ordinarily two light sources should be used for best results. The lamps should be placed so that the work place and the particular motions to be studied are properly lighted without deep shadows. If the person making the picture remembers that he is later going to study the motions in detail, he will be more likely to see that the motions are properly lighted.

With the recent development of "supersensitive" motion-picture film the need for artificial lighting has been reduced.

Courtesy of General Electric Co.

FIG. 28—Motion study laboratory at the Fort Wayne works of the General Electric Co.

Laboratory. Some insist that wherever possible the motion pictures should be made in a special laboratory apart from the main production floor. This requires that the regular tools and equipment be moved into the laboratory and the regular operators be brought in from the factory. Studies of the operation can then be made without disturbing regular production in the factory. Although this procedure has many advantages, it is now common practice to take the pictures at the regular work place in the factory. This is less costly, aids in securing the cooperation of the workers, and tends to remove some of the mystery of micromotion study. Where the work is of

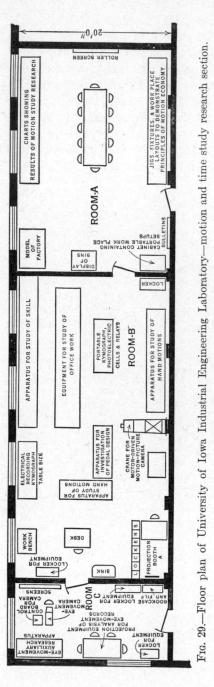

FIG. 29.—Floor plan of University of Iowa Industrial Engineering Laboratory—motion and time study research section.

such a nature that the laboratory setup is possible, and where an extended study is warranted, it is not unusual to carry the investigation into the laboratory. Laboratory setups are, nevertheless, exceptions rather than the rule in industry today.

There are other uses for the laboratory which justify its existence, even if not as a place in which to make the pictures. A laboratory is indispensable for storing the motion-picture equipment, for analyzing the film, for constructing the simo charts, and for showing the film to those concerned with improving the methods. The motion study laboratory may be used as a classroom by members of the organization interested in learning the micromotion study technique. The laboratory is frequently used as a classroom for training factory operators. Figure 28 shows the motion study laboratory at the Fort Wayne works of The General Electric Company. Figure 29 shows the floor plans of the research laboratory at the University of Iowa.

Motion-Picture Film. Professional motion pictures are made on negative film. This film is developed and, from it, positive prints are made for use in theater projectors. With the development of the amateur camera and 16-mm. film, a reversal process was perfected. The amateur 16-mm. reversal film now commonly used is coated with a photographic emulsion which permits the film to be exposed in the camera in the usual way. It is then sent to the manufacturer who processes it in such a way as to produce a positive directly on the original film base. Thus the user receives his original roll of film from the processing station as a positive and ready for projection on the screen. This greatly reduces the cost of the film. Moreover, the processing is done by the film manufacturer at one of his stations which relieves the motion-picture photographer of the difficult and costly task of doing his own developing and printing. Duplicates of the original 16-mm. film may be obtained when desired.

Ordinary panchromatic film is most commonly used for amateur motion-picture work. However, supersensitive panchromatic film is about twice as fast as ordinary panchromatic film in the daylight, and

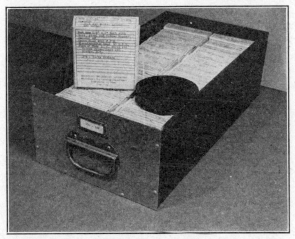

Fig. 30—Motion-picture film is filed in properly labeled cartons in a metal filing case.

three or four times as fast under artificial light. This means that satisfactory pictures can be made with considerably less light when this film is used. The supersensitive film is preferable to panchromatic for micromotion study work, although it is more costly. Colored motion pictures also are finding some use in this field.

All amateur motion-picture film is made from an acetate base, is non-inflammable, and is known as "safety" film.

Indexing and Storing Film. If motion pictures are used extensively, adequate provision should be made for indexing the film and caring for it. One method that has been found successful is to assign a number to each picture and place a small card bearing this number in the picture at the time the film is exposed.

A motion-picture data sheet similar to that shown in Fig. 33 is filled out at the time the picture is made and this sheet is kept as a permanent record. The roll of film or the film loop is then placed in a box and properly labeled as shown in Fig. 30. These boxes are filed by number in drawers in a metal filing cabinet which is properly humidified. The film may be cross indexed as to kind of operation (i.e., drilling, spray painting, inspection, etc.) and also as to department, kind of product, or in any other way that seems desirable.

Motion-Picture Projector. The motion-picture projector is indispensable for analyzing film as it must be studied frame by frame in minute detail. Frequently the motions of several members of the body, such as the fingers, arms, feet, must be studied. This requires that the same film be analyzed a number of times, once for each member of the body studied.

The most suitable projector for this purpose is a small one of very light weight so that it can be moved around easily on the desk or table. The projector should have a low-powered bulb so that the heat developed by it will not buckle or warp

FIG. 31—Motion-picture projector for film analysis.

the film when it remains stationary in front of the lens for a long period of time. The 100-watt bulb used in the projector shown in Fig. 31 was given a heavy coat of soap in order to reduce its power. The projector is more satisfactory if it is fitted with a lens of short focal length (one inch) so that a relatively large picture can be projected on a screen placed near the projector. The projector should have a hand crank attached to the sprocket drive for ordinary projection and a hand crank geared to the projector so that one turn of this crank advances the film one frame in front of the lens for film analysis. (Such as crank A in Fig. 31.) By giving this crank a quick turn the frame of film is pulled down in front of the projection lens so quickly that the movement of the subject may be noted on the screen. This aids in finding the points where motions begin, end, or where change direction occurs. This projector is also equipped with a mechanical counter which counts the frames passing by the lens. This counter is especially useful when analyzing film made with a constant-speed, motor-driven camera.

A projector with a high-power bulb is needed when pictures are to be shown to a large group of people. If this projector is fitted with a tachometer and a variable speed motor, it can be used to show

Fig. 32—Projection booth for film analysis.

pictures made with a constant-speed camera to advantage. The pictures may be shown at the exact speed at which the operator was working when the pictures were made or at faster or slower speeds of known value.[5]

List of Equipment for Micromotion Study Work. To summarize, the following equipment is recommended where a fairly extensive program of micromotion study work is to be carried on.

    1. One motion-picture camera, preferably with $f.1.9$ lens, adjustable focus from 4 feet to infinity, and film capacity of 100 feet.

    2. One metal tripod with tilting and panoraming head.

[5] See page **278** for a discussion of the use of motion pictures for rating skill and effort of operators.

3. One exposure meter.
4. Three or four photoflood lamps with reflectors.
5. Two tripods for photoflood lamp reflectors.
6. One microchronometer.
7. One motion-picture projector with low-power bulb for film analysis. (An inexpensive projector is satisfactory.)
8. One motion-picture projector with high-power bulb for showing pictures to large audiences.
9. One portable screen.
10. Suitable humidor cans or cabinets for storage of film.
11. One titling outfit.
12. One rewind and film splicer.
13. One steel cabinet for storage of equipment.

CHAPTER 8

MAKING THE MOTION PICTURES

It will be assumed that a particular operation to be studied has been selected from the process chart, and that an operation chart of the hand motions required for the performance of this operation has been constructed. It will be further assumed that the analyst has applied the principles of motion economy to the operation without finding an improved method that is entirely satisfactory. This being done, and having made certain that the operation is such as to justify a complete micromotion study of it, the analyst proceeds to make the study.

Operator to Be Studied. The first step is to select one or more operators as subjects for making the motion picture. It is of greatest value to make the pictures of those operators who are the most highly skilled and who perform the work in the most satisfactory manner. Every operator who gives promise of contributing something to the establishment of the improved method should be studied. It is often desirable from a psychological standpoint to make motion pictures of every one performing the operation. It is unlikely that information of much value will be obtained from the poorer workers, consequently only a few feet of film need be made of these. It has occasionally been found that the "lazy worker" may be using better methods than some of the more energetic operators. This, of course, comes from his attempt to get his work done with the least expenditure of energy.

It is very important and necessary that an explanation be made to the workers and the supervisor of just what is going to be done. Their cooperation should be sought from the very beginning. This is seldom difficult to obtain. In most cases the workers will give their very best performance while the motion pictures are being made, since they know that a permanent record is being made of their work by the motion-picture camera, and that their fellow workers as well as the executives may review their work on the screen.

Since it is not the method used by the average worker but the very best method that is required by motion study, it is essential that the very best operators, those most highly skilled and most proficient in performing their work, be studied in determining the proper method for doing the work.

It should be emphasized that motion study makes no effort to force the worker to "move faster" but studies his motions to find the shortest and best ones to use. Motion study aids in finding the easiest and least fatiguing way of doing the work. If the best operators obtainable are used as subjects for the study, the analyst is likely to progress more rapidly on the solution of his problem than if he uses the poorer and inexperienced workers. The motions that the operators use are the things being studied and not the speed or the "apparent effort" that the operators exhibit.

As stated at the beginning of Chapter 1 of this book, motion and time study has several objectives. It is the purpose of rate setting, for example, to determine a time value in minutes or hours which permits the average well-trained operator to work day after day and week after week without harm or undue fatigue to himself, always being able to perform the task in this standard or specified time. However, in making a micromotion study it is expected that the very superior and highly skilled workers who act as subjects for these studies will perform at a faster speed than the "standard rate" calls for. No one can object to this, for in motion study the discovery of the very best possible *way* of doing the work is the first and foremost object. Those operators who will aid most in determining this method are the ones who should be studied.

Placing the Camera. Assuming that the operator or operators to be studied have been selected and understand that a micromotion study is to be made, the motion study analyst is ready to set up his equipment and make the picture.

Although it is not necessary to have pictures of a quality equal to that of professional movies it is essential that the pictures should be sufficiently clear when projected to give details in the shadows. They should be sharply focused and they should be taken from such an angle as to give a satisfactory picture of all motions of the operator.

The camera should be placed as close to the subject as possible without omitting anything necessary from the picture. Both the work place and the actions of the operator should be considered in positioning the camera. The motions of the operator may occur in two directions—those made perpendicular to the line of sight and those made parallel to the line of sight. The camera should be placed at such an angle, relative to the operator and the work place, that a majority of the motions will be perpendicular to the line of sight.

Not only does such an arrangement tend to permit a sharp focus throughout the cycle but it also makes the analysis of the film easier. It is less difficult to judge the nature and extent of movements made at right angles to the line of sight than it is to judge movements made toward or away from the line of sight.

The view finder on most motion-picture cameras is sufficiently accurate even at close range to show what will be included in the picture.

The camera should preferably be placed to include the entire range of the worker's motions for the cycle. Seldom is it desirable to follow the movements of the operator by moving the camera as the cycle progresses. It is difficult to anticipate the movements of the operator and almost impossible to keep all of his motions in the picture at all times.

In some cases motion pictures may be made profitably from more than one position, although this is by no means required on every operation. It is, however, desirable to make a few pictures of the operator and the work place from a distance in order to have a complete record of the job, and incidentally a good picture of the operator.

It is sometimes advantageous to place a cross-sectioned screen, made with white lines drawn on a black background forming four-inch squares, behind the operator. In certain cases the work bench or the floor may be marked off in a similar manner. This is done to assist in determining the location and the extent of motions when the film is being analyzed. Everything should be done that will assist in making the analysis of the film easy. Such small details as the color of the operator's clothes (see Fig. 36) have an important effect upon the ease with which the motions may be analyzed.

On some occasions Gilbreth used what he called a "penetrating screen" because it gave further assistance in studying and measuring motions.[1] The penetrating screen resulted from a double exposure of the film. The first exposure was made of a screen of black material marked off into small squares with white lines. This screen was located on the work place at a position where the motions of the operator's hands normally occurred. Having been photographed, the screen was removed, the film was rewound in the darkroom on the original reel, and then the motion picture of the operator was made in the usual way. After the film was processed and projected,

---

[1] F. B. and L. M. Gilbreth, "Applied Motion Study," p. 86, Sturgis & Walton Co., New York, 1917.

the operator appeared to be working with this transparent cross-sectioned screen across the work place.

The camera should be mounted on a tripod and the tripod should be placed securely on the floor or on top of a solid table or bench so that the camera will be free from vibration while it is in operation.

Lighting. Daylight is preferable to artificial light for making pictures, but indoors it is usually necessary to use some artificial light to supplement daylight. Photoflood lamps with suitable reflectors are usually used to supply this additional illumination. These lamps should be located to light properly the darkest places in the picture. It is better to have too much illumination on the subject and stop the diaphragm opening of the camera down than it is to have too little illumination and get a dark picture.

In placing the lighting units it should be remembered that the intensity of illumination from the lamp falling on an object varies inversely as the square of the distance between the source and the object. If the lamp that is ten feet from the object is moved up to a distance of five feet, the intensity of illumination on the object is increased four times.

The surest way to know whether the object is sufficiently illuminated is by means of an exposure meter. The exposure meter should be directed towards the darkest part of the picture in which detail is required and the exposure should be made for that setting.

Making the Motion Picture. If a microchronometer is used, it should be placed so that its entire face will appear in the picture and yet not hide any of the motions of the operator or any part of the work place that should be included in the picture. Neither should motions of the operator interfere with the clock's being in full view at all times. The microchronometer should be placed in focus if it is to be easily read when photographed.

The camera is loaded with film, the film-footage meter set to zero, and the diaphragm opening adjusted for the lighting conditions present and for the speed at which the camera is to operate, if different from normal. The distance from the center of action of the operator to the lens of the camera should be carefully measured with a tape measure (estimating distance is not satisfactory) and the camera focused accurately. This is particularly important when the camera is placed near the work to be photographed.

Often a card bearing such information as operation name, part number, date of study, department number, and film number is placed in front of the camera and photographed on the first few frames of

MOTION-PICTURE DATA SHEET

Place	L. C. Smith & Corona Typewriters, Inc., Groton, N. Y.	Film No.	C1
OPERATION	Form Links	Op. No.	15
PART NAME	Link for Typewriter	Part No.	357

Machine Name	Special Bench Fixture	Machine Number	Fixture No. 1364	Dept.	No. 9

Operator Name and No.	M. S. Fost A1	Date	7-15-31

Experience on Job	An average operator, often on other work	Material M. S. wire cut to length

Begin 11:00 A.M.	Finish 11:50 A.M.	Elapsed	Units Finished	Rating

Camera Make EK Co.	Serial No. 03221	Lens f. 1.9	Diaphragm Opening f. 4. 0

Distance of Camera from Subject 4' 2''	Focus Setting 4'

Kind of Film E.K. Pan	No. of Spots Two	Wattage A–500 B–500

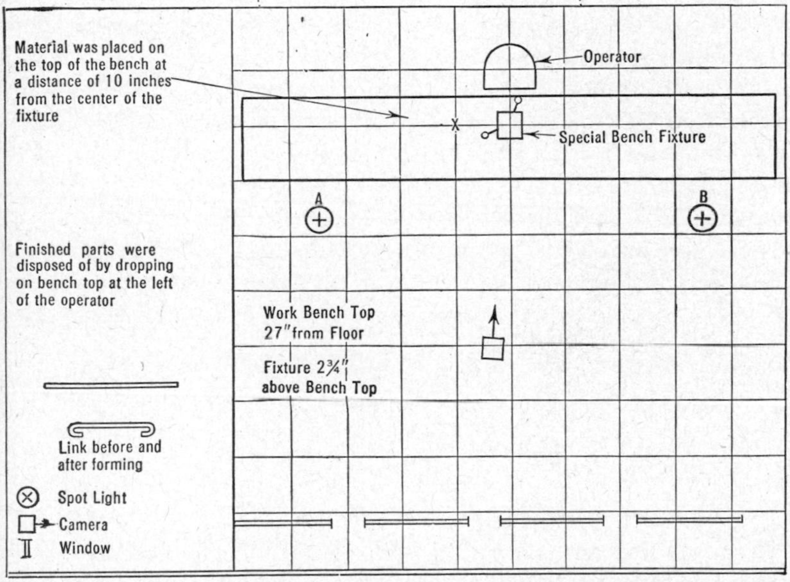

Material was placed on the top of the bench at a distance of 10 inches from the center of the fixture

Finished parts were disposed of by dropping on bench top at the left of the operator

Link before and after forming

⊗ Spot Light
□→ Camera
Ⅱ Window

Operator

Special Bench Fixture

Work Bench Top 27" from Floor

Fixture 2¾" above Bench Top

Tools, Jigs, Gauges: Special fixture operated with both the right and the left hands.   Made by S. S. J.

FIG. 33—Motion-picture data sheet.

film. This information identifies the film. A still better method than this is to use but a single number or symbol, which is placed in the picture during the entire "run." A different symbol is used for each setup or run. This symbol is referred to as the "film number." A special motion-picture data sheet bearing the film number such as the one shown in Fig. 33 is used to list all data pertaining to the particular study. This sheet, then, forms a permanent record of the information about the work being filmed, as well as of data pertaining to the mechanics of making the picture. Since the same symbol appears on each frame of the film in a given run, it is always possible to refer to the data sheet in order to identify any piece of film.

The analyst should estimate or measure with a watch the time required for a cycle if he has not already obtained this information from previous time standards or from the production department. There should be plenty of material ahead of the operator and everything should be in readiness so that there will be no unnecessary interruptions while the pictures are being made. The operator should be allowed to work some time after the lights are turned on before the camera is set in motion. Some operators require time to become accustomed to the new surroundings and to work off nervousness. Most workers present no serious problem on this last score.

The film is then exposed, making pictures of as many cycles of the operation as desired. It is impossible to give rules as to the number of cycles of an operation to be photographed. This depends upon the circumstances surrounding each case, but a sufficient number of cycles should be taken to give a representative record of the job. It is better to have made too many pictures of an operation than too few.

Outline of Procedure for Making Motion Pictures:

1. Secure the cooperation of the operator before attempting to make the picture.

2. Determine whether electricity is available for the photoflood lamps, microchronometer, and camera if an electric motor-driven camera is to be used.

3. Locate the camera to give the best picture of the cycle of the operation. Use the view finder to ascertain whether the entire cycle is covered.

4. Locate the photoflood lamps to give adequate intensity of illumination without deep shadows. See that the darkest places are properly lighted.

5. Place the microchronometer so that it will be in the picture, and in focus. See that it does not obscure any part of the operation.

6. Place the card bearing the film number or other identification in the picture, preferably near the microchronometer.

7. Have sufficient film in the camera for the number of cycles to be photographed.

8. Determine the proper diaphragm opening by means of an exposure meter and adjust the diaphragm setting on the camera.

9. Measure the distance of the subject from the camera lens and adjust the focus setting on the camera to correspond.

10. Fill in the motion-picture data sheet.

11. Turn on the lights, start the microchronometer, and make the picture.

CHAPTER 9

FILM ANALYSIS

After the motion picture has been made and the film processed it is placed in the projector and shown on the screen where it may be examined. It is customary for the analyst to run the film through the projector several times in order completely to familiarize himself with the operation. A particular cycle is then selected to be analyzed in detail.

The extent to which the analysis of the movements of the hands, arms, legs, head, and trunk will be made depends largely upon the nature of the work. Most operations selected for micromotion study analysis involve either bench work or short-cycle machine work requiring motions of the hands only. It is usually satisfactory to consider the hand as a unit in making the analysis. That is, it is not necessary to analyze the motions of each finger independently. Occasionally, however, an operation will be studied in which all the body movements take place. When such detailed analysis is required it is entirely possible to adapt the technique to this use although much more time is required for the analysis when all the members of the body must be considered separately.

In the bolt and washer assembly, which is to be an example, the simplest form of analysis will be used, that is, analysis of hand motions. Thus, when the thumb and index finger of the right hand grasp a washer it will be assumed that the right hand grasps the washer, etc.

Forms for Recording Motion-Analysis Data. As the film is analyzed the data are transferred to a data sheet, commonly called an analysis sheet. Various forms have been devised for this, and the one used will depend upon the type of the work studied and the extent to which the analysis is to be carried. The forms in Figs. 34 and 37 are very satisfactory for right-hand and left-hand analysis. The extra column on the form in Fig. 34 provides space for the analysis of a third member of the body, such as the foot in punch-press work, or the knee in knee-controlled sewing machine operation. The analy-

86

sis sheet in Fig. 35 is used by Macy's Department Store when a complete analysis is made.

Film Analysis of the Bolt and Washer Assembly. The enlarged print of one cycle of the film showing the operation, "Assemble Three Washers on Bolt," is reproduced in Fig. 36. The pictures were taken at normal speed of 16 exposures per second and the microchronometer speed was 20 revolutions per minute. The operation is described in detail on page 147. The enlarged print in Fig. 36 will be analyzed in the same manner, as if the analyst had the actual film before him. In that case, however, the task would be easier since he would have the film in a projector where he could greatly enlarge it on the screen.

Analysis of the Left-Hand Motions. The motions of the left hand of the operator are usually analyzed first. The film is then run back to the beginning of the cycle and is analyzed for the motions of the right hand.

To begin the analysis, the film is run through the projector until the beginning of a cycle is found. This is usually the point where the hand begins its first *transport empty* therblig. Sometimes it is best to begin the analysis at a point where both the right and the left hands begin or end their therbligs together. If the enlarged print of film in Fig. 36 is examined it will be noted that the microchronometer is located at the left of the operator, the card bearing the film number (B 21) appears above the clock,

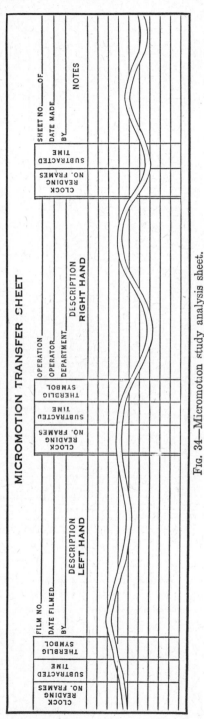

Fig. 34—Micromotion study analysis sheet.

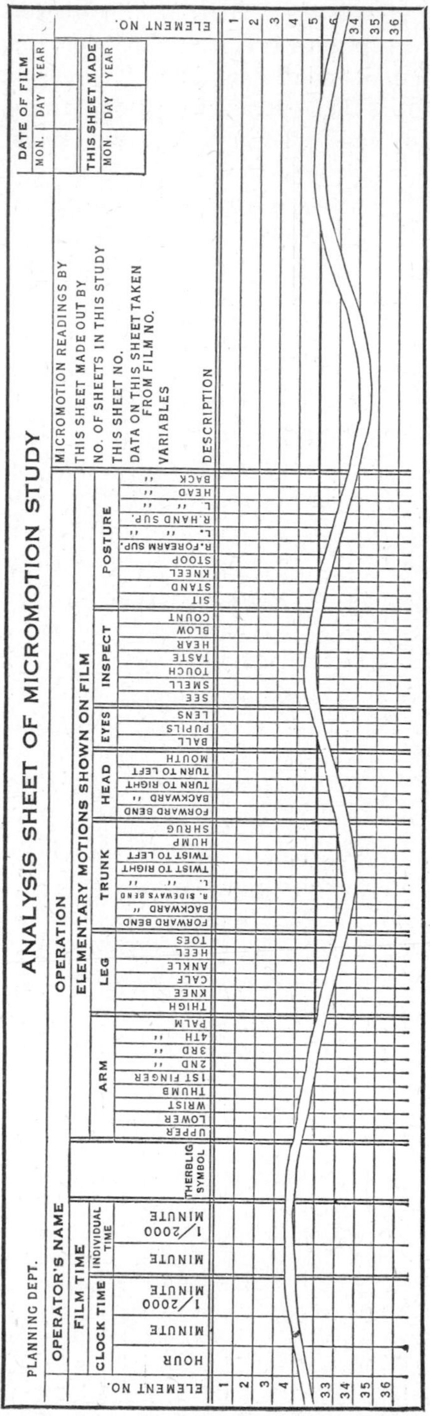

FIG. 35—Form for complete micromotion study analysis.

and the material to be assembled is located in small bins directly in front of the operator. The exact arrangement of the material is shown in Fig. 15 on page 40. The large clock hand makes 20 revolutions per minute; the small hand makes 2. There are 100 equal divisions on the dial of the clock; therefore, time is indicated directly in 1/2000 of a minute by the large hand. This time interval of 1/2000 of a minute was called a "wink" by Gilbreth.

The first frame of film in the upper left-hand corner of Fig. 36 shows the operator holding the head of the bolt with her left hand and completing the assembly of the last washer on the bolt with her right hand. The second frame shows the operator in the act of beginning to carry the finished assembly (with her left hand) to the bin nearest the clock, where she will dispose of it. This frame is an excellent place to begin the analysis as it shows the two hands at the instant they are beginning to separate. The clock reads 595, meaning 595/2000 of a minute from zero.

The motions of the left hand are recorded on the analysis sheet (see Fig. 37) in the column marked "Description Left Hand." The clock reading is recorded in the first column, 595 being the time at which the therblig *transport loaded* begins. The symbol for this therblig is placed in the third column and the motion is described "Carries assembly to bin." [1] The film is then examined frame by frame until this therblig (for the left hand) ends. The frame of film showing the left hand in the act of releasing the assembly also shows the clock to read 602. Therefore, 602 is recorded in the second horizontal line and in the first vertical column. Since the operator's left hand is now beginning the therblig *release load,* the symbol for this therblig is placed in the third vertical column and the description of the therblig "Releases assembly" is recorded in the fourth column. The analyst now turns to the film and examines it further, looking for the end of the therblig *release load* and for the beginning of the next therblig *transport empty.* The very next frame of film shows the operator's left hand in the act of moving empty to the bin of bolts; consequently the *release load* therblig has ended and the *transport empty* therblig has begun. The clock is read 604 and this is recorded in the third horizontal line and in the first vertical column. The symbol for *transport empty* is placed in the third column and the description of the therblig is noted in the fourth column. In a like manner the film is examined through the entire cycle, the analyst noting where one therblig ends and the next one begins and recording the data on the analysis sheet. After the analysis has been made for both hands, the clock readings are subtracted to get the elapsed time for each therblig. These subtracted times are recorded in the second vertical column.

Analysis of the Right Hand. After the motions of the left hand have been analyzed, the film is run back to the starting place and the motions made by the right hand are analyzed and recorded on the right side of the analysis sheet in Fig. 37. Referring to the second frame of film in the upper left-hand corner of Fig. 36, the operator's right hand is beginning the therblig *transport empty,* the hand moving to the bin of lock washers. Therefore, the clock reading 595 is recorded in the first vertical column under the heading "Clock Reading" for the right hand in Fig. 37. The therblig symbol for

---

[1] It is best practice to let the therblig symbol indicate the action, thus making it unnecessary to include the verb in the description. The description of the first therblig would therefore have been "Assembly to bin" instead of "Carries assembly to bin." The verbs have been included on the analysis sheets and simo charts in this book in order to aid the reader in learning the meanings of the therblig symbols.

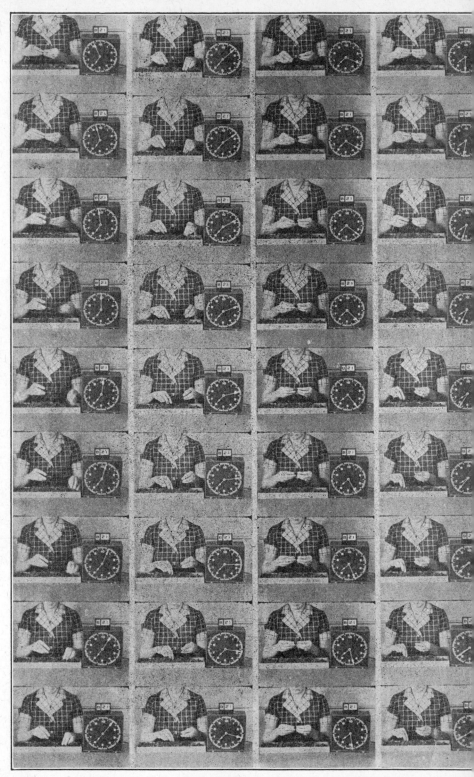

Fig. 36—Print of motion-picture film showing one com

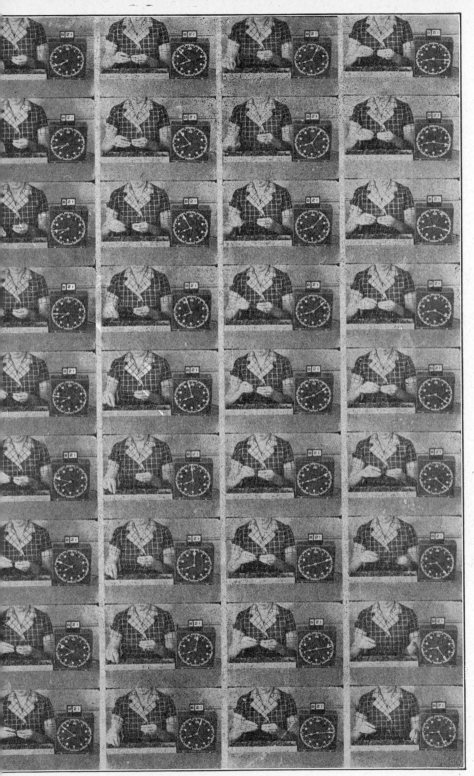

le of the bolt and washer assembly—old method.

transport empty is placed in the third vertical column and the description of the motion is recorded. The film is then studied frame by frame until the point is found where the therblig *transport empty* for the right hand ends and the next one begins. This therblig is a long one because the hand moves very slowly in order to allow time for the left hand to dispose of the assembly and procure a bolt. It is not until the frame in the middle of the second row of pictures of Fig. 36 that the operator begins to *select* and *grasp* a lock washer

MICROMOTION STUDY
ANALYSIS SHEET

PART Bolt and washer assembly–Old Method DEPARTMENT AY16 FILM NO B21

OPERATION Assemble 3 washers on bolt OP. NO. A32

OPERATOR M.Smith 1C634 DATE 1-26-37 ANALYSED BY M.E.R. SHEET NO 1 OF 1

CLOCK READING	SUBTRACTED TIME	THERBLIG SYMBOL	DESCRIPTION LEFT HAND	CLOCK READING	SUBTRACTED TIME	THERBLIG SYMBOL	DESCRIPTION RIGHT HAND
595	7		Carries assembly to bin	595	26		Reaches for lock washer
602	2		Releases assembly	621	6		Selects and grasps washer
604	4		Reaches for bolt	627	7		Carries washer to bolt
608	2		Selects and grasps bolt	634	6		Positions washer
610	17		Carries bolt to working position	640	12		Assembles washer onto bolt and releases
627	5		Positions bolt	652	8		Reaches for steel washer
632	104		Holds bolt	660	8		Selects and grasps washer
736	7		Carries assembly to bin	668	9		Carries washer to bolt
743	2		Releases assembly	677	3		Positions washer
745				680	10		Assembles steel washer and releases
				690	6		Reaches for rubber washer
				696	10		Selects and grasps rubber washer
				706	9		Carries washer to bolt
				715	5		Positions washer
				720	16		Assembles washer and releases
				736			

Fig. 37—Analysis sheet for bolt and washer assembly—old method.

from the bin on the bench. The clock is read 621 and the data are recorded on the analysis sheet, and so the analysis is continued for the remainder of the cycle. After the analysis has been made for both hands and the subtracted time obtained, it is then possible to picture the entire cycle easily and accurately. The left hand is analyzed independently of the right hand except that the cycle must begin and end at approximately the same point for the two hands. It must be remembered that the subtracted time shown in Fig. 37 is in 2000ths of a minute.

As many cycles of the operation may be analyzed as seem necessary. Usually one or two are all that are required if care is used in their selection.

CONSTRUCTION OF SIMULTANEOUS MOTION-CYCLE CHARTS

The time for each therblig recorded on the analysis sheet may be shown to scale by means of a simultaneous motion-cycle chart, com-

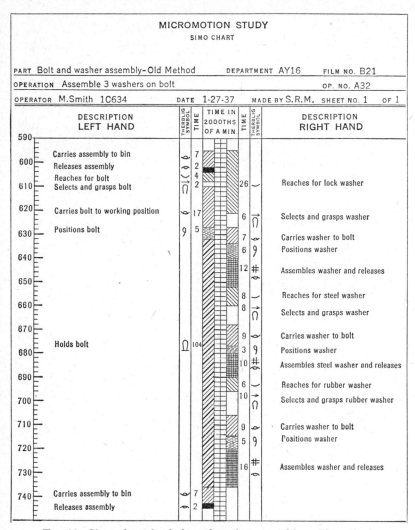

Fig. 38—Simo chart for bolt and washer assembly—old method.

monly called a "simo chart." Either the analysis sheet or the simo chart may be made independently, or the simo chart may be constructed from the data on the analysis sheet.

When a full simo chart showing every moving member of the body is made, it is customary to use a sheet of cross-section paper 22 inches wide with lines ruled 10 to the inch. For operations longer than one-half minute some analysts use paper with lines ruled 10 to the half inch, or paper ruled in millimeters in order to condense the chart. However, since the divisions are closer together, this paper is more difficult to use than the decimal-inch paper. Headings containing information such as that shown at the top of Fig. 35 are often printed in quantities and are pasted across the top of the cross-section paper.

For many operations, however, it is not necessary to construct a complete chart of all the moving members of the body. A simo chart of the two hands for the bolt and washer assembly is shown in Fig. 38. Exactly the same procedure would be used to construct a chart showing the motions of the arms, legs, head, trunk, and other parts of the body.

The vertical scale shown in the center of the chart in Fig. 38 represents time in 2000ths of a minute. The therblig description, symbol, color, and relative position in the cycle all appear on the chart. The time required for each therblig is drawn to scale in the vertical column and colored to represent the particular therblig. The sheet is arranged much like the analysis sheet. The clock read 595 at the beginning of the therblig *transport loaded* for the left hand, therefore this point is located on the vertical scale by a heavy black horizontal line at the top of the column. The first therblig, *transport loaded*, required seven winks (7/2000ths of a minute); therefore, seven divisions are marked off on the vertical column for the left hand and a heavy black line is drawn in. The space above this horizontal black line is then colored solidly in green [2] with a pencil, No. 375. The next therblig for the left hand is *release load* and it required two winks. In a similar manner this elapsed time is marked off on the vertical scale immediately below the heavy black line and another horizontal line is drawn in. The area for this therblig is colored red. And so for the remainder of the cycle the therbligs are marked off to scale and each area is colored with the standard therblig color. The motions made by the right hand are charted on the right-hand side of the sheet in exactly the same way as those for the left hand.

Figure 39 shows the simo chart for one cycle of the *improved method* of bolt and washer assembly as described on page 147.

---

[2] Since color cannot be reproduced in this book, color symbols are used instead. For standard therblig colors see Fig. 25 on page 63.

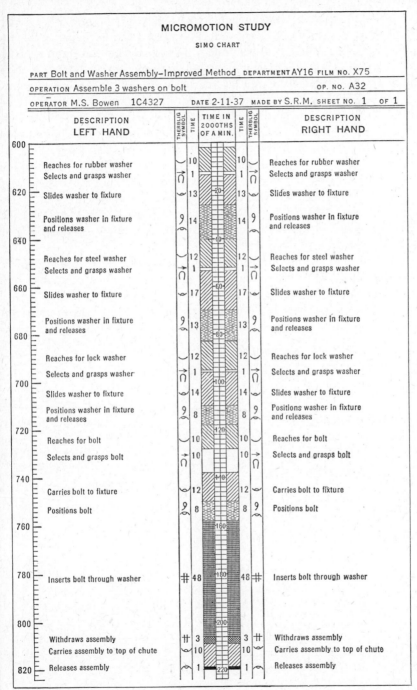

Fig. 39.—Simo chart for bolt and washer assembly—improved method.

Analysis of the Link-Forming Operation. The simple operation of bending a "hook" on each end of a short piece of wire to form a link (see Fig. 40) for a portable typewriter was the subject of a number of studies made by the author, and because this operation involves the use of a fixture and because it is short in length it will be used as an example.

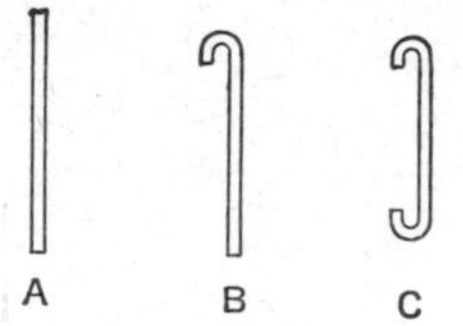

The camera used for making the motion pictures of this operation was driven by a synchronous motor and operated at a constant speed of 1000 exposures per minute. Therefore, no microchronometer was needed and the time interval from one frame of film to the next was exactly 1/1000th of a minute. See Fig. 42.

A   B   C

Fig. 40 — Link for portable typewriter. *A.* Soft steel wire; *B.* Link with one end formed; *C.* Finished link.

Description of the Link-Forming Operation. The material from which the link was formed consisted of soft steel wire cut from wire stock, 0.045 inch in diameter to uniform lengths of 1¼ inches. The material was supplied to the operator in metal containers and the operator emptied the stock of cut wire on the linoleum-topped bench

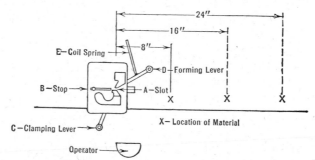

Fig. 41—Fixture and layout of the work place for forming link.

at the right of the fixture as she needed it. The link was formed in the following manner.

The pictures in Fig. 42 give a reproduction of each element of one complete cycle. The fixture was mounted securely on the bench so that its top surface was 2¾ inches above the top of the bench. The top of the bench was 27 inches above the floor. The material was spread out over the surface of the bench top so that it could be grasped more easily. The operator, seated behind the bench, picked up one piece of material with the thumb and index finger of her right hand, carried it to the left, and inserted it into the slot A in the fixture. See Fig. 41. The operator pressed the piece of material against a stop B in the fixture, and at the same time she clamped the piece into place by moving lever C to the left with her left hand. Then, with the right hand she grasped the knob of the forming lever D which extended to the right of the fixture and was about 3 inches above the top of the bench. The right hand rotated the forming lever in the clockwise direction about the center of the fixture as an axis, through approximately 180 degrees, the radius of rotation being 8 inches. The lever was moved in a plane parallel to the top of the bench. This movement of the lever formed the "hook" on one end of the link. The operator then returned the lever in the counter-clockwise direction toward its original position. A coil spring E, fastened to the forming lever and to the bench, assisted the operator in returning the lever to its original position. This spring made it possible for the operator to release the forming lever after she had returned it through about one-half of its return travel, the spring pulling the lever back the remainder of the distance.

After the operator had released the knob of the lever she moved her hand slightly to her right and into a position about 4 inches in front of her and waited an instant while her left hand removed the half-formed link from the slot in the fixture. Then the two hands together turned the link end for end and placed it back into the slot. Care was used to insure that the "hook" was turned in the proper direction so that after the link had been completely formed the two hooks would be on the same side. As the right hand held the link in place in the fixture, the left hand moved the lever C to the left, clamping the link in the slot as in the first part of the cycle. The right hand then grasped the knob of the forming lever and, as before, moved it through 180 degrees in the clockwise direction forming the second end of the link. While the right hand was forming the end of the link, the left hand continued to hold lever C in its position as far to the left as it would go, clamping the link in the fixture while it was being formed. After the link was formed, the right hand returned the forming lever toward its original position, releasing the knob of this lever directly in front of the operator. She then moved her hand to her right to pick up a piece of material from the bench for the beginning of the next cycle. In the meantime the left hand released the knob of lever C and reached forward to remove the finished formed link from the slot in the fixture. The left hand then carried the link to the left where it was dropped on top of the bench. During this

FILM ANALYSIS

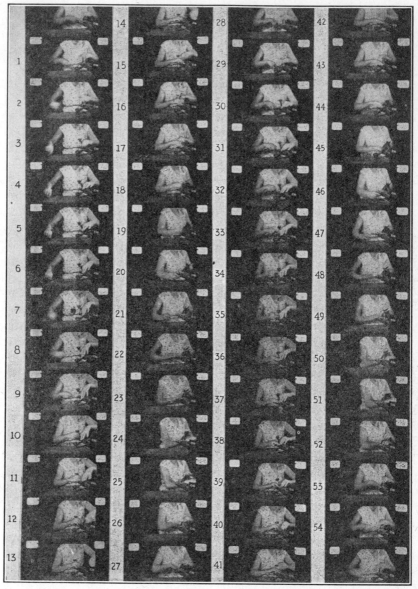

F<small>IG</small>. 42—Print of motion-picture film showing one complete cycle of the link-forming operation.

time the operator was looking to her right where the right hand was grasping a piece of material from the top of the bench for the next cycle.

Figure 43 shows the simo chart for the link-forming operation.

Complete Analysis of Hand Motions. Confusion sometimes occurs when making a right- and left-hand motion analysis because some members of the arm are performing certain therbligs while other members are performing other therbligs. The first therblig on the simo chart in Fig. 44, for example, shows the thumb, first, and second fingers of the right hand performing a grasp while the palm, third, and fourth fingers of the same hand are holding the bone. The operation is that of folding and creasing sheets of paper by the improved method described on page 166. The right hand carries the bone at all times, although it is used only during a small part of the cycle.

When a complete analysis of an operation is made each member of the arm is analyzed separately, i.e., the upper arm, lower arm, wrist, first finger, second finger, etc. The film is run back to the starting place after the analysis of each member and a separate vertical column on the simo chart is required for recording the motions of each. Although Fig. 44 does not show the movements of the head, trunk, and legs it does show all motions of the arms, hands, and fingers.

Had a simple right- and left-hand simo chart been made of the paper-folding operation it would have shown those therbligs performed by the thumb, first, and second fingers only. A note would have been included on the chart to show that the bone was carried in the right hand throughout the entire cycle.

Using the Simo Chart. After the simo chart of the operation has been made the task of finding a better way of doing the work has just begun. A thorough study of the chart is ordinarily the first step in this task.

The simo chart aids one in grasping a picture of the complete cycle in all of its details and assists in working out better combinations of the most desirable therbligs. The simo chart in Fig. 38 shows in a very clear way that the left hand is used during most of the cycle for holding the bolt. This at once suggests that some mechanical device be used which will permit the left hand as well as the right to do more useful work.

MICROMOTION STUDY
SIMO CHART

PART Link for typewriter   DEPARTMENT 9   FILM NO. C18

OPERATION Form link for typewriter   OP. NO. G11

OPERATOR A.S.Sanders   A2   DATE 2-15-37   MADE BY S.A.R.   SHEET NO. 1   OF 1

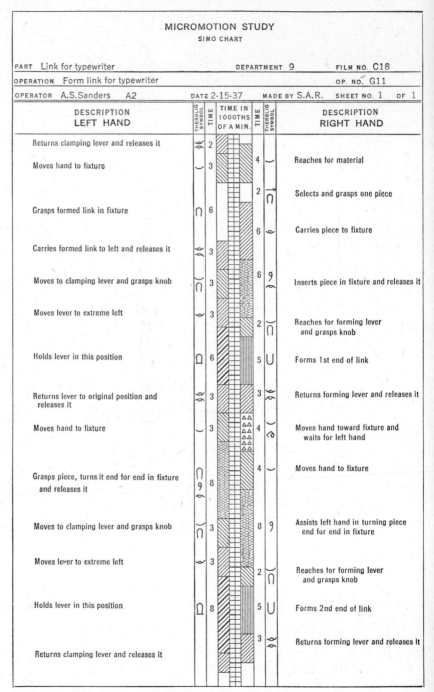

DESCRIPTION LEFT HAND	THERBLIG SYMBOL	TIME	TIME IN 1000THS OF A MIN.	TIME	THERBLIG SYMBOL	DESCRIPTION RIGHT HAND
Returns clamping lever and releases it		2				
Moves hand to fixture		3		4		Reaches for material
				2		Selects and grasps one piece
Grasps formed link in fixture		6				
				6		Carries piece to fixture
Carries formed link to left and releases it		3				
Moves to clamping lever and grasps knob		3		6		Inserts piece in fixture and releases it
Moves lever to extreme left		3				
				2		Reaches for forming lever and grasps knob
Holds lever in this position		6		5		Forms 1st end of link
Returns lever to original position and releases it		3		3		Returns forming lever and releases it
Moves hand to fixture		3		4		Moves hand toward fixture and waits for left hand
				4		Moves hand to fixture
Grasps piece, turns it end for end in fixture and releases it		8				
Moves to clamping lever and grasps knob		3		8		Assists left hand in turning piece end for end in fixture
Moves lever to extreme left		3				
				2		Reaches for forming lever and grasps knob
Holds lever in this position		8		5		Forms 2nd end of link
				3		Returns forming lever and releases it
Returns clamping lever and releases it						

FIG. 43—Simo chart of link-forming operation.

It is often found that the sequence of therbligs in one kind of work may be used in other kinds of work, or a particularly good se-

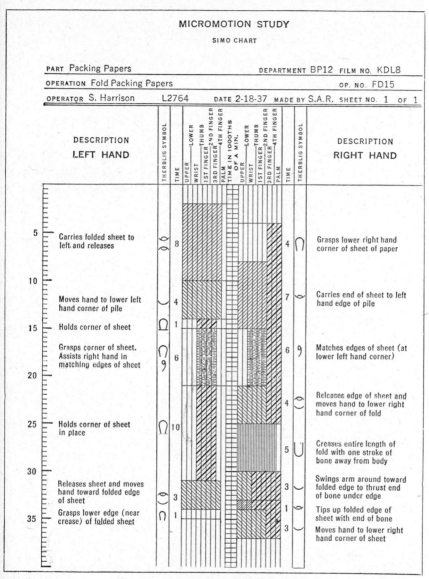

Fig. 44—Simo chart of folding paper.

quence in one operation may suggest a more efficient sequence in another operation. The simo chart shows very distinctly where delays occur in the cycle and it aids in finding an effective way of eliminating the delays.

The next five chapters give some methods of attack that may be useful in this problem of improving the method of doing a given task.

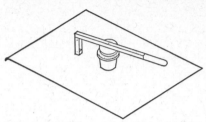

FIG. 45—Fixture used for pressing cheese in cup by the old method.

Possibility Charts. After the suggestions for the improvement of the method have been secured and when worthwhile changes seem practicable, a possibility chart may be constructed. This is a simultaneous motion-cycle chart showing the proposed method. A competent analyst will be able to draw up such a chart listing the necessary therbligs in order and indicating the time for each. Such possibility charts can be made with a surprising degree of accuracy by one trained in the micromotion study technique and experienced in making such charts.

Modified Simo Chart. Some organizations find it satisfactory to list the therbligs and the therblig times on the simo chart, plotting the

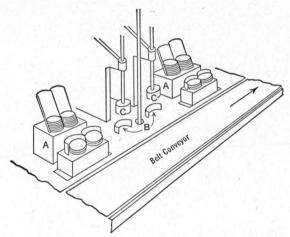

FIG. 46—Fixture used for pressing cheese in cups by the improved method. *A.* Supply of tinfoil liners, covers, etc.; *B.* Nests for positioning cups under plungers; *C.* Plungers (operated by foot) for pressing cheese into cups.

therblig time values on a graduated scale as shown in Figs. 47 and 48. The colored therblig identifications are not used. Moreover, such charts may be prepared with a typewriter using hectograph carbon paper on forms printed with hectograph ink. With such a master, a number of copies can be made. The simo charts for one operation in the process of packing Cheddar cheese in paper cups shown in Figs. 47 and 48 were made in this manner.

In this case the company had several branch plants packing cheese, and the charts together with films of the original method and of the improved method were sent to each plant so that they could benefit from this work.

The original method of "Crimp Foil Liner over Top, Press Cheese in Cup, Code Date, and Move to Wrapper" was as follows: The operator, standing at a table, picked up a cup from the table at her extreme left, placed it on the table directly in front of her, folded the tinfoil liner down on the cheese, placed it in a hand fixture as shown in Fig. 45, and lowered the lever which pressed the cheese down in the cup. Then the cup was removed from the fixture, an insert and a cover placed on top of the cup, and the cover pressed down. The cup was then turned over and a code date stamped on the bottom, using a hand stamp and an ink pad.

In investigating operations that seem to lend themselves to the use of duplicate fixtures it is often desirable to plot on the simo chart the therbligs used in producing two units, as it is easier to compare the old with the improved method. This was done in Fig. 47.

Having this new fixture in mind, the engineer drew heavy solid vertical lines beside the therbligs that he thought could be eliminated entirely, and heavy dotted vertical lines beside the therbligs that he thought probably could be reduced in time. This procedure gives a fairly definite idea of the potential savings that can be expected after the proposed fixture has been built and put into use.

The improved method, after it was worked out and put into effect in the factory, was filmed and a simo chart made of it (see Figs. 46 and 48). The improved method consisted of picking up two cups filled with cheese from a conveyor belt and placing them on the front edge of the table. The two hands then folded the tinfoil liner down on the first cup and placed it into a nest in the fixture. The foil was then folded down on the second cup and it was placed into the other nest in the fixture. The two hands held the two cups while the foot operated the two plungers which came down vertically, pressing the cheese into the cups. The operator then grasped an insert and then a cover in each hand and placed them on the cups. The cups were removed a few inches from the fixtures, the covers pressed

MICROMOTION STUDY
SIMO CHART

PART: ½ lb. and 1 lb. Cheddar Cheese	FILM NO.: S1486
OPERATION: Crimp Foil Liner over Top, Press Cheese in Cup,	OP. NO.:
Code Date, Move to Wrapper	DATE: 12-18-39
OPERATOR: M. Sanderson MADE BY: M.G.S.	SHEET NO.: 1 of 1
NO. UNITS PER CYCLE: 2-Cup Cycle ORIGINAL METHOD: X	IMPROVED METHOD:

FOOT	LEFT HAND	LH	1000THS OF A MINUTE	RH	RIGHT HAND
	T.E. to cup and aid right hand	10		10	T.E. to cup and move to position
	Crimp foil liner over cheese	28	25	26	Crimp foil liner over cheese
	Aid right hand	5		7	Aside cup
	T.E. to cup and grasp	8	50	17	Hold lever up
	Place cup in position to press	15			
				17	Lower lever pressing cheese to cup, raise
	Hold cup	11	75		
	Aside cup to table	7		7	Hold lever up
	T.E. pick up inserts, hold while right hand places, aside (6 at a time)	18	100	18	T.E. to instruction inserts in left hand, grasp and place on top of cheese in cup
	Aid place cover	13		32	Place cover and T.E. for next cover
	Shove cup aside	5			
	Move next cup in position	14	125		
	Turn cups upside down (1 in each hand)	10		10	Same as left
	T.E. for stamp pad, hold while right stamps, aside pad	13	150	13	T.E. for stamp-stamp cover-aside stamp- avg. 12 per time
	Shove to wrapper (1 each hand)	5		5	Same as left
	T.E. to cup and aid right hand	10		10	T.E. to cup and move to position
	Crimp foil liner over cheese	28	175	26	Crimp foil liner over cheese
	Aid right hand	5	200	7	T.L. and R.L. cup
	T.E. to cup and grasp	8		17	Hold lever up
	T.L. cup in position to press	15			
			225	17	Lower lever pressing cheese in cup, raise
	Hold cup	11			
	T.L. cup to table	7		7	Hold lever up
	T.E. pick up inserts, hold while right hand places, aside (6 at a time)	18	250	18	T.E. to instruction inserts in left hand, grasp and place on top of cheese in cup
	Aid place cover	13		32	Place cover and T.E. for next cover
	Shove cup aside	5	275		
	Move next cup in position	14			
	Turn cups upside down (1 in each hand)	10	300	10	Same as left
	Reach for stamp pad, hold while right stamps, aside pad	13		13	T.E. for stamp-stamp cover-aside stamp- avg. 12 per time
	Shove to wrapper (1 each hand)	5	324	5	Same as left

NOTE: In order to compare Old and New Methods a one-cup cycle of Old Method has been shown twice.

━━━ Indicates that element probably could be completely eliminated.

━ ━ ━ Indicates element probably could be reduced.

Fig. 47—Modified simo chart of one operation in the process of packing Cheddar cheese in paper cups by the old method. Size of chart 8½ × 17 inches.

MICROMOTION STUDY
SIMO CHART

PART: ½ lb. and 1 lb. Cheddar Cheese		**FILM NO.:** S1347
OPERATION: Crimp Foil Liner over Top, Press Cheese in Cup,		**OP. NO.:** c-27
Code Date, Move to Wrapper		**DATE:** 1-12-40
OPERATOR: M. Sanderson	**MADE BY:** M.G.S.	**SHEET NO.** 1 OF 1
NO. UNITS PER CYCLE: 2 Cup Cycle	**ORIGINAL METHOD:**	**IMPROVED METHOD:** X

FOOT	LEFT HAND	1000THS OF A MINUTE		RIGHT HAND
	T.E. and G. cup	7	8	T.E. and G. cup
	T.L. and R.L. cup	9	10	T.L. and R.L. cup
	Fold over tinfoil liner on first cup	28	25—26	Aid left hand to fold over tinfoil liner on first cup
	R.L. and T.E.	6	6	Slide forward into depression
	G. and T.L. to position	6	50—6	T.E. to next cup
	Fold over tinfoil liner on second cup	28	28	Aid left hand to fold over tinfoil liner on second cup
			—75—	
	Grasp cup	5	4	T.E. and G. first cup
	Slide into position to press	9	10	Idle
	Hold while press	7	100—7	Hold while press
	T.E. to insert	4	5	Idle
	Grasp insert	22	7	T.E. to insert
			14	Grasp insert
			—125—	
	T.L. to cover	5	8	T.L. to cover
	Position insert and G. cover	7	8	Position insert and G. cover
	T.L. to cup	10	150—6	T.L. to cup
	Position	6	6	Position
	Slide out 3″-4″	4	4	Slide out 3″-4″
	PRESS COVER DOWN	3	3	PRESS COVER DOWN
	Grasp	4	4	Grasp
	Turn over and R.L.	11	175—11	Turn over and R.L.
			3	T.E. TO STAMP
	Idle	29	5	G. and T.L. stamp to cup
			13	Stamp 2 cups
			—200—	
			210—8	T.L. and R.L. stamp
			—225—	
			—250—	
				Net reduction 35%
			—275—	
			—300—	
			324	
				Last 40 frames of this operation could be eliminated by stamping from bottom at the time of pressing.

FIG. 48—Modified simo chart of one operation in the process of packing Cheddar cheese in paper cups by the improved method. Size of chart 8½ × 17 inches.

into place, and the cups turned over and the code date stamped on the bottom of each cup.

The two simo charts when placed side by side make it easy to visualize the changes that were made in the method. Originally it required 0.324 minute for two cups, whereas by the improved method it requires but 0.210 minute for two cups, a reduction in time of 35 per cent.

CHAPTER 10

THE USE OF THE THERBLIGS

Although the definition of each therblig has been given in a preceding chapter, further explanation is needed in certain cases. Also, since each therblig requires, for its performance, time and energy on the part of the worker, the elimination of therbligs, or the better arrangement of such as are indispensable, constitutes part of the regular technique of improving methods of work. Information that will aid in making better use of the therbligs is included in this chapter, and a check list follows the discussion of each therblig.

Select. The time for select is frequently so short in duration that it is impossible to measure it with the camera at ordinary speeds. When this is the case it is advisable to combine it with either the preceding or the following therblig. Since select usually precedes grasp, it is good practice to combine these two. The symbols for both therbligs should be included on the analysis sheet and the color for the most important or the predominating therblig should be used in making the simo chart. Usually it will be the therblig other than select.

Color can be seen more quickly than shape; therefore, color should be used to aid in selecting or sorting whenever possible. For example, in sorting photographic snapshot prints into batches after the printing, developing, and drying operations, it was found desirable to use inks of different colors for stamping identification numbers on the back of the paper before printing. Sorting these prints by color of the ink is much easier and faster than sorting by key letters or figures.

Also, painting a tool the same color as the place where it is to be kept in the drawer saves time when putting it away and finding it the next time.[1]

Check List for Select

1. Is the layout such as to eliminate searching for articles?
2. Can tools and materials be standardized?

[1] F. B. Gilbreth, "Motion Study," p. 47, D. Van Nostrand Co., New York, 1911.

3. Are parts and materials properly labeled?

4. Can better arrangements be made to facilitate or eliminate select—such as a bin with a long lip, a tray that pre-positions parts, a transparent container, etc.?

5. Are common parts interchangeable?

6. Are parts and materials mixed?

7. Is the lighting satisfactory?

Grasp. There are two main types of grasp: (1) *pressure grasp* as in grasping a pencil lying flat on a table top; and (2) *full-hook grasp* as in grasping a pencil lying on a table top with one end raised an inch or so, so that the thumb and fingers are able to grasp by reaching around it (hook) instead of grasping by pinching.

An investigation [2] of grasping small pieces of wire used in making a link for a portable typewriter (see page 96) showed that it required twice as long to grasp a piece using a pressure grasp as it did using a full-hook grasp. A summary of these data is given in Table IV below. The same investigation revealed that the time for the grasp was not greatly affected by the distance through which the hand moved in either the therblig preceding or the one following the grasp, other conditions being constant.

TABLE IV

TIME REQUIRED FOR A PRESSURE GRASP VS. A HOOK GRASP

Link for Portable Typewriter

Time in Minutes

Study No.	Position of Material	Time Required to Grasp			
		Av.	Mode	Min.	Max.
X51	At random on table top (pressure grasp)	0.00558	0.0050	0.0035	0.0110
X53	Horizontal in grooves (hook grasp)	0.00225	0.0020	0.0020	0.0030

The results of a study [3] of the time required to grasp washers from a flat surface using a hook grasp and a pressure (pinch) grasp are given in Fig. 49 and Table V.

[2] Ralph M. Barnes, "An Investigation of Some Hand Motions Used in Factory Work," *Univ. Iowa Studies in Engg.*, Bul. 6, p. 29, 1936.

[3] Ralph M. Barnes and Marvin E. Mundel, "A Study of Hand Motions Used in Small Assembly Work," *Univ. Iowa Studies in Engg.*, Bul. 16, p. 10, 1939.

TABLE V

TIME REQUIRED TO GRASP, CARRY, AND DISPOSE OF WASHERS FROM A FLAT SURFACE, USING A "HOOK" GRASP AND A "PRESSURE" GRASP

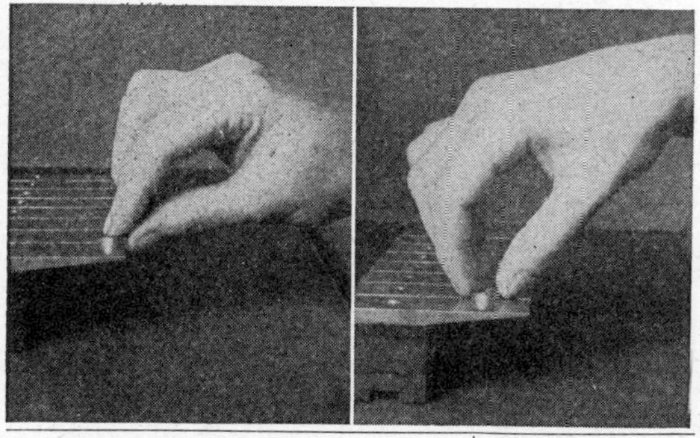

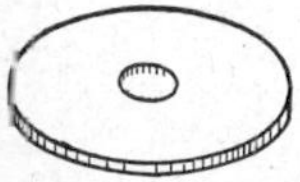

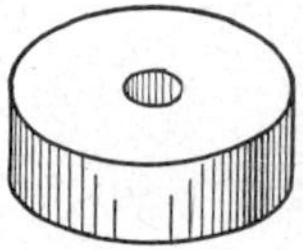

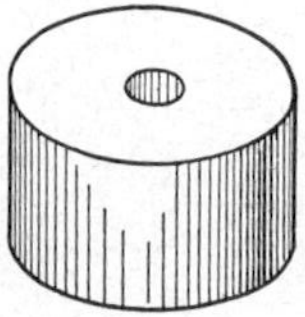

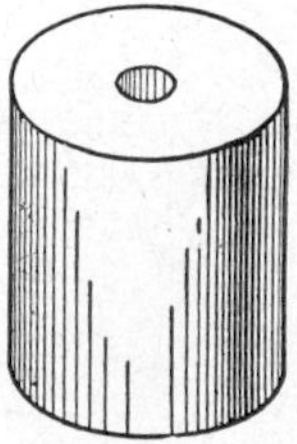

		1/32 Hook	1/32 Pressure	1/8 Hook	1/8 Pressure	1/4 Hook	1/4 Pressure	1/2 Hook	1/2 Pressure
GRASP Pick up washer from "Grasp" grid shown above.	Time in Minutes	0.00315	0.00629	0.00314	0.00308	0.00340	0.00233	0.00323	0.00158
	Time in Per Cent (Shortest Time = 100%)	101	397	100	195	109	147	103	100
TRANSPORT LOADED AND POSITION Carry washer through distance of 5 inches and position on "Release" grid.	Time in Minutes	0.00465	0.00628	0.00510	0.00571	0.00561	0.00514	0.00677	0.00473
	Time in Per Cent (Shortest Time = 100%)	100	132	110	121	121	108	146	100
TOTAL CYCLE (G. + T.L. + P. + R.L. + T.E.)	Time in Minutes	0.01527	0.01960	0.01524	0.01590	0.01630	0.01450	0.01750	0.01428
	Time in Per Cent (Shortest Time = 100%)	100	138	100	112	107	102	115	100

The operator merely picked up a washer from one flat surface, carried it through a distance of 5 inches, and disposed of it onto another flat surface. The time for the therbligs grasp, transport loaded

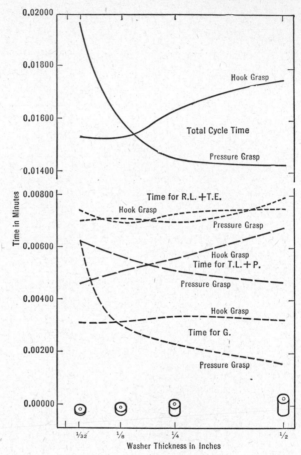

Fig. 49—Curves showing results of study of time required to grasp washers from a flat surface using a hook grasp and a pressure grasp. Four different thicknesses of washers were used. Averages of median time values for five male and five female operators are shown.

and position, and release load and transport empty was measured very accurately. Circular washers ½ inch in diameter, with a ⅛ inch hole in the center, and 1/32, ⅛, ¼, and ½ inch thick were used.

The time for grasp using the hook grasp tended to increase slightly as the washer thickness increased, whereas the time for grasp using the pressure grasp decreased markedly as the washer thickness increased. The time for grasping the thinnest washer ($\frac{1}{32}$ inch thick) using a pressure grasp was 297 per cent greater than when grasping the thickest washer ($\frac{1}{2}$ inch thick).[4]

It is usually quicker and easier to transport small objects by sliding than by carrying. In grasping a small object such as a coin or a washer preparatory to transporting it by sliding, the grasp consists merely of touching the ball of the index finger to the top surface of the object. Whereas, in grasping the same object preparatory to transporting it by carrying, the grasp consists of closing the thumb and index finger around the piece. A recent study [5] showed that the grasp preceding the slide required as little as $\frac{1}{30}$ as long as the grasp preceding the carry. The data pertaining to this point are given in Table VI.

TABLE VI

TIME REQUIRED TO GRASP SMALL WASHERS

(Grasp preceding carry, and grasp preceding slide)

Time in Minutes

Object Grasped	Study X74 Grasp Preceding Carry	Study X75 Grasp Preceding Slide
Rubber washer..............	0.00960	0.00033
Steel washer................	0.00895	0.00031
Lock washer................	0.00750	0.00038

Placing Inserts in Envelopes. There are many devices that aid in improving grasp. For example, Miss M. P. Sealy explains how R. H. Macy's Department Store uses a metal block about two inches long and triangular in shape to facilitate grasping inserts and monthly statements preparatory to inserting these in the envelope for mailing. The batch of inserts (advertising circulars) and the folded statements

[4] This investigation and the others carried on in the Industrial Engineering Laboratory at the University of Iowa and referred to in this book were made with most meticulous care and the data were taken with all the accuracy obtainable with the measuring devices that were used. However, the point must be noted that certain inevitable variations were introduced as a result of the fact that the movements being measured were those of human, as distinct from purely mechanical subjects.

The results given here are presented, not as general conclusions but merely as the findings of specific studies, details of which are fully described in the publications referred to in the footnotes.

[5] *Univ. Iowa Studies in Engg.,* Bul. 6, p. 32.

are stacked on each side of this block so that the thumb and index finger (using rubber finger tips) can grasp one of each, bringing it to the apex of the block and completing the grasp. The flaps of the envelopes have previously been opened and the envelopes positioned on the table with the envelope window face down and with the opening toward the grasp-block. The left hand holds the envelope open while the right hand carries the inserts over and places them in the envelope with the customer's name and address on the statement facing the window. The operator disposes of the filled envelope while her other hand returns to the block. If two or three inserts are to be enclosed, a second grasp-block is placed at the left of the operator and both hands are used for grasping. The statements vary in thickness depending upon the number of pages needed to list each customer's purchases during the month; consequently a machine cannot be used to insert the enclosures in the envelope.[6]

Check List for Grasp

1. Is it possible to grasp more than one object at a time?
2. Can objects be slid instead of carried?
3. Will a lip on front of the bin simplify grasp of small parts?
4. Can tools or parts be pre-positioned for easy grasp?
5. Can a special screwdriver, socket wrench, or combination tool be used?
6. Can a vacuum, magnet, rubber finger tip, or other device be used to advantage?
7. Is the article transferred from one hand to another?
8. Does the design of the jig or fixture permit an easy grasp in removing the part?

Transport Empty and Transport Loaded. Investigations [7] show (1) that it requires a slightly greater period of time to move the hand through a long distance than through a short distance, other conditions being constant; (2) that the average velocity of the hand is greater for long motions than for short ones; and (3) that in such motions as transport empty and transport loaded the hand of a skilled operator moves through almost identically the same path in going from one point to another in consecutive cycles of a repetitive operation. The particular study relating to this last point was made by projecting the film, one frame at a time, on a sheet of white paper

[6] L. Stone, M. P. Sealy, and E. B. Gage, "Office Gadgets," *Am. Management Assoc. Bul., Office Management Series*, No. 74, p. 20, 1936.
[7] *Univ. Iowa Studies in Engg.*, Bul. 6, p. 23, 1936.

and marking the position of the tip of the index finger. Connecting these points by pencil lines gave the path of the motion in two dimensions. By placing the camera perpendicular to the path of motion it was possible to secure a close approach to a true record of the motion path.

Table XVI on page 163 shows the results of some studies made of the operation of moving small pieces of wire through distances of 8, 16, and 24 inches in forming links for a typewriter.

A movement of the hand, such as transport empty or transport loaded, is ordinarily composed of three phases: (1) the hand, starting from a still position, accelerates until it reaches a maximum velocity; (2) it then proceeds at a uniform velocity; and (3) finally the hand slows down until it comes to a dead stop. If the hand changes direction and returns over the same path as in making a mark back and forth across a sheet of paper there will be an appreciable length of time at the end of the stroke during which the hand is motionless, that is, while the hand is changing direction.[8]

For example, in a simple hand motion 10 inches in length one study [9] showed the distribution of these events to be as follows: 38 per cent of the cycle time for acceleration, 18 per cent for movement at uniform velocity, 27 per cent for retardation, and 17 per cent for stop and change direction. See Fig. 81 on page 165.

The time required to move the hand is affected by the nature of the therbligs which precede and which follow the transport. For example, when a delicate or fragile object is transported and placed carefully in a small receptacle, the time for the transport will be longer than when the transport is followed by an ordinary disposal such as tossing a bolt into a box.

The manner in which an object is grasped and the way that it must be carried and positioned may also affect the time for the transport. This is shown by the results of an investigation [10] made to determine the time required to grasp various small cylinders from a flat surface. The results of this study are given in Fig. 50 and Table VII.

The operator picked up a cylinder from one flat surface, carried it through a distance of 5 inches, and placed it on another flat surface, sliding it between two small flat copper springs. The time for the therbligs grasp, and transport loaded and position was measured very

[8] *Ibid.*, pp. 37-51.
[9] *Ibid.*, p. 48.
[10] *Univ. Iowa Studies in Engg.*, Bul. 16, p. 20, 1939.

TABLE VII

Time Required to Grasp Various Small Cylinders from a Flat Surface

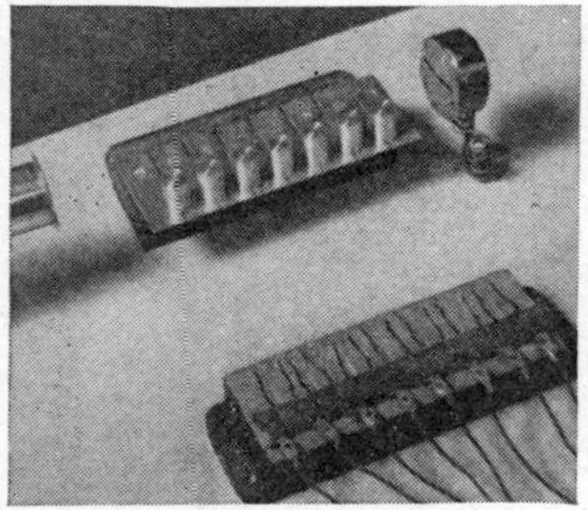		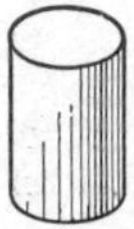 1 Plain Cylinder Wt., 0.182 oz.	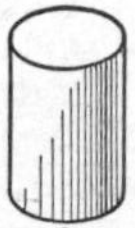 2 Plain Cylinder Wt., 1.92 oz.	 3 Plain Cylinder Wt., 3.12 oz.	 4 Ink-Filled Glass Cylinder	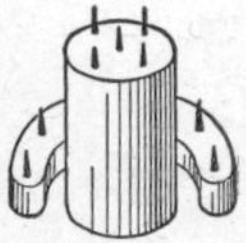 5 Cylinder with Needle Points
GRASP Pick up cylinder from "Grasp" grid shown above.	Time in Minutes	0.00128	0.00151	0.00126	0.00120	0.00128
	Time in Per Cent (Shortest Time = 100%)	107	126	106	100	107
TRANSPORT LOADED AND POSITION Carry cylinder through a distance of 5 inches and place on special "Release" grid.	Time in Minutes	0.00551	0.00540	0.00505	0.00631	0.00557
	Time in Per Cent (Shortest Time = 100%)	109	107	100	125	110
GRASP, TRANSPORT LOADED AND POSITION	Time in Minutes	0.00679	0.00691	0.00631	0.00751	0.00685
	Time in Per Cent (Shortest Time = 100%)	107	110	100	119	108
TOTAL CYCLE (G. + T.L. + P. + A. + R.L. + T.E.)	Time in Minutes	0.01460	0.01403	0.01367	0.01552	0.01430
	Time in Per Cent (Shortest Time = 100%)	107	103	100	113	105

accurately. Five cylinders 23/32 inch in diameter and 1 inch high were used. Three of these were identical except for weight. Cylinder 1 weighed 0.184 ounce, cylinder 2, 1.92 ounces, and cylinder 3, 3.12 ounces. Cylinder 4 was a glass cup filled with ink, and cylinder 5 was

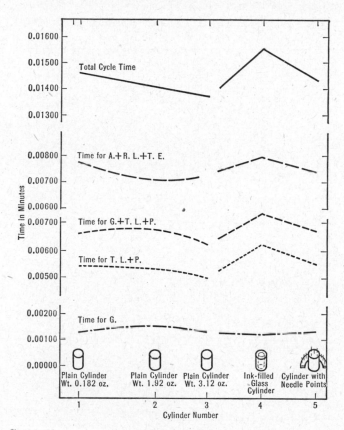

FIG. 50—Curves showing results of study of time required to grasp various small cylinders from a flat surface. Averages of median time values for five male and five female operators are shown.

a brass cylinder identical in size and weight with 2 but studded on top with needle points.

To transport loaded and position the heaviest of the cylinders (3) required the least time. The lightest cylinder (1) required 9 per cent more time, the solid brass cylinder (2) 7 per cent more time, the ink-filled glass cylinder 25 per cent more time, and the cylinder with the needle points 10 per cent more time than did cylinder 3.

Gauging Hard Rubber Washers. Mention has already been made of the fact that it is usually quicker and easier to transport small objects by sliding than by carrying. That a "grasp and slide" is definitely faster than a "grasp and carry" apparently results from the shorter grasp rather than from a saving in time in the transportation.

The inspection of small hard rubber washers for thickness is an-

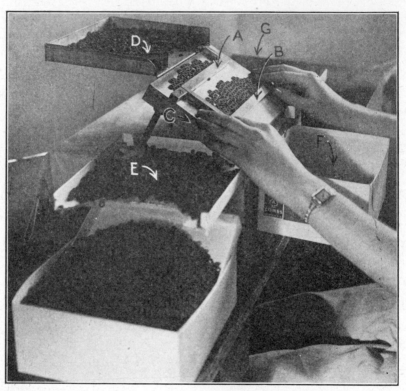

FIG. 51—Special gauge for inspecting hard rubber washers for thickness. *A.* Go gauge; *B.* No-go gauge; *C.* Base place of gauge; *D.* Supply of washers; *E.* Rejected washers (oversize); *F.* Rejected washers (undersize); *G.* Good washers.

other illustration of the use of a sliding transport. The gauge used for this operation was developed by W. R. Mullee at the American Hard Rubber Company. The purpose of this operation is to reject all washers that are too thick or too thin as well as those having burrs on the edges. The washers have the following dimensions: outside diameter 0.280 ± 0.002 inch, inside diameter 0.188 ± 0.002 inch, and thickness 0.085 ± 0.005 inch.

The metal bar A forms a "go" gauge and the bar B a "no-go" gauge with the base C, which is a heavy metal plate set at an angle with the bench top. The washers to be inspected are drawn from the hopper D by hand into the upper section of the inclined go gauge. Those washers that do not slide underneath the bar A are too thick and are slid in multiple to the chute E at the left of the gauge. The pieces that go through the gauge A drop down into the middle compartment. If they are too small they slide under the gauge B and drop into the box F directly in front of the operator. Washers that are the correct size are slid off into the chute G at the right. (See Fig. 51.)

All movements of the washers in this operation are sliding transports. The washers are not picked up at any place in the cycle. They are not handled individually but are shuffled back and forth in groups across the metal plate and against the bar gauges so that gravity is able to act as the force which tends to pull them through the gauge.

The height and angle at which the gauge is mounted above the bench are such as to make the task as easy and comfortable as possible. With this arrangement one operator inspects 30,000 washers per day.

Check List for Transport Empty and Transport Loaded

    1. Can either of these therbligs be eliminated entirely?

    2. Is the distance traveled the best one?

    3. Are the proper means used, i.e., hand, tweezers, conveyors, etc.?

    4. Are the correct members (and muscles) of the body used, i.e., fingers, forearm, shoulder, etc.?

    5. Can a chute or conveyor be used?

    6. Can "transports" be effected more satisfactorily in larger units?

    7. Can transport be performed with foot-operated devices?

    8. Is transport slowed up because of a delicate position following it?

    9. Are proper trays or bins used and is the operation laid out correctly?

    10. Are the preceding and following operations properly related to this one?

    11. Is it possible to eliminate abrupt changes in direction?

    12. For the weight of material moved, is the fastest member of the body used?

    13. Are there any body movements that can be eliminated?

    14. Can arm movements be made simultaneously, symmetrically, and in opposite directions?

Position and Pre-position. The difference between position and pre-position may be illustrated by the simple operation of picking up a fountain pen, writing, and returning it to its holder.[11] The therbligs involved in this operation are shown in Table VIII below.

TABLE VIII

MOTIONS USED IN WRITING

Steps Used in Writing	Name of Motions	Time in Thousandths of a Minute
1. Reaches for pen.............	Transport empty...........	10
2. Grasps pen..................	Grasp.....................	3
3. Carries pen to paper.........	Transport loaded...........	8
4. Positions pen for writing......	Position..................	3
5. Writes.....................	Use......................	44
6. Returns pen to holder........	Transport loaded...........	9
7. Inserts pen in holder.........	Pre-position...............	6
8. Lets go of pen...............	Release...................	1
9. Moves hand to paper.........	Transport empty...........	9

After the pen is carried to the paper it is necessary to *position* it, that is, to bring the pen down on the sheet of paper at the correct place on the line to begin writing. This is a *position* therblig. The writing completed, the pen is returned to the holder. The therblig *transport loaded* is followed by *pre-position* (rather than by position) because the pen rests in the holder in such a way that it can be grasped in the position in which it will be used the next time. Had the pen been placed in a horizontal pen holder on the desk top, the therblig sequence would then have been *transport loaded* and *position* (rather than pre-position) because the pen would have been resting in such a way that it could not have been grasped in the correct position for using. However, had the pen merely been dropped on the desk top the therblig sequence would have been *transport loaded* and *release load* since no positioning or pre-positioning would have occurred.

Positioning Pins in Bushings with Beveled Holes. Beveled holes in bushings, funnel-shaped openings in fixtures, and bullet-nosed pins all tend to reduce positioning time.

The results of a study [12] of the time required to position and insert pins in bushings with beveled holes is given in Figs. 52 and 53 and Table IX.

[11] This refers to the usual form of fountain-pen desk set.

[12] Ralph M. Barnes and Marvin E. Mundel, "Studies of Hand Motions and Rhythm Appearing in Factory Work," *Univ. Iowa Studies in Engg.,* Bul. 12, p. 19, 1938; also, "Motion Study Research: 1. How Bevel Affects Pin-Positioning Time," *Factory Management and Maintenance,* Vol. 97, No. 1, pp. 51-54, January, 1939.

TABLE IX

TIME REQUIRED TO POSITION PINS IN BUSHINGS WITH BEVELED HOLES

Operation		1		2		3		4		5	
		Clearance Between the Pin and the Hole in the Bushing in Inches									
		0.002	0.010	0.002	0.010	0.002	0.010	0.002	0.010	0.002	0.010
TRANSPORT LOADED — Carry pin from magazine at A (see figure above) through distance of 5 inches to edge of bushing at B.	Time in Minutes	0.00519	0.00564	0.00506	0.00531	0.00579	0.00542	0.00616	0.00592	0.00640	0.00716
	Time in Per Cent (Shortest Time = 100%)	102	106	100	100	114	102	121	111	126	135
POSITION — Place pin in hole C of bushing D.	Time in Minutes	0.00469	0.00271	0.00544	0.00285	0.00483	0.00386	0.00492	0.00377	0.00809	0.00672
	Time in Per Cent (Shortest Time = 100%)	100	100	116	106	103	143	105	139	173	248
TRANSPORT LOADED AND POSITION	Time in Minutes	0.00988	0.00835	0.01050	0.00816	0.01062	0.00928	0.01108	0.00969	0.01449	0.01388
	Time in Per Cent (Shortest Time = 100%)	100	102	106	100	108	114	112	119	147	170
ASSEMBLE AND DISASSEMBLE — Insert pin down into hole C and withdraw pin.	Time in Minutes	0.00316	0.00333	0.00306	0.00321	0.00298	0.00324	0.00293	0.00283	0.00222	0.00201
	Time in Per Cent (Shortest Time = 100%)	142	165	138	160	135	160	132	141	100	100
TOTAL OF TRANSPORT LOADED, POSITION, ASSEMBLE, AND DISASSEMBLE	Time in Minutes	0.01304	0.01168	0.01358	0.01138	0.01360	0.01250	0.01400	0.01253	0.01670	0.01588
	Time in Per Cent (Shortest Time = 100%)	100	103	104	100	105	110	107	110	128	140

The operation consisted of grasping a one-quarter inch brass pin 1¼ inches long from a magazine, carrying it through a distance of 5 inches, positioning and inserting it in the hole in the bushing, withdrawing the pin, and disposing of it in a tray on the table top. The time for the therbligs transport loaded, position, and assemble and disassemble was accurately measured.

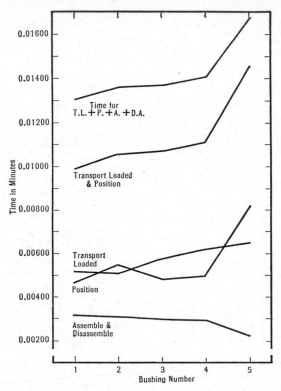

FIG. 52—Curves showing results of study of time required to position pins in beveled holes when the clearance between the pin and the hole in the bushing was 0.002 inch. Averages of median time values for seven male operators are shown.

The study was conducted in two parts, one where the clearance between the pin and the hole in the bushing was 0.002 inch, and the other where the clearance was 0.010 inch.

Least time was required to position the pin in the bushing with the 45-degree bevel (1). Seventy-three per cent more time was required to position the pin in the bushing with no bevel (5) when the clearance was 0.002 inch.

Positioning Bars on Pins.   The results of another study [13] similar to the preceding one are shown in Figs. 54 and 55 and Table X.

The operation consisted of grasping a flat bar ⅛ inch thick, ⅝ inch wide, and 3 inches long, removing it from two pins near the front edge of the table, carrying it through a distance of 5 inches, positioning it on two accurately machined pins (called a "pin set"), and dropping

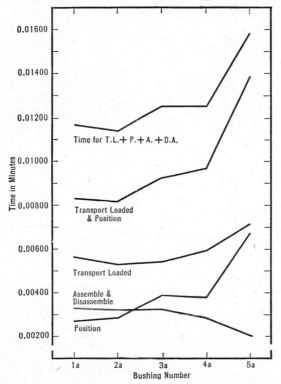

Fig. 53—Curves showing results of study of time required to position pins in beleved holes when the clearance between the pin and the hole in the bushing was 0.010 inch. Averages of median time values for seven male operators are shown.

it over the pins.   The time for the therbligs transport loaded and position was accurately measured.

The study was conducted in two parts, one where the clearance be-

[13] Ralph M. Barnes and Marvin E. Mundel, "Motion Study Research: 2. How Shape of Pins Affects Bar-Positioning Time," *Factory Management and Maintenance,* Vol. 97, No. 3, pp. 59-62, March, 1939; also *Univ. Iowa Studies in Engg.,* Bul. 12, p. 31, 1938.

tween the pin and the hole in the bar was 0.003 inch, and the other where the clearance was 0.011 inch.
The results of the study are shown in Table X. For example, least time was required to position the bar over the pins with the bullet nose (4). The pins with the square ends (2) required approximately 156 per cent more time with a clearance of 0.003 inch.

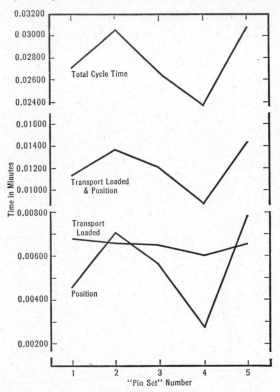

FIG. 54—Curves showing results of study of time required to position bars on five different pin sets when the clearance between the pins and the holes in the bar was 0.003 inch. Averages of median time values for ten male operators are shown.

Positioning Blocks in Slots. A study [14] was made by John M. MacKenzie to determine the time required to position and release small wood blocks (½ inch cubes) in slots with varying amounts of clearance.

[14] Ralph M. Barnes and John M. MacKenzie, "Motion Study Research: 5. How Amount of Clearance Affects Time to Position Small Parts," *Factory Management and Maintenance,* Vol. 98, No. 3, March, 1940; also *Univ. Iowa Studies in Engg.,* Bul. 21, 1940.

The operation consisted of selecting and grasping a block from a rectangular container, carrying it through a distance of 5 inches, and inserting it in a slot in a mask and releasing it. The slots were all 3½ inches long and the clearance was varied as follows: ¼₄, ⅓₂, ¼₆, ⅛ and ⅜ inch. The latter slot permitted the block to be dropped through without lining the sides up with the sides of the slot. In

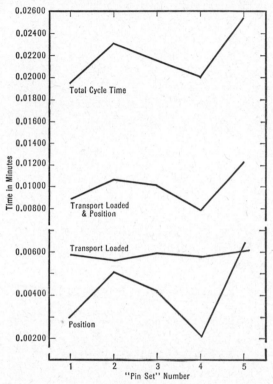

Fig. 55—Curves showing results of study of time required to position bars on five different pin sets when the clearance between the pins and the holes in the bar was 0.011 inch. Averages of median time values for ten male operators are shown.

the first part of the study the slot was placed vertical or perpendicular with the front edge of the work table and in the second part of the study it was placed horizontal or parallel with the front edge.

The results of the study given in Fig. 56 and Table XI show that in general, for a given set of conditions, a decrease in the minimum clearance between the block and the disposal opening causes an increase in the position plus release load time. It takes 151 per cent

TABLE X

Time Required to Position Bars on Pins

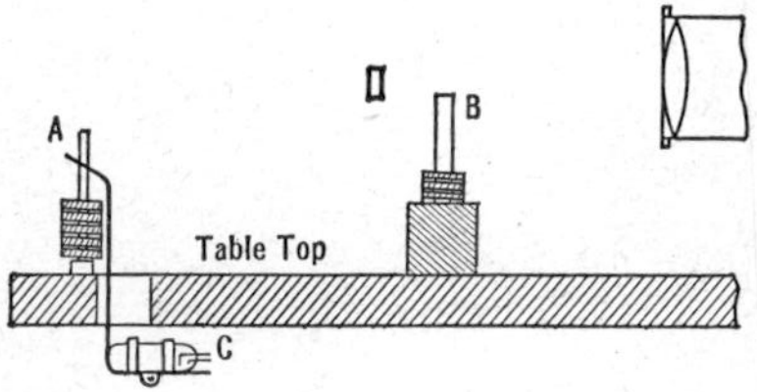

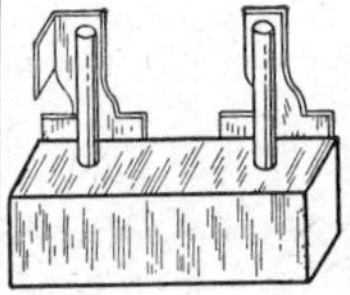

		1. Pins of equal height with square ends, Guides at left end and back.	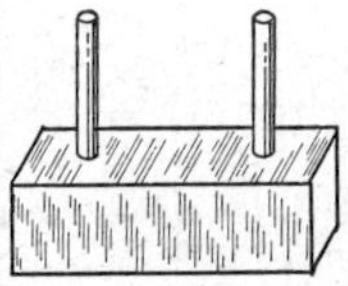	2. Pins of equal height with square ends.	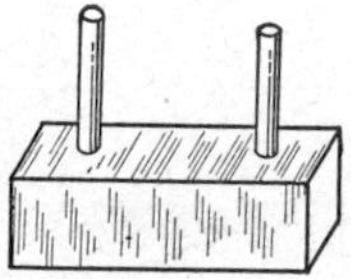	3. Pins of unequal height with square ends.	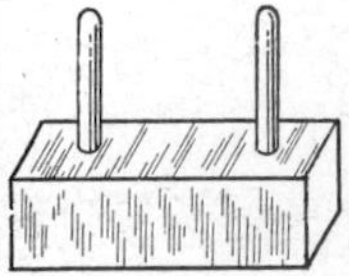	4. Pins of equal height with round ends.	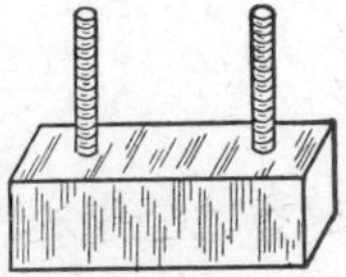	5. Threaded pins of equal height with square ends.	
		Clearance Between the Pin and the Hole in the Bar in Inches									
		0.003	0.011	0.003	0.011	0.003	0.011	0.003	0.011	0.003	0.011
TRANSPORT LOADED Carry bar from supply at A (see figure above) to the pin set at B.	Time in Minutes	0.00679	0.00587	0.00657	0.00557	0.00645	0.00585	0.00600	0.00567	0.00654	0.00590
	Time in Per Cent (Shortest Time = 100%)	113	105	109	100	108	105	100	102	109	106
POSITION Place bar on pin set at B.	Time in Minutes	0.00452	0.00302	0.00706	0.00502	0.00552	0.00410	0.00275	0.00198	0.00785	0.00614
	Time in Per Cent (Shortest Time = 100%)	164	152	256	253	201	207	100	100	286	309
TRANSPORT LOADED AND POSITION	Time in Minutes	0.01131	0.00889	0.01363	0.01059	0.01197	0.00995	0.00875	0.00765	0.01439	0.01204
	Time in Per Cent (Shortest Time = 100%)	129	116	156	138	137	130	100	100	164	157
TOTAL CYCLE (T.L. + P. + A. + R.L. + T.E. + G. + D.A.)	Time in Minutes	0.02705	0.01960	0.03051	0.02312	0.02647	0.02147	0.02362	0.01995	0.03082	0.02527
	Time in Per Cent (Shortest Time = 100%)	115	100	129	118	112	110	100	102	131	129

TABLE XI

TIME REQUIRED TO POSITION AND RELEASE SMALL BLOCKS IN SLOTS WITH VARYING AMOUNTS OF CLEARANCE

Position of Slot Relative to Front Edge of Work Table

		$\frac{1}{2}'' \times \frac{1}{64}''$		$\frac{1}{2}'' \times \frac{1}{32}''$		$\frac{1}{2}'' \times \frac{1}{16}''$		$\frac{1}{2}'' \times \frac{1}{8}''$		$\frac{1}{2}'' \times \frac{3}{8}''$	
		Vertical	Horizontal	Vertical	Horizontal	Vertical	Horizontal	Vertical	Horizontal	Vertical	Horizontal
BOTH HANDS											
POSITION AND RELEASE — Place block through slot in mask at B and release.	Time in Minutes	0.01380	0.01215	0.01340	.01188	0.01013	0.00993	0.00922	0.00922	0.00548	0.00713
	Time in Per Cent (Shortest Time = 100%)	251	170	244	167	185	139	168	129	100	100
TOTAL CYCLE — Select and grasp block from container A above, carry block 5 inches, insert in slot in mask at B, and release.	Time in Minutes	0.03367	0.03127	0.03307	0.03013	0.02927	0.02708	0.02750	0.02670	0.02182	0.02303
	Time in Per Cent (Shortest Time = 100%)	154	136	152	131	134	118	126	116	100	100
RIGHT HAND ONLY											
POSITION AND RELEASE — Place block through slot in mask at B and release.	Time in Minutes	0.00893	0.00110	0.00875	0.00983	0.00698	0.00858	0.00793	0.00810	0.00445	0.00525
	Time in Per Cent (Shortest Time = 100%)	201	210	197	187	157	163	178	154	100	100
TOTAL CYCLE — Select and grasp block from container A above, carry block 5 inches, insert in slot in mask at B and release.	Time in Minutes	0.02205	0.02270	0.02095	0.02263	0.02075	0.02090	0.02010	0.01988	0.01528	0.01667
	Time in Per Cent (Shortest Time = 100%)	144	136	137	136	136	125	131	119	100	100

more time to position and release a block, both hands being used and slots vertical, when there is a clearance of $\frac{1}{64}$ than it does when there is a clearance of $\frac{3}{8}$ of an inch.

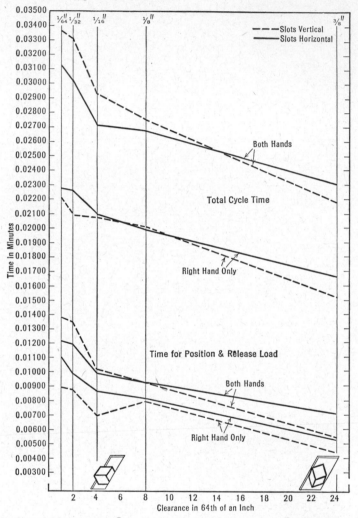

Fig. 56—Curves showing the results of study of time required to position blocks in slots. Averages of median time values for five male operators are shown.

For a given set of conditions, the time required for position plus release load when using both hands is 25 per cent greater than the time required when using one hand alone. However, two blocks are being carried instead of one.

Some devices which aid in pre-positioning tools and materials are shown on pages 227 and 228.

Check List for Position

1. Can tolerances be changed?
2. Can square edges be eliminated?
3. Can a guide, funnel, bushing, gauge, stop, swinging bracket, locating pin, spring, drift, recess, key, pilot on screw, or chamfer be used?
4. Can a foot-operated collet be used?

Check List for Pre-position [15]

1. Can the object be pre-positioned in transit?
2. Can tool be balanced so as to keep handle in upright position?
3. Can holding device be made to keep tool handle in proper position?
4. Can tools be suspended?
5. Can tools be stored in proper location to work?
6. Can a guide be used?
7. Can design of article be made so that all sides are alike?
8. Can a magazine feed be used?
9. Can a stacking device be used?
10. Can a rotating fixture be used?

Assemble, Use, and Disassemble. The following explanation is included here to clarify the meaning of assemble and use. Use always refers to the use of a tool or device for the purpose for which it was intended. Thus, the actual writing (see Table VIII) was a use therblig. Similarly, painting, drilling, and sawing are all use therbligs. If a nut is assembled onto a bolt by hand this therblig is assemble; whereas if a wrench is used for this operation the sequence is assemble (fit wrench to nut), use (turn nut down), and disassemble (remove wrench from nut).

Frequently a tool will be held in the palm of the hand when not in use. For example, the clerk checking boxes in a shipping department may place a crayon mark on certain items as they pass by on a conveyor. The use therblig would not include the entire cycle but only that part during which the crayon is actually used for marking. The use of the bone in folding paper presents another example of this. See page 166.

Some analysts advocate limiting *use* to ultimate objectives and restricting assemble to such temporary acts as fitting a tool to its work. Thus, any permanent assembly of two or more parts would be

---

[15] Pre-position is discussed at length on pages 226 to 228.

use even when no tool is involved.[16] Since this interpretation is likely to result in some confusion to the beginner, and in view of the fact that the former interpretation is more widely accepted, use will, in this book, always refer to the use of a tool or device for the purpose for which it was intended; and assemble will be understood to consist of placing one object into or onto another object with which it becomes an integral part.

Painting with Spray Gun. The scope of the use therblig is so wide that it is impossible to cite representative cases. However, one illustration will be included because it gives an interpretation of this therblig that is often overlooked. The operation is painting with a spray gun the enclosed motor unit of an electric refrigerator. The unit had a number of irregular projections and, since it occupied a prominent position on the refrigerator, a first-class painting job was required. From observation of the operation it was apparent that the operator was wasting paint, owing to the fact that he was missing the surface, "spraying air" by spraying past corners, and making sweeping flourishes during which little or none of the paint was being directed at the refrigerator unit. In this operation the use therblig not only involved time but material as well. Therefore, shortening the use therblig meant saving both time and paint.

A micromotion study of this operation, made of the best operator in the plant, showed that during 23 per cent of the time the spray gun was in use the paint was not hitting the surface of the unit being sprayed, but was being wasted "spraying air."

By careful training of the operator, and by some changes in the work place, including a power-driven, foot-controlled, turntable for the work and three fixed spray guns mounted above the turntable, the following results were obtained:

(*a*) Savings in time .... 50.6 per cent
(*b*) Reduction in rejects .... 60 . per cent
(*c*) Direct labor savings per year $3750.00
(*d*) Savings in paint per year $5940.00
(*e*) Cost to develop and install new method $1040.00

Not only did the total savings in direct labor and paint resulting from the improved method amount to a substantial sum, but also of importance was the great reduction in rejects. In the old method of spraying most of the rejects resulted from "runs" in the paint. In

[16] L. P. Alford, Ed., "Cost and Production Handbook," p. 523, Ronald Press, New York, 1934.

such cases the excess paint had to be scraped off and the unit re-painted, which was an expensive operation. The improved method eliminated most of this type of reject.

Check List for Assemble, Use, and Disassemble

1. Can a jig or fixture be used?
2. Can an automatic device or machine be used?
3. Can the assembly be made in multiple?
4. Can a more efficient tool be used?
5. Can stops be used?
6. Can burrs be removed while machine is making cut?
7. Should a power tool be used?
8. Can a cam or air-operated fixture be used?

Inspect. In inspection work [17] the time for the therblig inspect is usually proportional to the reaction time of the individual and the type of the stimulus used. Only an individual with fast reaction time should be employed on inspection operations. Incidentally, good eyesight is a second essential requirement for success on this kind of work.

As to the type of stimulus, the data in Table XII show that, other

TABLE XII

AVERAGE SPEED OF REACTION

Time in Thousandths of a Second

Type of Stimulus	Reaction Time
Simple reaction—visual stimulus. Subject was instructed to press telegraph key as quickly as possible after light flashed.	225
Simple reaction—auditory stimulus. Subject was instructed to press telegraph key as quickly as possible after electric buzzer sounded.	185
Simple reaction—touch stimulus. Subject was instructed to press telegraph key as quickly as possible after feeling bar touch hand.	175
Simple reaction—electric shock stimulus. Subject was instructed to press telegraph key as quickly as possible after receiving electric shock on hand.	140
Choice reaction—visual stimulus. Subject could react to two lights. If the right light flashed, the subject pressed the right key. If the left light flashed, the subject pressed the left key.	325
Timed action stimulus—touch stimulus. Subject is given notice of the approaching stimulus. The subject watched the operator's descending hand and was instructed to react as soon as the operator's hand touched the key.	50

[17] See also pages 203 to 207.

conditions being equal, a person would react more quickly to sound than to light, the time being 0.185 second for the former and 0.225 second for the latter. Reaction to touch is the quickest of all, being 0.175 second.[18]

Check List for Inspect

1. Can inspect be eliminated or overlapped with another operation?
2. Can multiple gauges or tests be used?
3. Can a pressure, vibration, hardness, or flash test be used?
4. Can the intensity of illumination be increased or the light sources rearranged to reduce the inspection time?
5. Can the operator use spectacles to advantage?

Release Load. Although release load is often of very short duration, it should always be included in the analysis. In the operation "assemble bolt and washers" described on page 147 the operator released the washer after having assembled it onto the bolt. This therblig required such a short time that it could not be measured with the clock at ordinary speeds and consequently this therblig was combined with the preceding one as shown in Fig. 38.

Release load should be short. If it is of long duration some change should be made in the operation to shorten it. The discussion on page 189 under drop delivery suggests some possible changes.

Check List for Release Load

1. Can this therblig be eliminated?
2. Can a drop delivery be used?
3. Can the release be made in transit?
4. Is a careful release load necessary? Can this be avoided?
5. Can an ejector (mechanical, air, gravity) be used?
6. Are the material bins of proper design?
7. At the end of the release load, is the hand or the transportation means in the most advantageous position for the next therblig?
8. Can a conveyor be used?

Hold. Hold is a therblig that frequently occurs in assembly work and in hand-manipulated machine operations. It is one of the easiest therbligs to eliminate and often leads to substantial increases in output. The elimination of the hold therblig in the bolt and washer as-

---

[18] A slight difference in reaction time results from different attitudes of mind on the part of the operator. For example, if the operator's mind is primarily concentrated on the *stimulus,* the reaction times are likely to be a little slower than those indicated. However, if his attention is primarily directed to the *muscular sensations* involved in reacting, the reactions will be a little faster.

sembly (see page 149), for example, was largely responsible for the 50 per cent increase in output.

The hand should not be used for a "vise"—a mechanical device of some kind is usually much more economical for holding. In fact, when one hand is used for holding, the operator has reduced his capacity for productive hand work by 50 per cent. Although not every hold therblig can be eliminated, certainly all such therbligs in a cycle are vulnerable points of attack for improving the method.

Check List for Hold

1. Can a vise, clamp, clip, vacuum, hook, rack, fixture, or other mechanical device be used?
2. Can an adhesive or friction be used?
3. Can a stop be used to eliminate hold?
4. When hold cannot be eliminated can arm rests be provided?

ACCURATE MEASUREMENT OF THERBLIG TIME

The therblig time values for several of the investigations referred to in this chapter were given in hundred thousandths of a minute. An electrical recording kymograph (see Fig. 57) was used for making these time measurements.

Paper tape, similar to adding-machine tape, is drawn across the kymograph table by means of the two rollers shown at the left of the machine. A synchronous motor drives the rollers, drawing the paper through at a uniform velocity of 2000 inches per minute.

Solenoid-operated pencils are mounted above the paper tape so that each of six pencils makes contact with it and draws a straight line on the tape as it passes through.

Each pencil is connected to a solenoid in such a way that closing the solenoid circuit jerks the pencil toward the solenoid and perpendicular to the motion of the paper through the kymograph, thus putting a jog in the pencil line on the moving tape (see Fig. 58).

Figure 58 is a reproduction of the record made by the solenoid-operated pencils for the study of grasping washers of varying thickness.

Washers were placed in a row on the grid shown in Table V (see also Table VII), a thin flat beam of light was passed across the top of the row of washers, and allowed to fall on a photoelectric cell mounted at the end of the grid. This photoelectric cell was connected through relays to pencil B on the kymograph. As the finger and thumb interrupted the beam of light to grasp the washer the first jog in the line B was made, marking the beginning of the grasp therblig.

Since the brass bars in the grid were insulated from each other by a thin fiber strip or spacer between the bars, a circuit could be closed by placing brass washers across the insulators (fiber strip) and thus

FIG. 57—Electrically operated kymograph measures and records time. Paper tape passes through the machine at a uniform speed of 2000 inches per minute and solenoid-operated pencils mounted above the tape may be used to mark the beginning and end points of therbligs or of other subdivisions of an operation to be timed.

connecting all grids together. Such a circuit was used and connected to solenoid A. Thus, when the washer rested on top of the grid and across the insulating strip, the circuit was closed and line A was drawn.

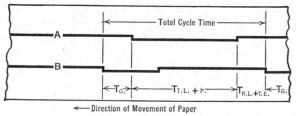

FIG. 58—Reproduction of record made by solenoid-operated pencils on kymograph for study of grasping washers of varying thickness.

However, as soon as the washer was grasped by the thumb and fingers and started to be removed from the grid, the circuit was interrupted and the first jog was made in line A in Fig. 58. The distance between the first two jogs was a measure of the time required to grasp the washer. One-fiftieth of an inch on the tape represented $\frac{1}{100,000}$ of a minute.

By means of photoelectric cells and other devices it is possible to measure various parts of an operation without interfering in any way with the natural movements of the operator.

CHAPTER 11

FATIGUE

Since one of the main objectives of motion and time study is to reduce fatigue and to make the work as easy and satisfying for the individual as possible, it is desirable at this time to define fatigue.

The term fatigue has various meanings depending upon the point of view that is taken in considering the subject. Fatigue in industry refers to three related phenomena:

1. A feeling of tiredness.
2. A physiological change in the body. The nerves and muscles fail to function as well or as fast as is normal owing to chemical changes in the body resulting from work.
3. A diminished capacity for doing work.

Feeling of Tiredness. A feeling of tiredness is commonly associated with long periods of work. It is subjective in nature and consequently the extent of tiredness cannot be determined by an observer. Tiredness may be localized in some particular muscle or it may be a general sensation of weariness.

This feeling of fatigue acts as a protective device in preventing exhaustion but there is often no direct correlation with physiological fatigue which manifests itself in decreased ability to do work. A person may feel tired and yet he may work as efficiently as ever, or he may feel normal and yet he may be actually working at a low rate because of physiological fatigue. Therefore, the feeling of tiredness does not seem to be a valid basis for judging the effect of work on the individual.

Physiological Changes Resulting from Work. From the physiological point of view the human body may be thought of as a machine [1] which consumes fuel and gives out useful energy. The principal mechanisms of the body involved are (1) the circulatory system, (2) the digestive system, (3) the muscular system, (4) the nervous system, and (5) the respiratory system. Continuous physical work affects these mechanisms both separately and collectively.

Fatigue is the result of an accumulation of waste products in the

[1] A. V. Hill, "Living Machinery," Harcourt, Brace and Co., New York, 1927.

muscles and in the blood stream which reduces the capacity of the muscles to act. Very possibly the nerve fiber terminals and the central nervous system may also be affected by work, thereby causing a person to slow up when tired. Muscular movements are accompanied by chemical reactions which require food for their activities. This food is furnished as *glycogen*, a starch-like substance which is carried in the blood stream and is readily converted into sugar. When the muscle contracts, the glycogen is changed into lactic acid, a waste product which tends to restrict the continued activity of the muscle. In the recovery phase of muscular action, oxygen is used to change most of the lactic acid back to glycogen, thus enabling the muscles to continue moving. The supply of oxygen and the temperature affect the speed of recovery. If the rate of work is not strenuous, the muscle is able to maintain a satisfactory balance. Excessive lactic acid does not accumulate and the muscle does not go into "oxygen debt," both of which diminish the capacity of the muscle to act.

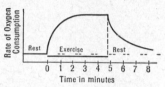

Fig. 59—Rate of oxygen consumption before, during, and after exercise. The period of exercise is marked by a heavy horizontal line.

An athlete running the mile might be used as an example of an individual exerting himself to the utmost. He is using the supply of fuel and oxygen at a rapid rate and therefore will require time for recuperation, that is, time to bring his muscles back to equilibrium.

The diagram in Fig. 59 shows the rate of oxygen consumption before, during, and after exercise.[2] The period of exercise is marked by the thick horizontal line. As the diagram shows, the rate of oxygen consumption starts to rise as soon as exercise begins and starts to fall as soon as it ceases. Since the exercise pictured in Fig. 59 was moderate, recovery was completed after a few minutes. After severe physical exercise, recovery may not be completed for an hour or more.

Experiments in the Physiological Cost of Doing Work. Physiologists have conducted many studies of physical work in which the energy expended was measured in terms of "physiological cost"[3] or

---

[2] *Ibid.*, p. 142.

[3] "The physiological cost of a given piece of work is the amount of oxygen used during work and recovery in excess of the amount used during an equal period of time, the subject being in the resting state." G. P. Crowden, "The Physiological Cost of the Muscular Movements Involved in Barrow Work," *Ind. Fatigue Research Bd.*, Report 50, p. 2, 1928.

the excess of oxygen consumed while the subject was working. Since oxygen is used by man in proportion to the "fuel" burnt in his body, the amount of oxygen absorbed from the inhaled air during the period of work and recovery is a measure or an index of the extent of the vital process involved.[4]

The subject to be studied is fitted with apparatus (Douglas-Haldane Apparatus) for collecting exhaled air over a definite period of time. Usually the subject carries a mouthpiece in his mouth, so equipped with valves that fresh air is admitted from the outside and exhaled air is led through a tube to a large rubberized fabric bag carried on the back of the subject. A nose-clip is placed on the nose so that breathing is possible only through the mouth. Using this technique, investigators have arrived at such conclusions as the following:

1. Wheelbarrow Work: [5]

(a) The optimum speed for wheeling a barrow is a normal brisk walk, as Table XIII shows.

TABLE XIII

PHYSIOLOGICAL COST OF WHEELING BARROW AT VARIOUS RATES

	Slow Walk	Normal Brisk Walk	Very Quick Walk	Gentle Run
Excess O_2	2520 cc.	2480 cc.	4040 cc.	3660 cc.
Relative values	1.01	1	1.63	1.47
Excess O_2	2515 cc.	2280 cc.	4405 cc.	3887 cc.
Relative values	1.1	1	1.77	1.7
Excess O_2	1560 cc.	1240 cc.	2040 cc.	1960 cc.
Relative values	1.26	1	1.64	1.58
Mean relative values	1.12	1	1.68	1.58

(b) The best conditions for barrow work are attained when the load is balanced to suit the worker's stature.

(c) Greatest energy is expended in starting and stopping, therefore the elimination of interruptions brings greater efficiency.

2. Walking on Level: [6]

(a) On a truly horizontal surface, the most economical rate of progress is

[4] Ibid., p. 2.

[5] Ibid., p. 15. Table XIII reproduced by permission of the Controller of H. M. Stationery Office, London.

[6] Jules Amar, "The Physiology of Industrial Organization and the Reemployment of the Disabled," p. 133, Macmillan Co., New York, 1919.

4.5 kilometres (2.8 miles) an hour. This enables an unburdened man to cover 45 to 50 kilometres (28 to 31 miles) in the day, with two minutes' rest at every kilometre.

(b) When the man is carrying a burden the economical pace, that which costs the organism least, is 4.2 kilometres (2.6 miles) an hour, the burden weighing from 20 to 22 kilogrammes (44 to 48.4 pounds). But to realize the maximum daily performance, the weight of the load should be 45 kilogrammes (99 pounds) and the rate of progress 4.8 kilometres (3 miles) an hour, while the day's work should consist of 7½ hours, with 2 minutes' rest every 600 metres (650 yards). An adult of 25 to 40 years of age can carry this load of 99 pounds for an average distance of 26 kilometres (16 miles) a day. But if the pace is increased to 5.5 kilometres (3.4 miles) an hour, the distance will be reduced by almost one-half, no matter how the intervals of rest may be arranged.

3. Methods of Carrying Loads: [7]

The best methods of carrying a load are those which interfere least with the normal body posture. Between the usual method and the best method there may be as much as 50 per cent difference.

4. Performing Home Laundering Operations: [8]

The energy cost of laundry processes as compared with resting is given in the table below:

Kind of Activity	Total Number of Tests	Average Per Cent above Resting
Resting (100 per cent).............................	36	
Washing clothes by hand...........................	25	191
Rinsing clothes...................................	21	161
Wringing clothes with hand-power wringer...........	7	197
Wringing clothes by hand..........................	23	138
Drying clothes in extractor........................	21	125
Wringing clothes with electric dryer................	23	99
Putting up and removing clothes line...............	7	135
Hanging clothes with basket on floor...............	21	184
Hanging clothes from utility table.................	22	118

[7] E. P. Cathcart, "The Physique of Women in Industry," *Ind. Fatigue Research Bd.*, Report 44, 1927.

[8] State College of Washington Agricultural Experiment Station, Bul. 282, "The Human Energy Cost of Certain Household Tasks," p. 13. See also Bul. 317, "Time and Cost Evaluation of Home Laundering," 1935.

Decrease in Output a Measure of Fatigue. The most practical and useful measure of fatigue resulting from work is its effect upon

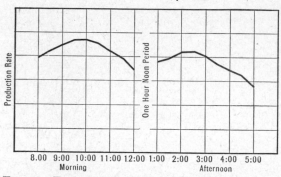

the quantity and the quality of the individual's work. The amount of work done per unit of time may be shown by means of a production curve, sometimes called an output curve or a work curve. Figure 60 shows a typical daily production curve for an individual engaged in heavy manual

Fig. 60—Typical daily production curve. For an individual engaged in heavy muscular work.

work. The upward slope of the curve indicates a "warming up" period in the morning. This is followed by an increase in output until the middle of the morning, when a falling off in production occurs, possibly due to the fatigue of the worker. The curve for the afternoon is similar in shape to that for the forenoon, except that it falls off more rapidly towards the end of the day.

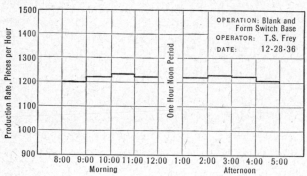

Fig. 61—Production curve for blanking and forming switch base on No. 21 Bliss press.

Much work in industry today is light and requires little physical exertion on the part of the operator. The production curve shown in Fig. 61 seems to be typical for such work, there being a fairly uniform output throughout the day. The operator has such a reserve of energy and the physical requirements of the task are so small that it is entirely possible for the operator to maintain a steady output for the entire day.[9] In fact, it is not uncommon to find an operator actually increasing his speed during the last hour of the day when a delay has existed early in the day causing him to fall behind, or when a rush job has been put into production.[10]

There are many factors which affect the amount of work that an individual will do in a day and the extent of the physical fatigue that will result from this work. With a given set of working conditions and equipment, the amount of work done in a day will depend upon the skill and ability of the worker, and the speed and effort at which he works. This latter factor depends directly upon the individual's inclination or his "will to work," which itself is affected by many things. The fatigue resulting from a given level of activity will depend upon such factors as (1) hours of work, i.e., the length of the working day and the weekly working hours, (2) the number, location, and length of rest periods, (3) working conditions, such as lighting, heating, ventilation, and noise, and (4) the work itself.

Hours of Work. The findings of the Health of Munition Workers Committee organized in Great Britain in 1915 gave impetus to the movement for decreasing the length of the working day. At that time the twelve- to fifteen-hour day was common. The reports of this committee and of many other investigations made since that time indicate the economy of shorter working hours. There is evidence to show that on most work, except in operations whose output depends mainly upon the speed of the machine, the reduction of the length of the working day to eight hours results in an increase in hourly and daily output.[11]

Since, in this country, the eight-hour day and the five-day week are now in effect in many industries, there seems to be little to be gained from a further reduction in the length of the working day in so far as preventing physical fatigue is concerned. When increased demands for output cannot be met with an eight-hour day, the possibility of two eight-hour shifts per day offers a practical way out. This also tends to reduce the overhead costs of operating the plant

[9] G. J. Stegemerten, "What Fatigue Does to Output," *Factory Management and Maintenance*, Vol. 93, No. 9, p. 381, September, 1935.

[10] A. G. Anderson, "A Study of Human Fatigue in Industry," an abstract of a thesis, pp. 20-22, Univ. of Ill., 1931.

[11] H. M. Vernon, "Industrial Fatigue and Efficiency," George Routledge & Sons, London, 1921. Also, "Two Studies on Hours of Work," *Ind. Fatigue Research Bd.*, Report 47, 1928.

since the overhead expenses would be distributed over a larger number of units.

Rest Periods. Rest is a physical necessity during heavy work, and whether "official" rest periods are allowed by the management or not workers will rest during a considerable part of the day. Vernon found that on heavy work, men rested from one-half to one-fourth of the working time.[12] Taylor, in his classic experiment of handling pig iron, increased the output from $12\frac{1}{2}$ tons to 47 tons per day mainly by requiring that the workmen rest 57 per cent of the time and work but 43 per cent of the time.[13] Several investigations of workers on medium heavy muscular work and on an eight-hour day show that the worker cannot give his maximum output unless he rests approximately 15 per cent of the time during the working day.[14] It should be noted that these examples are taken from heavy and medium heavy work and that much work in industry today is very light and requires little physical exertion on the part of the operator.

In many kinds of work, both heavy and light, rest periods are desirable for the following reasons: (1) rest periods increase the amount of work done in a day, (2) the workers like the rest periods, (3) rest periods decrease the variability in the rate of working and tend to encourage the operator to maintain a level of performance nearer his maximum output, (4) rest periods reduce physical fatigue, and (5) they reduce the amount of personal time taken during the working hours.

Rest periods are usually placed in the middle of the morning and the middle of the afternoon and range in length from five to fifteen minutes, seven to ten minutes being most common. The proper number of rest periods and the proper length of each will depend upon the nature of the work and can be determined most satisfactorily by experiment. A study of the output curve may indicate the time at which output reaches its maximum, which is the point where a rest period should be introduced. Rest periods are particularly effective in heavy manual work, in operations that require close attention and concentration, such as fine inspection work, and in work that is highly repetitive and monotonous.

Tests show that definite rest periods sanctioned by the management have a far greater recuperative effect than those which must be

[12] H. M. Vernon and others, "Rest Pauses in Heavy and Moderately Heavy Industrial Work," *Ind. Fatigue Research Bd.*, Report 4i, p. 20, 1927.

[13] F. W. Taylor, "The Principles of Scientific Management," p. 57, Harper & Bros., New York, 1911.

[14] G. H. Shepard, "Effect of Rest Periods on Production," *Personnel J.*, Vol. 7, No. 3, p. 186, August, 1928.

taken surreptitiously. Whether the rest is in the form of "soldiering" or whether it is enforced because of lack of materials, such hit or miss rests may have as little as one-fifth the value of prescribed rests in relieving fatigue.[15]

Lighting, Heating, and Ventilation. Lighting, heating, and ventilation have a definite effect upon the physical comfort, mental attitude, output, and fatigue of the worker. Working conditions should be so adjusted as to make the shop and office a comfortable place in which to work. The requirements for proper illumination, heating, and ventilation are well understood, and equipment that will supply comfortable physical conditions for work is now available.

Of these three factors, illumination is perhaps most inadequately provided in most plants. Where the work is of such a nature that visual perception is required for its satisfactory performance, the output is invariably increased when adequate illumination is provided. Inspection operations such as those described on pages 203 to 209 are examples of work of this nature.

Noise and Vibration. Although noise is annoying to practically everyone, adaptation to such conditions is readily made by most people and the psychological and physiological effects of noise are not so serious as many people believe.[16] Viteles draws the following conclusions from his study of noise:

(1) No experimental evidence is available to show that automatic performance is adversely affected by noise or by vibration.

(2) Nevertheless, except with certain "meaningful" noises, there is a wide agreement that both noise and vibration are "disagreeable" or "uncomfortable" accompaniments of work.

(3) A continuous noisy background often appears to have an initial stimulating effect, and this taken together with (2) appears to indicate that the noise should be regarded as an adverse condition which is met by an unwitting increase of effort.

(4) With constructive work involving mental effort fairly consistent slight deterioration is observed, particularly in continued effort. Although so far as the experiments go, the deterioration is barely or only just statistically significant, it may be "psychologically" significant. The consistency of the small deterioration seems to point to this.

(5) Discontinuous noise is more subjectively disturbing than continuous noise; "meaningful" noise may be more or less disturbing than "unmeaning" noise according as it is interesting or familiar.[17]

[15] H. M. Vernon, *Ind. Fatigue Research Bd.*, Report 41, p. 21, 1927.

[16] K. G. Pollock and others, "Two Studies in the Psychological Effects of Noise," *Ind. Health Research Bd.*, Report 65, p. 30, 1932.

[17] M. S. Viteles, "Industrial Psychology," p. 510, W. W. Norton & Co., Inc., New York, 1932.

Since noise and vibration are annoying they are undesirable and should be reduced or eliminated in so far as possible. Stamping, cutting, and press work are often segregated in one part of the factory so that the remainder of the plant may be kept relatively free from noise. Where large numbers of employees are affected and where the work requires a high degree of concentration or attention, it may be economical to reduce the noise by covering the ceilings and walls with acousticon as is done in many places.[18]

Effect of Mental Attitude on Fatigue. Fatigue is by no means the simple, easily defined thing that many would have us believe it to be. Cathcart,[19] Dill,[20] and Mayo,[21] all of whom have written very clearly on this subject, point out the many-sided nature of fatigue.

A carefully conducted study of fatigue lasting over a period of several years, made of factory operators on regular production work at the Western Electric Company, showed that the mental attitude of the workers was by far the most important factor governing the employee's efficiency.

Specific conclusions [22] relating to this point are:

(1) The amount of sleep has a slight but significant effect upon individual performance.

(2) A distinct relationship is apparent between the emotional status or home conditions of the girls and their performance.

(3) Total daily productivity is increased by rest periods, and not decreased.

(4) Outside influences tend to create either a buoyant or a depressed spirit which is reflected in production.

(5) The mental attitude of the operator toward the supervisor and working and home conditions is probably the biggest single factor governing the employee's efficiency.

Additional statements bearing on this point were selected by

[18] B. E. Lies and Marie P. Sealy, "Motion Study Principles and Their Application in a Department Store," *Trans. A.S.M.E.*, Vol. 50, No. 29, Man-50-17A, p. 21, 1928.

[19] E. P. Cathcart, "The Human Fatigue in Industry," Oxford Univ. Press, London, 1928.

[20] D. B. Dill, "Fatigue and Work Efficiency," *Personnel J.*, Vol. 9, No. 4, pp. 112-116, May, 1933, Am. Management Assoc.

[21] E. Mayo, "The Human Problems of an Industrial Civilization," Macmillan Co., New York, 1933.

[22] G. A. Pennock, "Industrial Research at Hawthorne, an Experimental Investigation of Rest Periods, Working Conditions, and Other Influences," *Personnel J.*, Vol. 8, No. 5, p. 311, February, 1930.

Mayo [23] from "progress reports" of the experiment made at Hawthorne. Some of these are given here.

There has been a continual upward trend in output which has been independent of the changes in rest pauses. This upward trend has continued too long to be ascribed to an initial stimulus from the novelty of starting a special study.

There has been an important increase in contentment among the girls working under test-room conditions.

There has been a decrease in absences of about 80 per cent among the girls since entering the test-room group. Test-room operators have had approximately one-third as many sick absences as the regular department during the last six months.

Observations of operators in the relay assembly test room indicate that their health is being maintained or improved and that they are working within their capacity. . . .

Important factors in the production of a better mental attitude and greater enjoyment of work have been the greater freedom, less strict supervision and the opportunity to vary from a fixed pace without reprimand from a gang boss.

The operators have no clear idea as to why they are able to produce more in the test room; but as shown in the replies to questionnaires . . . there is the feeling that better output is in some way related to the distinctly pleasanter, freer, and happier working conditions.

Improving the Method of Doing the Work. It has been estimated that 25 to 50 per cent of the manual work done in our shops, offices, factories, and homes is unnecessary—that the work might be done in a much better way, producing the same output with less expenditure of energy on the part of the workers. The industrial engineer has, in the past, played an important part in increasing labor effectiveness and his opportunities in this field are greater today than ever before. In performing his task, motion and time study serves as one of his most valuable tools.

It so happens that in finding a better way of doing work, the task is nearly always made easier and more satisfying for the worker because the improved way is a logical and convenient way, permitting smooth, natural, rhythmical motions.

The next three chapters give principles and rules which have been found useful in improving methods of doing work. These twenty-two principles have the common purpose of suggesting ways of using the capacities of the human body most effectively—indicating methods that permit the greatest economy of motion.

[23] E. Mayo, *Op. cit.,* p. 67.

PRINCIPLES OF MOTION ECONOMY

A CHECK SHEET FOR MOTION ECONOMY AND FATIGUE REDUCTION

The following twenty-two rules or principles of motion economy may be profitably applied to shop and office work alike. Although not all of these principles are applicable to every operation, they do form a basis or a code for improving the efficiency and reducing fatigue in manual work.

Use of the Human Body

1. The two hands should begin as well as complete their therbligs at the same instant.

2. The two hands should not be idle at the same instant except during rest periods.

3. Motions of the arms should be in opposite and symmetrical directions, instead of in the same direction, and should be made simultaneously.

4. Hand motions should be confined to the lowest classification with which it is possible to perform the work satisfactorily.

5. Momentum should be employed to assist the worker wherever possible, and it should be reduced to a minimum if it must be overcome by muscular effort.

6. Continuous curved motions are preferable to straight-line motions involving sudden and sharp changes in direction.

7. Ballistic movements are faster, easier, and more accurate than restricted (fixation) or "controlled" movements.

8. Rhythm is essential to the smooth and automatic performance of an operation and the work should be arranged to permit easy and natural rhythm wherever possible.

Arrangement of the Work Place

9. Definite and fixed stations should be provided for all tools and materials.

10. Tools, materials, and controls should be located around the work place and as close in front of the worker as possible.

11. Gravity feed bins and containers should be used to deliver the material as close to the point of assembly or use as possible.

12. "Drop deliveries" should be used wherever possible.

13. Materials and tools should be located to permit the best sequence of therbligs.

14. Provisions should be made for adequate illumination is the first requirement for satisfactory visual perception.

15. The height of the work place and the chair should preferably be so arranged that alternate sitting and standing at work are easily possible.

16. A chair of the type and height to permit good posture should be provided for every worker.

Design of Tools and Equipment

17. The hands should be relieved of all work that can be performed more advantageously by the feet or other parts of the body.

18. Two or more tools should be combined wherever possible.

19. Tools and materials should be pre-positioned wherever possible.

20. Where each finger performs some specific movement, such as in typewriting, the load should be distributed in accordance with the inherent capacities of the fingers.

21. Handles such as those used on cranks and large screwdrivers should be designed to permit as much of the surface of the hand to come in contact with the handle as possible. This is particularly true when considerable force is exerted in using the handle. For light assembly work the screwdriver handle should be so shaped that it is smaller at the bottom than at the top.

22. Levers, crossbars, and handwheels should be located in such positions that the operator can manipulate them with the least change in body position and with the greatest mechanical advantage.

CHAPTER 12

PRINCIPLES OF MOTION ECONOMY AS RELATED TO THE USE OF THE HUMAN BODY

Although the phrase "principles of motion economy" is used very frequently in engineering literature, it seems impossible to find a satisfactory statement of these principles in sufficient detail to be of value to those who are not expert in the field.

On several occasions Gilbreth listed certain "rules for motion economy and efficiency" [1] which govern hand motions, and from time to time other investigators in this field have added to this list.

Additional research which will enlarge our knowledge of the inherent capacities of the various members of the human body is greatly needed. There is much yet to be done in determining the fundamental laws which permit the maximum amount of productive effort with a minimum of fatigue. Although the material in this chapter is discussed under the heading "principles of motion economy," it might perhaps have been more accurately designated as "some rules for motion economy and fatigue reduction."

In attempting to collect and codify the authentic information which is already available for use as a guide in determining methods of greatest economy, one is confronted with many difficulties. If general principles are stated they are likely to be abstract and of little practical use; whereas if narrower rules with specific illustrations are presented they may lack universality of application. In the past it has been customary to make general statements of the principles without including additional information or practical applications. This has been very unsatisfactory and has greatly retarded the use of motion and time study.

[1] F. B. and L. M. Gilbreth, "A Fourth Dimension for Measuring Skill for Obtaining the One Best Way," *Soc. Ind. Engg. Bul.*, Vol. 5, No. 11, Nov. 1923. Gilbreth gave sixteen rules for motion economy in the above article and these rules have been listed in a more recent publication: W. J. Donald, Ed., "Handbook of Business Administration," Chapter 8, p. 640, McGraw-Hill Book Co., New York, 1931. See also: A. H. Mogensen, "Common Sense Applied to Motion and Time Study," pp. 98-99, McGraw-Hill Book Co., 1932, and F. B. Gilbreth, "Motion Study," pp. 10-85, Van Nostrand Co., New York, 1911.

It is the purpose of this and the following two chapters to interpret by means of specific illustrations some of the general rules or principles of motion economy which have been and are now being successfully used in industry. All the principles presented in these chapters are not of equal importance nor does this discussion include all the factors which enter into the determination of better methods for doing work. These principles do, however, form a basis—a code, or a body of rules—which, if applied by one trained in the technique of micromotion study, will make it possible to increase greatly the output of manual labor with a minimum of fatigue.

These principles will be presented under the following three subdivisions:

I. Principles of motion economy as related to the use of the human body.

II. Principles of motion economy as related to the arrangement of the work place.

III. Principles of motion economy as related to the design of tools and equipment.

Principles of Motion Economy as Related to the Use of the Human Body.

1. THE TWO HANDS SHOULD BEGIN AS WELL AS COMPLETE THEIR THERBLIGS AT THE SAME INSTANT.

2. THE TWO HANDS SHOULD NOT BE IDLE AT THE SAME INSTANT EXCEPT DURING REST PERIODS.

3. MOTIONS OF THE ARMS SHOULD BE MADE IN OPPOSITE AND SYMMETRICAL DIRECTIONS, INSTEAD OF IN THE SAME DIRECTION, AND SHOULD BE MADE SIMULTANEOUSLY.[2]

These three principles are closely related and can best be considered together. When it is possible for the two hands to move at the same time in opposite directions by arranging similar work on the right- and left-hand sides of the work place, the operator performs his task faster and with less mental and physical effort. The symmetrical movements of the arms tend to balance each other and so reduce the shock and jar on the body. There is less bodily strain present when the hands move in opposite directions than when they move in the same direction because of this matter of balance.

A specific case will be cited to show how an operation might be arranged to comply with these three closely related principles.

[2] These three principles were first stated by: F. B. and L. M. Gilbreth, "A Fourth Dimension for Measuring Skill for Obtaining the One Best Way to Do Work," *Soc. Ind. Engg. Bul.,* Vol. 5, No. 11, p. 6, November, 1923.

Bolt and Washer Assembly. A manufacturing concern uses eight bolts ⅜ inch × 1 inch fitted with three washers each (see Fig. 62) in the final assembly of one of its products. This operation was facilitated by having the three washers previously assembled onto the bolt. Consequently the bolt and washers were assembled by girl operators at benches in another department.

Old Method of Assembly. The bolt and washer assembly was originally made in the following manner. Containers with the bolts,

lock washers, steel washers, and rubber washers were arranged on the top of the bench as shown in Fig. 15 on page 40. The operator reached over to the container of bolts with her left hand. She picked up a bolt with her left hand and brought it up to position in front of her. Then with the right

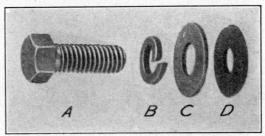

Fig. 62—Bolt and washer assembly. *A*. ⅜ inch × 1 inch bolt; *B*. Lock washer; *C*. Plain steel washer; *D*. Special rubber washer.

hand she in turn picked up a lock washer from the container on the bench and placed it on the bolt, then a plain steel washer, and then a rubber washer. This completed the assembly and with the left hand the operator disposed of it in the container to her left. Figure 37 on page 92 gives the analysis sheet for this operation and Fig. 36 shows the pictures of one cycle.

It is readily seen that every one of the three principles named above were violated when the operation was performed in this way although it is the customary method of doing such work.

Improved Method of Assembly. A simple fixture was made of wood and surrounded by metal bins of the gravity feed type as shown in Figs. 63 and 65. The bins containing the washers were arranged in duplicate so that both hands could move simultaneously, assembling washers for two bolts at the same time. As seen from Fig. 63 bins 1 contain the rubber washers, bins 2 the plain steel washers, bins 3 the lock washers, and bin 4, located in the center of the fixture, contains the bolts. The bottom of the bins slope toward the front at a 30-degree angle so that the materials are fed out onto the fixture board by gravity as the parts are used in assembly.

Two countersunk holes or recesses were made in the front of the fixture (see Fig. 64) into which the three washers fitted loosely, the rubber washer on the bottom, the plain steel washer next, and the lock washer on top. A small hole slightly larger than the diameter

Fig. 63—Bins and chute for bolt and washer assembly.

of the bolt went through the fixture as shown in Fig. 64. A metal chute was placed around the front of the wood fixture with openings to the right and to the left of the two recesses so that assembled bolts and washers might be dropped into the top of this chute and carried down under the bench to a container.

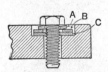

Fig. 64 — Enlarged view of recess in wood fixture for assembling bolt and washers.

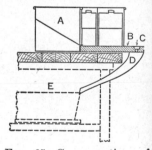

Fig. 65—Cross section of bins showing chute for drop delivery.

In assembling the bolt and washers, as the chart in Fig. 39 on page 95 shows, the two hands move simultaneously toward the duplicate bins 1, grasp rubber washers which rest on the wood fixture in front of the bins, and slide the rubber washers into place in the two recesses in the fixture. The two hands, then, in a similar way, slide the steel washers into place on top of the rubber washers, and then the lock washers are slid into place on top of these. Each hand, then, grasps a bolt and slips them through the washers which are lined up so that the holes are concentric. The hole in the rubber washer is slightly smaller than the outside diameter of the threads on the bolt so that when the bolt is forced through the hole it is gripped and thus permitted, with the three washers, to be withdrawn vertically upward without losing the washers. The two hands release the assemblies simultaneously over the metal chute. As the operator begins on the next cycle with the hands in this position, the second finger of each hand is in position to reach for the rubber washer which is almost at the tip of the finger.

A detailed study of the old and the improved methods of assembling the bolt and washers shows:

Average time [3] required to make one bolt and washer assembly
    by the old method .... 0.0838 minute
Average time [4] required to make one bolt and washer assembly
    by the improved method .... 0.0546 minute

      Time saved .... 0.0292 minute
0.0292/0.0546 = 53 per cent possible increase in output

    The improved method as opposed to the old method of assembling the bolt and washers conforms to each of the three principles of motion economy already mentioned. The two hands begin and end their therbligs at the same instant and they move simultaneously in opposite directions. There is no idle time, and neither hand is used as a "vise" for holding material while the other one does the work, as under the old method.

    Frequently the nature of the work prevents the operator from moving his arms simultaneously in opposite and symmetrical directions. When this is the case it may be that the

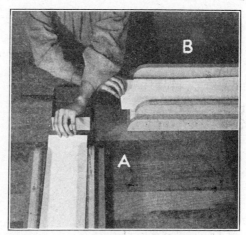

FIG. 66—Simultaneous motions of the arms perpendicular to each other. The operation is that of wrapping and boxing electric switches.

[2] Average of 12 consecutive cycles by operator A1.
[4] Average of 10 consecutive cycles by operator A1.

work can be arranged so that the operator can move his arms simultaneously in directions perpendicular to each other. An example of this type of movement is shown in Fig. 66. The operation is that of wrapping and boxing electric switches. The old method was to place the product to be wrapped on one end of a sheet of wrapping paper and then by a folding and rolling process to finish the operation. The product was then placed in a fiber box and the lid was put on. This method of wrapping and boxing was wasteful of time and effort, as well as of paper.

In the improved method two narrow strips of paper are drawn from supply boxes at *A* and *B* (Fig. 66) across the top of the fiber box by perpendicular motions of the two arms. The switch is then placed on top of the paper and pushed down into the box, both ends of the paper being folded over the switch with simultaneous motions of the two hands. Finally the lid is placed on the box. Incidentally the new method of wrapping and boxing the electric switch requires 40 per cent less time than did the old method.

There is a certain balance and ease of muscular control to these motions performed at right angles which make them definitely superior to motions of the arms in the same direction. However, they are not as easy as simultaneous motions of the arms in opposite directions and should be used only when the former motions are impossible.

Eye Movements. Although some kinds of work can be performed with little or no eye direction, where visual perception is required, it is essential that the task be so arranged that the eyes can direct the work effectively, that is, the work place should be so laid out that the eye fixations are as few and as close together as possible.

Figure 67 shows head, eye, and hand motions of the operator performing a simple assembly operation. Small steel washers enameled green on one side and black on the other were to be assembled with green side up in the fixture directly in front of the operator. Duplicate bins containing the washers were located on either side of the fixture. As the figure shows, it was necessary for the operator to look first to the right and then to the left before grasping the washers. The first strip of film in Fig. 67 shows the operator looking to her right preparatory to grasping a washer from the bin at her right. The second and third strips of film show her looking to her left and grasping a washer from the bin at her left; and the fourth strip of film shows the two hands moving simultaneously carrying washers to the fixture. The 36 consecutive frames of film reproduced in Fig. 67 were made at 1000 exposures per minute.

FIG. 67—Print of motion-picture film showing eye and hand motions of the operator assembling small parts.

151

The distance that the eyes and the hands have to move and the nature of the operation will determine whether the hands must wait for the eyes, thus increasing the time to perform the task. In the above case had the containers been placed directly in front of the operator, the head movements would have been eliminated entirely and the eye movements would have been greatly reduced.

FIG. 68—Arrangement of the work place for study requiring visual direction of the hands.

The angle which the motion path of each hand made with the plane of the front of the operator's body is shown in each of the four photographs. The circular insert shows a close-up of the operator inserting an electrode into the hole in an uncovered unit.

Arrangement of the Work Place. The results of an investigation [5] made by Marvin E. Mundel to evaluate the effect of the angle which the motion paths of the operator's hands made with the plane of the

[5] Ralph M. Barnes and Marvin E. Mundel, "A Study of Simultaneous Symmetrical Hand Motions," *Univ. Iowa Studies in Engg.*, Bul. 17, 1939; also, *Factory Management and Maintenance*, Vol. 97, No. 8, pp. 47-50, August, 1939, and Vol. 97, No. 12, pp. 56-58, December, 1939.

front of the worker's body upon the efficiency with which the worker moved his hands away from and towards his body in a simultaneous, symmetrical fashion are shown in Figs. 68 and 69.

Fig. 69—Arrangement of the work place for study not requiring visual direction of the hands. Only one arrangement is shown—the motion path of each of the operator's hands makes an angle of 60 degrees with the plane of the front of the operator's body.

In the first part of the study the operator was seated at a table (see Fig. 68) and simultaneously carried with each hand an electrode about the size of a pencil back and forth between points on the

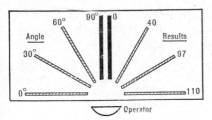

Fig. 70—Results of study requiring visual direction of the hands.

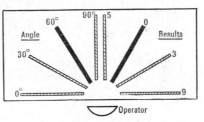

Fig. 71—Results of study not requiring visual direction of the hands.

work place. These points were located symmetrically for the two hands, and the operator inserted the electrodes simultaneously into ⅜-inch holes in metal plates on the work place surface at the terminal points. Two sets of holes located 10 inches apart required 10-inch motions of each of the two hands.

In the second part of the study the operator moved small slides (wood blocks) simultaneously back and forth on smooth wood bars (see Fig. 69). Stops at either end of the bar permitted the operator

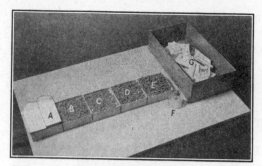

FIG. 72—Layout of work place for packaging wood screws—old method. *A.* Envelopes with gummed flap; *B.* ½-inch No. 5 wood screws; *C.* ¾-inch No. 5 wood screws; *D.* 1-inch No. 7 wood screws; *E.* 1-inch No. 9 wood screws; *F.* Moistener; *G.* Filled envelopes.

FIG. 73—Layout of work place for packaging wood screws—first improvement.

FIG. 74—Layout of work place for packaging wood screws—second improvement.

to make 10-inch movements of the blocks without conscious direction. The time required to make this back and forth motion with the two hands was measured in thousandths of a second.

In the first case visual direction was required to perform the task, while in the second case the eyes were not used. The results of this investigation showed that the 90-degree position was the best when visual direction was required, whereas the 60-degree angle required the least time when the eyes were not needed to direct the hands. (See Figs. 70 and 71.)

Packaging Small Parts. A study [6] of various methods of packaging small parts was made in order to find the most effective one. The operation consisted of placing seven small screws of four different sizes in a small envelope and then sealing it. Figure 72 shows the layout of the work place for the old method. By arranging the materials as shown in Fig. 73 a substantial saving in time resulted. However, a second im-

[6] This study was made in 1939 by Bert H. Norem and John M. MacKenzie.

provement was made later, as shown in Fig. 74, which further reduced the time for the operation. Some visual direction was required in this operation, and the work place as finally arranged enabled the

I. As the tweezers start to open when releasing the part in the die, the eyes shift to the part in the left hand to direct the tweezer-grasping of the next part. First fixation at A.

II. Before the right hand releases the part in the tweezers, the eyes shift to the supply tray to select the next part. Second fixation at B.

III. After the left hand is sufficiently well directed towards the part on the supply tray, the eyes shift to the die to direct the right hand in locating the part over the pilot pins. Third fixation at C.

IV. The eyes remain fixed on the die until the part is properly located. The part is ejected by a foot pedal as the right reaches for the next part.

FIG. 75—Punch press operation showing eye fixations and hand motions of a beginner. Three fixations were used per cycle.

operator to reduce the extent of the head and eye movements and also to shorten the hand motions. This further illustrates that eye motions should always be considered in determining the best method of doing a task.

Eye-Hand Coordination. In a study of the effect of practice on individual therbligs of a punch-press operation made in the University of Iowa Industrial Engineering Laboratory in cooperation with Western Electric Company, one of the observations was the effect of practice on eye movements.

The operation was the forming of a relay contact bar. The fixture and work-place arrangement shown in Figs. 75 and 76 were designed to duplicate the mechanical movements and hand motions of the actual factory operation.

The eye movements and the hand motions of the beginner are shown in Figs. 75 and 76-I and are as follows:

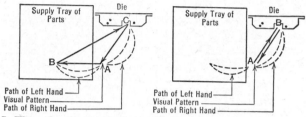

I. Three fixation method.   II. Two fixation method.

FIG. 76—Punch-press operation. Schematic drawings, showing eye fixations and hand motions.

As the tweezers start to open when releasing the part in the die the eyes shift to the part in the left hand to direct the tweezer-grasping of the next part. The first fixation of the eyes occurs at A in Fig. 75-I.

Before the right hand releases the part into the tweezers, the eyes shift to the supply tray to select the next part. The second fixation occurs at B in Fig. 75-II.

If the left hand is sufficiently well directed towards the part on the supply tray, the eyes shift to the die to direct the right hand in locating the part over the pilot pins. The third fixation occurs at C in Fig. 75-III.

The eyes remain fixed on the die until the part is properly located. The part is ejected by a foot pedal as the right hand reaches for the next part.

However, after 10,000 cycles of practice 56 per cent of the cycles had three fixations while the remaining 44 per cent had two fixations.[7] At first the cycle time averaged 0.05837 minute, and after 10,000 cycles of practice the average time was 0.02584 minute. When only two fixations occurred the hand movements were the same, but the

[7] Based on the data for one subject.

eyes did not fixate on the supply of parts. The eyes would fixate
on the part as it was transferred from the left hand to the right hand
at *A* in Fig. 76-II, and then the eyes would move to the fixture to
direct in locating the part over the pilot pins at *B* in Fig. 76-II.
Although at first it was necessary to look at the parts in the tray to
facilitate the grasping, after practicing a less-defined picture was
necessary. It is believed that attention was directed to the parts
and to the hand in grasping them but that it was not essential for
the eyes to see the parts so clearly.

It seems that the better coordination resulting from practice
not only enabled the operator to perform each of the therbligs in less
time (although they were not all affected in the same way with
practice) but also reduced the number of fixations required.

One- and Two-Handed Work. The results of a study [8] of the time
to select and grasp, transport, and dispose of machine screw nuts from
two types of bins with the right hand alone, with the left hand alone,
and with both hands working together are shown in Fig. 77 and
Table XIV.

The operation consisted of selecting and grasping machine screw
nuts (Nos. 2 and 8) from a bin, carrying them through a distance of
five inches, and disposing of them in a hole in the table top. The
study was made using a rectangular bin and was then repeated using
a bin with tray. These bins are shown on page 187. The operator
worked first with the right hand alone, then with the left hand alone,
and finally with both hands.

Least time was required for a total cycle when only the right hand
was used. A cycle for the left hand required 6 per cent more time
with the rectangular bin, and 12 per cent more time with the bin with
tray; and a cycle with both hands required 30 to 40 per cent more
time. However, since two cycles were performed simultaneously
when the two hands were used, the time chargeable to each cycle was
considerably less than when only the right hand was used.

Under the conditions observed in this investigation and with the
operators studied, there was considerable evidence to indicate that a
good "one-handed" operator was also a good "two-handed" operator,
and a relatively poor one-handed operator was also a relatively poor
two-handed operator. This suggests that the introduction of two-

[8] Ralph M. Barnes and Marvin E. Mundel, "Motion Study Research: 3. A
Study of One-Hand and Two-Hand Work," *Factory Management and Mainte-
nance*, Vol. 97, No. 6, pp. 63-66, June, 1939; also, *Univ. Iowa Studies in Engg.*,
Bul. 21, 1940.

handed simultaneous work in place of less efficient one-handed work will not inconvenience any one operator very much more than another operator.

Redesign of Parts to Facilitate Assembly.   In order to avoid microphonics in radio sets, one radio manufacturer uses rubber grom-mets in mounting certain tube sockets or bases onto the radio frame.

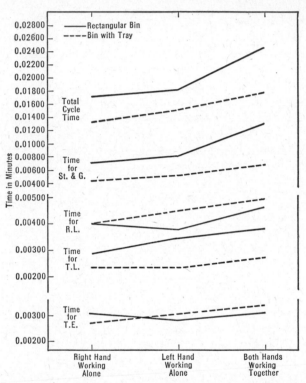

FIG. 77—Curves showing results of study of one- and two-handed work. Averages of the medians selected by total cycle time were used. Results from five male operators working with No. 2 nuts and five who worked with No. 8 nuts have been combined.

The original method of inserting the rubber grommets into the hole in the tube socket (see Fig. 78) was a tedious and difficult one. By cutting out a slot in the two sides of the metal base plate (see Fig. 79) it was simple to squeeze the rubber grommet together and insert it through the slot into the hole.   Moreover, by mounting the base on a fixture, two grommets, one held in each hand, could be assembled into the holes at the same time.

TABLE XIV

STUDY OF ONE- AND TWO-HANDED WORK

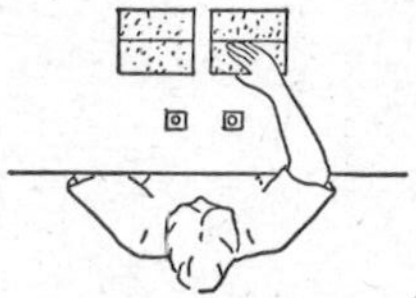

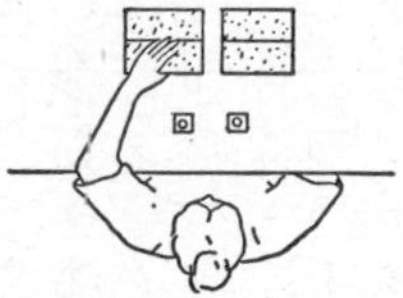

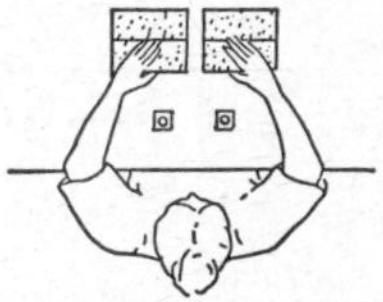

		Right Hand Working Alone		Left Hand Working Alone		Both Hands Working Together	
		Rectangular Bin	Bin with Tray	Rectangular Bin	Bin with Tray	Rectangular Bin	Bin with Tray
SELECT AND GRASP Nut from bin at A (see figure above).	Time in Minutes	0.00723	0.00438	0.00822	0.00520	0.01307	0.00674
	Time in Per Cent (Shortest Time = 100%)	100	100	114	118	181	154
TRANSPORT LOADED Carry nut through distance of 5 inches —from A to B.	Time in Minutes	0.00492	0.00235	0.00347	0.00234	0.00380	0.00270
	Time in Per Cent (Shortest Time = 100%)	100	100	119	100	130	115
RELEASE LOAD Drop nut into 1-inch hole in table top at B.	Time in Minutes	0.00403	0.00403	0.00380	0.00453	0.00463	0.00500
	Time in Per Cent (Shortest Time = 100%)	106	100	100	112	122	124
TRANSPORT EMPTY Move hand to bin at A for nut.	Time in Minutes	0.00314	0.00277	0.00282	0.00304	0.00308	0.00337
	Time in Per Cent (Shortest Time = 100%)	111	100	100	110	110	122
TOTAL CYCLE	Time in Minutes	0.01730	0.01351	0.01832	0.01510	0.02459	0.01778
	Time in Per Cent (Shortest Time = 100%)	100	100	106	112	142	131

The time to insert the grommet in each of the two holes in the
base using the old method was
142.5 minutes per 100 sockets.
The improved method permitted
the operator to perform the same
operation at the rate of 40 minutes
per 100 sockets. The sockets were
purchased by the radio manufacturer, and it was possible to have
the supplier furnish the improved
design of socket at no extra cost.

FIG. 78—Radio tube socket—original
design.

The only expense involved in making the change in the method was
a few dollars for an assembly fixture which was made of wood.

FIG. 79 — Radio
tube socket — im-
proved design.
A—Socket assem-
bly
B—Base showing
slots cut out
of two sides of
metal plate to
facilitate as-
sembly of rub-
ber grommets
C—Nuts
D—Lock washers
E—Rubber grom-
mets
F—Bolts for
mounting
socket onto
radio base

FIG. 80—Drilling and counterboring
operation. The material to be drilled is
poorly placed resulting in slow fatiguing
work.

Jigs and Fixtures. One of the important things about motion study applications is that usually only simple jigs, fixtures, and special apparatus are needed. Where the number of units to be manufactured is limited, a temporary fixture is often satisfactory.

One radio manufacturer has a group of three men who spend their entire time making fixtures, mainly for assembly operations. The group consists of a designer and two carpenters. The designer is a practical man with ingenuity, imagination, and considerable inventive ability. The designer, as well as the carpenters, is well grounded in the principles of motion economy. Although the foremen, industrial engineers, and operators all make suggestions as to the fixtures needed for the best method of doing a task, the three men contribute much to the success of the motion study program in the plant.

Nearly all assembly fixtures in this plant are made from maple wood, impregnated with oil to prevent change in dimensions due to change in weather conditions. Standard bins, holders for soldering irons and screwdrivers, and supports for power wrenches are available. A laboratory has been set up to try out ideas that are likely to require considerable experimentation. One of the important developments coming from the laboratory is a new design of soldering iron which is much more effective than any that can be purchased on the market.

4. HAND MOTIONS SHOULD BE CONFINED TO THE LOWEST CLASSIFICATION WITH WHICH IT IS POSSIBLE TO PERFORM THE WORK SATISFACTORILY.

The five general classes of hand motions are listed in progressive order in the table below. The lowest classification which is shown first usually requires the least amount of time and effort and consequently produces the least fatigue.

General Classification of Hand Motions:

1. Finger motions.
2. Motions involving fingers and wrist.
3. Motions involving fingers, wrist, and forearm.
4. Motions involving fingers, wrist, forearm, and upper arm.
5. Motions involving fingers, wrist, forearm, upper arm, and shoulder. This class necessitates disturbance of the posture.

The above classification of hand motions is given here because it helps emphasize that material and tools should be located as close as possible to the point of use and that motions of the hands should be as short as the work permits.

A glaring example of poor location of material is shown in Fig. 80. Not only must the operator use the fifth classification of hand motions here but he must also twist and bend his back in order to get parts from the tote box at the right of the drill press. By simply emptying the parts from the tote box into a bin with a sloping bottom located on the drill press table, the task of procuring parts is made easier and requires less time than in the first case.

The results of a study [9] of the time required to make hand motions of varying lengths are given in Tables XV and XVI. The operation was the forming of links for a portable typewriter. Although no general conclusions can be drawn from these data it is apparent that on this operation 30 to 75 per cent more time was required to make motions 24 inches long than motions 8 inches long.

As desirable as it may be to keep hand motions as short as possible, it is incorrect to assume that finger motions are less fatiguing than motions of the forearm. One has only to remember his early instructions in writing to know that free, loose, forearm and wrist movements are easier, faster, and more uniform than finger motions. In fact the substitution of a telegraph key which moved in the lateral direction for the vertical movement key was the result of the observation that the lateral movement permitted the operator to work with a freer and looser wrist.[10]

TABLE XV

SUMMARY OF TIME REQUIRED FOR HAND MOTIONS OF VARYING LENGTHS

Transport Empty

Study No.	Operator No.	Distance in Inches	Time in Minutes			
			Average	Mode	Maximum	Minimum
C17	A2	8	0.0037	0.004	0.004	0.003
C18	A2	16	0.0035	0.004	0.004	0.003
C19	A2	24	0.0049	0.005	0.005	0.004
C20	A1	8	0.0037	0.004	0.004	0.003
C21	A1	16	0.0053	0.005	0.006	0.005
C22	A1	24	0.0066	0.0065	0.008	0.006

[9] See page 96.
[10] M. Smith, M. Culpin, and E. Farmer, "A Study of Telegrapher's Cramp," *Ind. Fatigue Research Bd.*, Report 43, 1927.

TABLE XVI

SUMMARY OF TIME REQUIRED FOR HAND MOTIONS OF VARYING LENGTHS

Transport Loaded

Study No.	Operator No.	Distance in Inches	Time in Minutes				Average Velocity in Feet per Minute
			Average	Mode	Maximum	Minimum	
C17	A2	8	0.0040	0.004	0.004	0.004	167
C18	A2	16	0.0057	0.006	0.006	0.005	234
C19	A2	24	0.0059	0.003	0.007	0.005	339
C20	A1	8	0.0050	0.005	0.005	0.005	133
C21	A1	16	0.0070	0.006	0.010	0.006	190
C22	A1	24	0.0080	0.008	0.012	0.006	250

In another investigation of movements, it was found that the finger motions were more fatiguing, less accurate, and slower than the motions of the forearm.[11] All evidence seems to show that the forearm is the most desirable member to use for light work and that in highly repetitive work the motions about the wrist and elbow are in all respects superior to those of the fingers or shoulders.

5. MOMENTUM SHOULD BE EMPLOYED TO ASSIST THE WORKER WHEREVER POSSIBLE, AND IT SHOULD BE REDUCED TO A MINIMUM IF IT MUST BE OVERCOME BY MUSCULAR EFFORT.

The momentum of an object is its mass multiplied by its velocity. In most kinds of factory work the total weight moved by the operator may consist of three things: the weight of the material moved, the weight of the tools or devices moved, and the weight of the part of the body moved.[12] It is often possible to make use of momentum of the hand, the material, or the tool to do useful work. When a forcible stroke is required, the motions of the worker should be so arranged that the stroke is delivered when it reaches its greatest momentum.[13] In laying a brick wall, for example, "If the bricks are conveyed from

[11] R. H. Stetson and J. A. McDill, "Mechanisms of the Different Types of Movement," Psychol. Monograph, Vol. 32, No. 3, Whole No. 145, p. 37, 1923.

[12] F. B. Gilbreth, "Motion Study," p. 63, D. Van Nostrand Co., New York, 1911.

[13] C. S. Myers, "Industrial Psychology in Great Britain," p. 88, Jonathan Cape, Ltd., London 1926.

the stock platform to the wall with no stops, the momentum can be made to do valuable work by assisting to shove the joints full of mortar. If, instead of being utilized, the momentum must be overcome by the muscles of the bricklayer, fatigue . . . will result." [14]

The improved method of candy dipping explained on page 168 is another illustration of the utilization of momentum for the performance of useful work. The piece to be dipped was submerged under the surface of the melted sugar by the right hand at the end of a long return stroke of the hand. The momentum developed in this movement of the hand and the empty dipping fork was used in doing useful work instead of being dissipated by the muscles of the dipper's arm.

There are many times when momentum has no productive value. Its presence is undesirable in that the muscles must always counteract the momentum developed. When such is the case the three classes of weight or mass named above should be studied for the purpose of reducing each to the minimum. In addition, the velocity of the motions should be kept low by using the shortest motions possible.[15] There are a number of tools that are most effective when they are made as light in weight as possible. Such tools do not depend upon momentum or the use of a blow to function properly. For many kinds of work a heavy shovel or a heavy trowel is more fatiguing to use than a light one of the same dimensions and rigidity.

There are many additional considerations which enter into the determination of the proper size and weight of materials and tools to be used to produce maximum efficiency. Unfortunately there are little accumulated data that are of value here. Each case, as a rule, is surrounded by circumstances and conditions peculiar to itself. Consequently each problem must be the subject for special investigation.

6.   CONTINUOUS CURVED MOTIONS ARE PREFERABLE TO STRAIGHT-LINE MOTIONS INVOLVING SUDDEN AND SHARP CHANGES IN DIRECTION.

The results of a study [16] of the simple hand motions *transport loaded* (away from the body), *stop* and *change direction,* and *transport loaded* (toward the body) are given in Fig. 81. This figure shows that 15 to 24 per cent of the cycle was used in changing direction of the hand. Such abrupt changes in direction are not only time con-

[14] F. B. Gilbreth, "Motion Study," p. 78, D. Van Nostrand Co., New York, 1911.

[15] Short motions are relatively slow motions. For data on average velocities of hand motion see Table XVI.

[16] *Univ. Iowa Studies in Engg.,* Bul. 6, pp. 37-51, 1936.

suming but they are fatiguing to the operator. Smooth curved motions are always preferred.

In many jobs in the shop and office it is possible to use these smooth curved motions. Some examples will be given. The first is that of folding rectangular sheets of paper in the middle. The sheets vary in size from 3 inches × 5 inches to 12 inches × 15 inches folded. Although several million of these sheets of paper are folded per year it was found to be more economical to fold them by hand than by machine because of the many different sizes used.

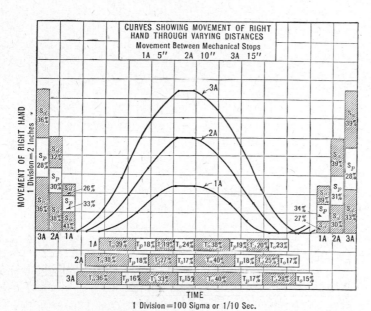

Fig. 81—Curves showing movement of right hand through varying distances—between mechanical stops.

Old Method of Folding Paper. The worker, holding a smooth piece of bone in the palm of her right hand (see Fig. 82a), grasped the lower right-hand corner A of the sheet of paper to be folded. She folded this end of the sheet over to point B, where the two hands matched or lined up the two corners of the sheet of paper. Then, swinging the right hand away from the body and using the bone as a creasing tool, she struck the folded sheet of paper about mid-point at C, creasing the fold from C to D. At D she stopped and changed direction abruptly, doubled back, creasing the entire length of the fold from D to E. At E the hand again changed direction and swung around to *F*, where the end of the bone was inserted under the edge of the creased sheet to assist the left hand in disposing of it on the pile of folded sheets at *G*.

Improved Method of Folding Paper. In the improved method the worker grasps the lower right-hand corner *A* of the sheet of paper to

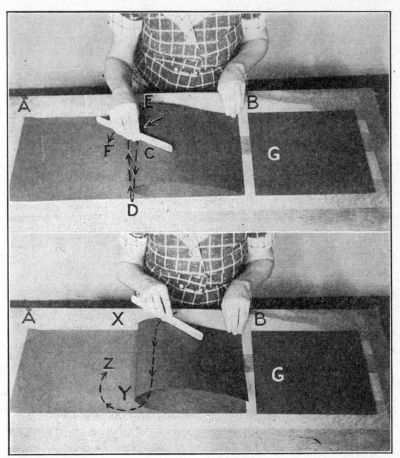

Fig. 82—Path of hand in creasing folded sheet of paper. (*a*) Above—old method. (*b*) Below—improved method.

be folded. (See Fig. 82*b*.) She folds this end of the sheet over to point *B*, where the two hands match or line up the two corners of the sheet of paper. She then moves the right hand through a smooth "S" curve, the bone striking the paper and beginning to crease at *X* and ending at *Y*. Thus the entire crease is completed with the single stroke of the bone. The hand then swings around in a curved motion from Y to Z, where, as in the old method, the end of the bone is inserted under the creased sheet to assist the left hand in disposing of it on the pile of folded sheets at G.

Results. By using the improved method described above only one creasing motion was required to complete the cycle instead of the two (one short and one long one) in the old method. Moreover, in the improved method two curved motions of the hand were used instead of two complete change directions and one 90° change direction in the old method.

A micromotion study of these two methods shows that 0.009 minute was required to crease the fold by the old method and 0.005 minute by the improved method. The improved method of creasing the fold, plus some other changes in the cycle, reduced the total time from 0.058 to 0.033 minute per cycle.

Another illustration of the value of curved motions over straight-line motions involving sudden changes in direction is given below.[17] The operation is dipping candy.

Old Method of Dipping Candy. The dipping process was carried out in the following manner. A "center" (an almond, walnut, Brazil nut, or caramel) was placed in a pot containing melted sugar by using the left hand, and was covered with the melted sugar by working it with a fork held in the right hand. The finished piece of candy was then placed with the right hand on the tray to the right of the operator. Approximately two seconds were required to dip each piece.

Although the lines in Fig. 83 do not show the exact movements of the right hand, they give a picture of the principal motions used. While the left hand was placing a center in the container of melted sugar, the right hand carried the empty fork from the tray A to the container B, and took up some of the thick melted sugar and pulled it over the center at X. When the hand reached C it moved to the left side of the container, the center being carried along with the end of the fork under it. The center was picked up at D and carried to the tray where it was deposited. The objections to this method of dipping were that the hand stopped at B (in Fig. 83) and changed direction sharply, and then at C the direction was almost reversed. This stopping and sudden changing of direction placed unnecessary strain on the muscles of the arm.

[17] E. Farmer, "Time and Motion Study," *Ind. Fatigue Research Bd.*, Report 14, pp. 36-41, 1921. Figures 83 and 84 reproduced by permission of the Controller of H. M. Stationery Office, London.

Improved Method of Dipping Candy. The improved method of dipping is shown diagrammatically in Fig. 84. The center is dipped by a smooth sweeping motion of the hand instead of by a number of short zigzagging motions as in the old method. In the improved method the hand, after disposing of the finished piece of candy on the tray, moves from A to B as before, but reaches B "in the middle of an inward and downward curve with the hand in its strongest position for doing work." This makes it possible to utilize the momentum developed in the movement A-B in doing the most fatiguing part of the work, the dipping being the part of the process that offers the greatest resistance to the hand. In the old process this dipping motion was made by a short backward movement just after the hand had stopped

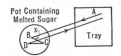

FIG. 83—Old method of dipping candy.

FIG. 84—Improved method of dipping candy.

and changed its direction. Furthermore, the momentum developed during the motion A-B was wasted in the old method since the hand motion was checked at B in order to change its direction. By using the downward motion of the hand in the improved method, the melted sugar is swept over the center and, going under the surface in the second part of the curve, it comes up at C. The piece of candy is then deposited on the tray with a circular motion to "finish off" the candy. In the new method the hand takes easy smooth movements with all changes in direction effected by curves.

Results. The improved method was taught to a group of workers in the factory and after a short period of training an average increase in production of 27.1 per cent resulted. However, since many workers had used the old method for years it was difficult to persuade some of them to give the new method a fair trial. As a new dipping room equipped with new-style tables and trays was being started, new operators were trained in the proper method of dipping. After three months' work in this new room these new workers were producing an average of 88 per cent more than the workers of the same standing in the original room.

Coal Mining. In an investigation in coal mining it was found that the miners tired themselves unnecessarily by the sudden checking of the upward stroke of the pick and in accelerating again for the downward stroke. They were taught to use a slightly continuous path in swinging the pick, and to strike harder at a slower speed against the coal face.[18]

7. BALLISTIC MOVEMENTS ARE FASTER, EASIER, AND MORE ACCURATE THAN RESTRICTED (FIXATION) OR "CONTROLLED" MOVEMENTS.

Voluntary movements of the members of the human body may be divided into two general classes or groups.

A. In the *fixation* or controlled movements, opposing groups of muscles are contracted, one group against the other. For example, in bringing the pencil down to the paper preparatory to writing, two or more sets of muscles are in action. The positive sets of muscles propel the hand and the antagonistic sets oppose the movement. When the two sets of muscles act in an uneven or unbalanced manner, motion of the hand results. When the two sets of muscles exactly balance each other, the hand remains in a fixed position, although it is ready to act in any direction at any instant. The finger-and-thumb method of writing is an excellent illustration of fixation movements.

B. The *ballistic* movement is a fast easy motion caused by a single contraction of a positive muscle group with no antagonistic muscle group contracting to oppose it. The contraction of the muscles throws the member of the body into motion and since these muscles act only through the first part of the movement the member sweeps through the remainder of the movement with its muscles relaxed. The ballistic movement is controlled by the initial impulse and once under way its course cannot be changed.[19] A ballistic stroke may terminate (1) by the contraction of the opposing muscles, (2) by an obstacle, or (3) by dissipation of the momentum of the movement, as in swinging a golf club.

The ballistic movement is preferable to the fixation movement and should be used whenever possible. It is less fatiguing since the muscles contract only at the beginning of the movement and are relaxed for the remainder of the movement. The ballistic movement is more powerful, faster, more accurate, and is less likely to cause muscle cramp. It is smoother than the fixation movement which is caused by the contraction of two sets of muscles, one acting against the other

[18] E. Farmer and others, "An Investigation in a Coal Mine," *J. Nat. Institute Ind. Psychol.*, Vol. 1, No. 4, pp. 125-131, October, 1922.

[19] L. D. Hartson, "Analysis of Skilled Movements," *The Personnel J.*, Vol. 11, No. 1, pp. 28-43, June, 1932.

continuously. The skilled carpenter swinging his hammer in driving a nail illustrates a ballistic movement. He aims his hammer, then throws or swings it. The muscles are contracted only during the first part of the movement; they idle along the rest of the way. The swinging curves of an orchestra conductor's baton is another illustration of ballistic movement. P. R. Spenser understood the value of ballistic movements, for the "free-hand writing" which he taught is known to every one to produce greater speed and accuracy with less fatigue than is possible with the finger-and-thumb method of writing, where the muscles of the hand are tightly drawn. The ballistic movement is the one taught to telegraph operators, piano players, violin players, athletes, etc., all of whom must use fast and accurate motions or movements.

It is not difficult to develop the free, loose, easy movements of the wrist and forearm. The hand should move about the wrist for the shorter motions and the forearm about the elbow for the longer motions. Experiments show that the wrist and elbow movements are faster than finger or shoulder movements.[20]

8. RHYTHM IS ESSENTIAL TO THE SMOOTH AND AUTOMATIC PERFORMANCE OF AN OPERATION AND THE WORK SHOULD BE ARRANGED TO PERMIT AN EASY AND NATURAL RHYTHM WHEREVER POSSIBLE.

Rhythm may be interpreted in two different ways. Perhaps it is most frequently understood to mean the speed or the rapidity with which repeated motions are made. The reference is commonly made to the rhythm of walking or breathing. The operator feeding material into a machine is said to work with a rhythm depending upon the speed of the machine. Rhythm, then, in this sense, refers to the regular repetition of a certain cycle of motions by an individual.

Rhythm may be interpreted in a second way. "A movement may be perfectly regular, uniform, and recurrent and yet not give the impression of rhythm. If one moves the hand or the arm in a circle, the hand may be made to pass a point in a circle much oftener per second than the tempo of the slower rhythms requires, and yet there will be no feeling of rhythm *so long as the hand moves uniformly and in a circle.* In order to become rhythmic in the psychological sense, the following change in the movement is necessary: The path of the hand must be elongated to an ellipse; the velocity of the movement

[20] Wm. L. Bryan, "On the Development of Voluntary Motor Ability," *The Am. J. of Psychol.,* Vol. 5, No. 2, p. 171, November, 1892.

in a part of the orbit must be much faster than in the rest of the orbit; just as the hand comes to the end of the arc through which it passes with increased velocity, there is a feeling of tension, of muscular strain; at this point the movement is retarded, almost stopped; then the hand goes on more slowly until it reaches the arc of increased velocity. The rapid movement through the arc of velocity and the sudden feeling of strain and retarding at the end of this rapid movement constitute the beat. In consciousness they represent one event, and a series of such events connected in such a movement-cycle may be said provisionally to constitute a rhythm. Every rhythmic beat is a *blow*. . . . In all forms of activity where a rhythm is required, the stroke, the blow, the impact, is the thing; all the rest is but connection and preparation." [21]

Rhythm, either in the sense of a regular sequence of uniform motions, or in the sense of a regular sequence of accented motions, is of value to the worker. Uniformity, ease, and even speed of work are promoted by the proper arrangement of the work place, tools, and materials. The proper sequence of therbligs enables the worker to establish a rhythm which assists in making the operation practically an automatic performance—the operator does the work without mental effort.

In many kinds of work there is an opportunity for the operator to accent certain points in a cycle of motions. For example, every punch-press operator, feeding the press by hand, tends to feed the sheet of material forward with a sudden thrust which constitutes an accented point in the cycle. Where the work permits it is most natural for the worker to fall into a rhythm in this second sense.

Individual Rhythm. Some have suggested that each individual has a "natural" rhythm or speed of movement that permits him to work with least effort. Some have urged that individuals should be permitted to work at this natural speed and that no outside force, such as a wage incentive, should be exerted to cause the individual to work faster than his natural rhythm. [22] Since it seems difficult to determine what the natural rhythm is for any person and since most workers can be taught to change their rhythm in performing the same work (such as working at different speeds or using different sets of motions), it seems that too much emphasis should not be

[21] R. H. Stetson, "A Motor Theory of Rhythm and Discrete Succession," *Psychology. Rev.*, Vol. 12, No. 4, p. 258, 1905.

[22] E. Farmer, "Time and Motion Study," *Engg. and Ind. Management,* Vol. 7 (N.S.), No. 5, p. 138, London, Feb. 2, 1922.

placed on this, so-called, natural rhythm. Habit acts in a powerful way to affect the speed and the sequence of motions which a worker uses in performing a task. Once the habit is formed, it *does* require real effort on the part of the worker to change or modify this habit. To illustrate this point, a typewriter company had several polishers of long experience who had for several years been polishing a particular part of the typewriter. These polishers had been accustomed to take a definite number of strokes across the polishing wheel and they knew the finish that the piece should have to pass inspection. In a new design of the typewriter this particular piece was located in a more obscure position than formerly and so it did not need such a high polish. The polishers were told just how the piece was to be polished for the new typewriter and they were carefully instructed as to the finish that would now be required to pass inspection. The operators, however, found it difficult to change their habits. They "forgot" to take fewer strokes and as a result they were turning out work that was of higher quality than needed and their output was lower than it should have been. With constant and persistent attention these polishers, after four days, were able to produce the parts of just the quality finish required and at a proportionately faster speed in pieces per hour.

Nearly every worker finds that a conscious effort and some persistence are required to do a new task or to perform an old one in a new way. However, for most people this change is by no means impossible and usually it can be readily made. There are cases where a certain sequence of motions has been made by a person for such a long period of time that it is unwise to try to change it. This can, perhaps, also be said about the speed at which some people work.

When a worker becomes fatigued or when he is distracted or voluntarily wishes to produce less, he may either slow down his speed and maintain a slower rhythm, or he may introduce delays or interruptions, in the form of extra therbligs, into the cycle of motions.

Effect of Fatigue on Rhythm. In a study of polishing in a silverware factory, it was found that during the morning the polishers worked at a uniform rate and the units were finished at regular intervals.[23] In the afternoon, however, the time per unit increased. Also the pressure used in holding the knife or the spoon against the polishing wheel increased; more strokes were used and the time for polish-

[23] E. Farmer and R. S. Brooke, "Motion Study in Metal Polishing," *Ind. Fat. Research Bd.*, Report 15, pp. 1-65, 1921.

ing each piece was greater than in the morning when a regular rhythm was maintained.   Fatigue, then, seems to break up the rhythm and disturb the coordination that makes for rapid and easy work.   Quoting from the report, "The tired worker is, therefore, not only working slower than when she is fresh, but is also expending her energy extravagantly." [24]

[24] *Ibid.,* p. 51.

CHAPTER 13

PRINCIPLES OF MOTION ECONOMY AS RELATED TO THE WORK PLACE

9. DEFINITE AND FIXED STATIONS SHOULD BE PROVIDED FOR ALL TOOLS AND MATERIALS.

The operator should always be able to find the tools and materials in the same location. Likewise, finished parts and assembled units should be disposed of in fixed places. For example, in the assembly of the bolt and washers, the hand should move without mental direction to the bin containing the rubber washers, then to the bin containing the steel washers, then to the lock washers, and finally to the bolts. It should be unnecessary for the operator to have to think where the materials are located.

Definite stations for materials and tools aid the worker in habit formation, permitting the rapid development of automaticity. It cannot be emphasized too strongly that it is greatly to the worker's advantage to be able to perform the operation with the least conscious mental direction. Frequently, materials and tools are scattered over the work place in such a disorderly fashion that the operator must not only exert mental effort, but must also hunt around in order to locate the part or tool needed at a given instant. The workers are very much in favor of having definite stations for materials and tools, since this reduces fatigue and saves time. There can be no virtue in requiring the worker to exert the unnecessary effort of deciding just what tool to pick up next or what part to assemble next, when, by simply arranging the materials and tools properly, the operator, with a little practice, will automatically perform the work in the proper sequence, at a rapid rate, and with a minimum expenditure of effort.

Since the eye must direct the hand in reaching for an object, the eye ordinarily precedes the hand. However, if materials or tools are located in a definite place and if they are always grasped from the same point, the hand automatically finds the right location and the eyes may be kept fixed on the point where the tools or materials are used.

19. TOOLS, MATERIALS, AND CONTROLS SHOULD BE LOCATED AROUND THE WORK PLACE AND AS CLOSE IN FRONT OF THE WORKER AS POSSIBLE.

Very frequently the work place, such as a bench, machine, desk, or table, is laid out with tools and materials in straight lines. This is incorrect, for a person naturally works in areas bounded by lines which are arcs of circles.

Normal Working Area. Considering the horizontal plane, there is a very definite and limited area which the worker can use with a normal expenditure of effort. There is a normal working area for the right hand, and for the left hand, working separately, and for both hands working together. (See Fig. 85.) The normal working area for the right hand is determined by an arc drawn with a sweep of the right hand across the table. The forearm only is extended and the upper arm hangs at the side of the body in a natural position until it tends to swing away as the hand moves toward the outer part of the work place. The normal working area for the left hand is determined in a similar manner. The normal arcs drawn with the right and left hands will cross each other at a point in front of the worker.

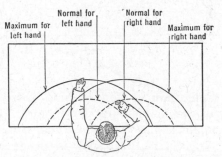

FIG. 85—Normal and maximum working areas.

The overlapping area constitutes a zone in which two-handed work may be done most conveniently.

Maximum Working Area. There is a maximum working area for the right hand and for the left hand, working separately, and for both hands working together. (See Fig. 85.) The maximum working area for the right hand is determined by an arc drawn with a sweep of the right hand across the table with the arm pivoted at the right shoulder. The maximum working area for the left hand is determined in a similar manner by an arc drawn with a sweep of the left hand. The overlapping area formed by these two maximum arcs constitutes a zone beyond which two-handed work cannot be performed without causing considerable disturbance of posture accompanied by excessive fatigue.

Each hand has its normal working space in the vertical plane as well as in the horizontal plane in which work may be done with the least time and effort. A maximum work space in the vertical plane may also be determined beyond which work cannot be performed without disturbing the posture. In locating materials or tools above the work place consideration should be given to these facts.

Figures 86 and 87 have been included in order to emphasize the importance of arranging the material *around* the work place and as close in as possible. In Fig. 86 the six bins containing material are all outside the maximum working area, necessitating bending the body to reach them. In Fig. 87 the bins have been arranged on the border

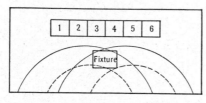

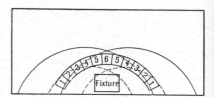

Fig. 86—Incorrect arrangement of work place.

Fig. 87—Correct arrangement of work place.

of the normal working area, permitting a third-class motion which requires no movement of the body. The use of a duplicate fixture and duplicate bins arranged symmetrically on either side of the fixture permits the two hands to make simultaneous motions in opposite directions in performing the operation. Such an arrangement makes possible natural, easy, rhythmical movements of the arms.

Those tools and parts that must be handled several times during an operation should be located closer to the fixture or working position than tools or parts which are handled but once. For example, if an operation consists of assembling a number of screws into a metal switch plate, the containers for the screws should be placed closer to the fixture than the containers for the plates. This is done because only one plate must be transported from the container to the fixture per operation, whereas several screws would have to be transported from their containers to the fixture.

In considering the above point it is equally important to remember that the parts must be arranged in such a way as to permit the shortest eye movements, the fewest eye fixations, the best sequence of therbligs, and arranged to aid the operator in rapidly developing automatic and rhythmical movements.

Operating-Room Setup. The accepted operating-room practice causes much useless motion and delay on the part of assistants and nurses in handling instruments and supplies. The redesigned arrangement shown in Fig. 88 eliminates many motions in that the instruments and supplies are on either side of the surgeon, enabling the nurses to face the operating table instead of turning around to procure necessary articles from tables ordinarily located behind them.[1]

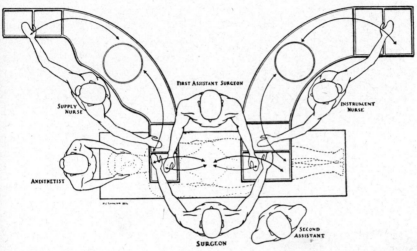

FIG. 88—Operating-room setup showing tables for instruments and supplies designed to facilitate the work of the surgeon, his assistants, and the nurses.

The two tables are adjustable in height, built with removable metal tops and separate basins for clean and soiled instruments.

Office Desks. The application of motion economy principles to many kinds of office and shop work has lead to concentrated effort to improve the office desk. The way this problem was solved by Frank Lloyd Wright, designer of plant and furnishings for C. S. Johnson and Son, Inc., is given here.

Desks were designed and built to suit the operations to be per-

[1] W. H. Lawrence and C. H. Berry, "Rhythmic Surgery," *The American Journal of Surgery*, Vol. XLI, No. 3, pp. 393-398, September, 1938. Figure 88 is used with the permission of *The American Journal of Surgery*.

For other material in this field see: T. S. Welton, "In Regard to 'Rhythmic Surgery,'" *The American Journal of Surgery*, Vol. XLI, No. 3, pp. 371-373, September, 1938; E. H. Pool and F. W. Bancroft, "Systematization of a Surgical Service," *J.A.M.A.*, Vol. 59, pp. 1599-1603, November 10, 1917; F. B. Gilbreth, "Motion Study in Surgery," *Canadian J. Medicine and Surgery*, July, 1916.

formed on them. The basic desk has a top 84 inches long and 32 inches wide, a subshelf, and a top shelf for stationery racks and "in and out" letter trays. The subshelf is used to hold papers and reference books which might otherwise be piled on top of the desk; yet these are located conveniently for use when needed. The working surface is 28½ inches from the floor instead of 30 inches.

The typist's desk shown in Fig. 89 has a section cut out of the top

FIG. 89—Typist's desk.

so that the typewriter sits on the lower level. Several variations of the standard desk have been developed with openings for comptometers, billing machines, and filing boxes cut out to bring the working surface to the proper height for easy use.

Among the advantages claimed for the desk is the substitution of hanging tills hinged to the front leg for drawers, making it possible for the operator to swing the till over to her for ease in use. Tills are either 5½ inches or 11 inches deep and are interchangeable so that different combinations can be made to fit the operator's needs. The wastepaper basket is hung on the desk frame, where it is more convenient to use, less conspicuous, and out of the way when the floor is being cleaned.

The entire office consists of a single work room 128 feet by 208 feet with a 17-foot mezzanine all around it, all without partitions or obstructions. The arrangement of the office so that work flows in straight lines from department to department together with the new equipment has resulted in at least a 15 per cent increase in output for each division of the office, with some departments producing 25 per cent more work.

Figure 90 shows the arrangement of the work place for packing a book in shipping carton (see Fig. 91 B) and sealing the carton by an improved method. The carton is folded around the wrapped book and the ends of the carton are folded over. The carton is then placed in a simple three-sided fixture which holds the edges in place while both hands apply the tape around three sides.

FIG. 90—Arrangement of work place for placing book in shipping carton and sealing carton with tape—improved method.

This improved method, worked out by James Morrison, saves 22 per cent in time, 43 per cent in amount of tape used, and produces a neater package and one that is several times stronger than the original one.

A   B

FIG. 91—Shipping carton containing encyclopedia. A. Carton sealed old way; B. Carton sealed improved way.

The following statement might be considered as a corollary to rule 10. In the continuous or progressive type of manufacturing, machines, process apparatus, and equipment should be arranged so as to require the least possible movement on the part of the operator.

The machines in Fig. 92 are laid out in a straight line along a trucking aisle. Space is provided between the machines for a skid platform on which material is placed before and after being processed. When one man operates several machines it is necessary for him to walk a considerable distance because the machines are spread out over so much floor space.

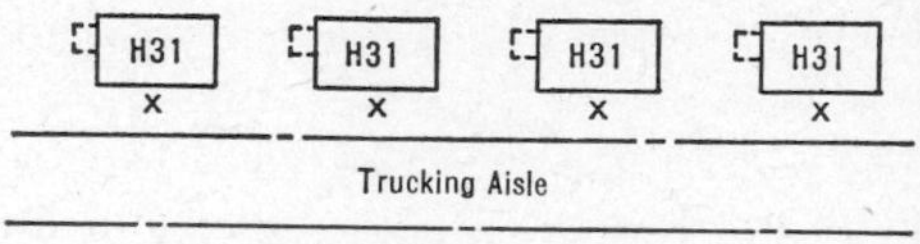

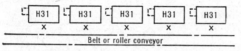

Fig. 92—Machines laid out in the conventional way. Material is moved to and from the machines on skid platforms by lift trucks. An aisle permits access to each machine.

The trucking aisle is unnecessary and walking is reduced when the machines are located along a conveyor. Machines are frequently placed parallel to the conveyor as in Fig. 93. Such an arrangement, although better than the one illustrated in Fig. 92, still requires the operator to turn completely around in transporting material from the machine to the conveyor, and vice versa. A better arrangement is shown in Fig. 94, where the machines are placed perpendicular to the conveyor and close to it. This permits the operator to move material to and from the conveyor with less movement of the body.

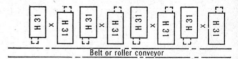

Fig. 93—Machines laid out parallel to a belt or roller conveyor. Material is moved to and from the machines by conveyor and no trucking aisle is needed. The operator turns through 180 degrees to use the conveyor.

There is still a fourth method of laying out machines which can often be used to advantage. (See Fig. 95.) The machines that can be operated by one man are grouped close together, so that the time required for the operator to move from loading one machine to removing the finished piece from the next, and loading it, is a minimum. Often machines used to perform successive operations on a part can be grouped together so

Fig. 94—Machines laid out perpendicular to a belt or roller conveyor. The operator turns through 90 degrees to use the conveyor.

that the part, in the form of a casting or forging, might begin the process at A (skid platform in Fig. 95), the first operation being performed by machine H31, the next by machine L12, and the third operation by H31B. The machine time and the handling time would have to be so balanced that the operator could keep the machines in operation without too much loss of machine time. From the third machine the part is sent, if necessary, to the next group of machines by means of a chute shown at *D*.

The Cadillac factory rearranged a number of their departments in a manner similar to that shown in Fig. 95. In one department, in particular, where front-wheel spindles were machined in a continuous process, the new arrangement saved 40 per cent of the floor space and seventeen men did the work of twenty-seven.[2]

FIG. 95—Machines arranged in groups. Machine time and handling time are so balanced that one man can keep the entire group in operation. Material is moved by short conveyor or chute to the next group of machines where succeeding operations are performed on the part.

Shipping-Department Operations. The application of motion economy principles to shipping-department operations may result in substantial savings in time and labor costs.

A packing bench and a checker's table designed by C. H. Cox for use in the shipping department of Merck & Company shows how the principle of locating materials and tools close in front of the operator made it possible for the operator to do his work easier and faster.[3]

Packing Bench. The packing operation consisted mainly of packing for shipment bottles and boxes containing chemicals. Figure 96 shows the original 9-foot-long flat-top packing bench containing a tape machine, glue pots, nail boxes, hammer, stencil brush, knife, scissors, etc. Hoods, wrappers, and pads for individual container protection and special box labels were stored along the back half of the bench and in the cabinets below the working surface. None of the equipment or material was pre-positioned in definite locations. Since the actual packing was not done on this bench, all equipment and material were outside the maximum working area. Boxes were set up and packed on the 2-foot by 3-foot packing "buck" which was set perpendicular to the packing bench. A loose bale of excelsior was placed on the floor opposite the bench and on the left side of the buck.

The operator carried each piece of stock from shelf truck to bench; hooded or wrapped each item; carried it to the box; placed it in position; stepped to the left for excelsior; stepped back to the

[2] F. J. Van Poppelen, "See What Motion Study Has Done to Plant Layout," *Factory and Ind. Management*, Vol. 82, No. 6, pp. 797-799, December, 1931.

[3] C. H. Cox, "Work Simplification Applied to the Shipping Department," *Am. Management Assoc.*, Production Series No. 115, p. 3, 1939.

box; and placed the excelsior. Each use of glue, labels, or stencil brush meant several steps along the packing-bench area. The operator in Fig. 96 is cutting tape for sealing the packed box on the buck.

The new packing bench shown in Fig. 97 combines all three former units into one fixture. All equipment and material are conveniently

FIG. 96—Packing bench—old design.

positioned within the maximum working area. On the left is a tin-lined excelsior bin and on the right is a packing buck. A compartment for hammer, stencil brush, knife, etc., is located above the buck; above this is a drawer for nails and tacks; to the left of this drawer is a holder for the operator's pencil and a slide for his production record.

On the extreme right side of the bench, a shelf holds the tape dispenser; a large compartment houses a new-style glue-dispenser; then come four compartments for commonly used corrugated separators; and a small pigeonhole slot for special stencils. The extreme left-

FIG. 97—Packing bench—improved design.

hand side of the fixture contains material infrequently used, such as six sizes of special labels, asbestos pads, large-sized hoods, and long strips of corrugated wrappers.

If the operator desires to do so, he may stand in one position to select and make up the box; select stock to be packed from the mono-rail carrier; reach glue and tape; select all internal packing material; reach necessary stencils and stencil brush; and record the work on his production record. Although it is not recommended that the operator stay in one fixed location, this packing bench has eliminated thousands of unnecessary steps for each packer every day.

Checker's Table. The checker's table shown in Fig. 98 is semi-circular in shape with individual compartments for shipping papers, orders, packing memos, envelopes, rubber stamps, stamp pads, and

FIG. 98—Checker's table—improved design.

other auxiliary equipment and materials.[4] Working edges of the compartments are within the maximum working area. The table also provides a sloping working surface of convenient height for an operator in standing position. The lower shelf provides space for the storage of special "put-ups" to be assembled with the regular stock items.

This improved table replaced an old-style bench, nine feet long with four large storage cabinets under the working surface, where miscellaneous material and equipment were kept.

The improved table eliminated the walking required to cover the old straight-table area; saved time because of conveniently located material and the proper height of writing surface; and conserved floor space.

4 *Ibid.*, p. 10.

11. GRAVITY FEED BINS AND CONTAINERS SHOULD BE USED TO DELIVER THE MATERIAL AS CLOSE TO THE POINT OF ASSEMBLY OR USE AS POSSIBLE.

Bins with sloping bottoms permit the material to be fed to the front by gravity and so relieve the operator from having to dip down into the container to grasp parts. It is not always possible to slide material into position as in the bolt and washer assembly. More frequently bins such as those shown in Fig. 99 are used. Where many

Fig. 99—Standard bins.

different parts are required, as in the assembly of an electric switch, it becomes necessary to nest the bins, one above the other, in order to have the material within convenient reach of the operator.

Bins of standard sizes (see Fig. 99) have been designed and are standard equipment at the Philadelphia plant of the General Electric Company. The bins are interchangeable and are made in three heights and three widths. By the use of these standard-unit bins, any combination can be made to suit the particular job. It is difficult to give a general rule as to the proper size of bins for a particular operation. Some companies try to have their bins large enough to hold material for four hours' work, which probably is an economical size for many kinds of material.

Figure 100 shows how these bins were arranged for the assembly of a two-plate clamp.[5] With such standard bins available it is a simple

[5] Ralph M. Barnes, "Cutting Costs by Motion Study," *Am. Machinist*, Vol. 78, No. 3, pp. 120-122, Jan. 31, 1934.

task to set up for a new job. This one took less than three hours, and that included time for making a fixture for locating the bolts in the vise jaws.

FIG. 100—Standard bins are used in the layout of the work place for the assembly of clamps.

Figure 101 shows a bin with a long spout or tray attached. This tray facilitates the grasping of very small parts. A number of parts are drawn from the bin to the tray. It is then easy to select and grasp individual parts. The ordinary gravity bin (see Fig. 99) may have a tray spout attached to it. This type of bin is superior to that shown in Fig. 101, since it does not need to be refilled so often.

A Study of Three Types of Bins. The results of a study [6] of the time to grasp machine screws (Nos. 2, 4, 8, and 12) and machine-screw nuts from various types of bins are shown in Figs. 102 and 103. The operation consisted of selecting and grasping with the right hand a machine screw or nut from a bin, carrying it through a distance of five inches, and releasing it into a hole in the table top. The time

FIG. 101—Bin with tray attached to facilitate *select* and *grasp* of parts.

for each of the therbligs select and grasp, transport loaded, release load, and transport empty was accurately measured.

As Table XVII shows, the bin with tray (3) required the least

[6] *Univ. Iowa Studies in Engg.*, Bul. 16, p. 28, 1939; also *The Iron Age*, Vol. 19, No. 13, pp. 32-37, March 30, 1939.

TABLE XVII

Time Required to Grasp, Carry, and Dispose of Machine-screw Nuts and Machine Screws from Various Types of Bins

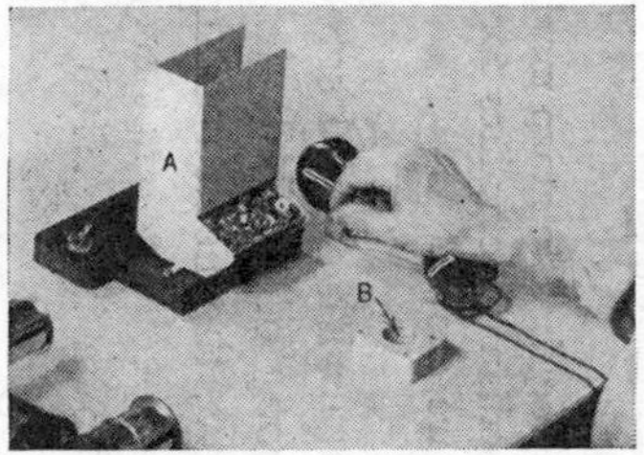		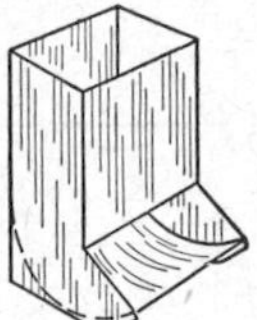 Hopper Type Bin		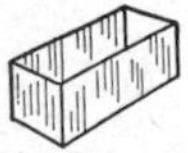 Rectangular Bin		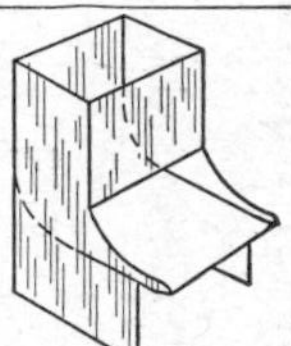 Bin with Tray	
		Nuts	Screws	Nuts	Screws	Nuts	Screws
SELECT AND GRASP — Nut or screw from bin at A (see figure above).	Time in Minutes	0.00629	0.00586	0.00653	0.00541	0.00390	0.00465
	Time in Per Cent (Shortest Time = 100%)	161	126	168	117	100	100
TRANSPORT LOADED — Carry nut or screw through distance of 5 inches—from A to B.	Time in Minutes	0.00193	0.00339	0.00236	0.00418	0.00205	0.00318
	Time in Per Cent (Shortest Time = 100%)	100	106	123	132	106	100
RELEASE LOAD — Drop nut into 1-inch hole in table top at B.	Time in Minutes	0.00404	0.00397	0.00360	0.00350	0.00368	0.00385
	Time in Per Cent (Shortest Time = 100%)	112	113	100	100	102	110
TRANSPORT EMPTY — Move hand to bin at A for nut.	Time in Minutes	0.00152	0.00245	0.00233	0.00305	0.00198	0.00258
	Time in Per Cent (Shortest Time = 100%)	100	100	154	125	131	106
TOTAL CYCLE (G. + T. L. + R. L. + T. E.)	Time in Minutes	0.01377	0.01567	0.01480	0.01614	0.01160	0.01428
	Time in Per Cent (Shortest Time = 100%)	119	110	128	113	100	100

time to select and grasp the nuts.   The hopper type bin (1) required
61 per cent more time, and the rectangular bin (2) required 68 per
cent more time than did bin 3.

Trays such as those shown in Figs. 104 and 105 are used to position

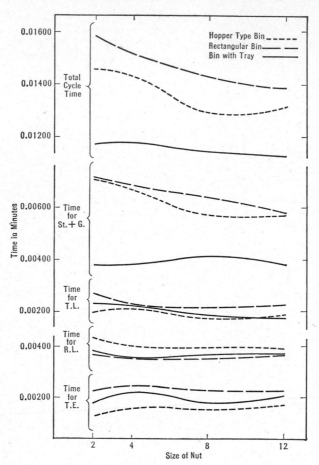

FIG. 102—Curves showing results of study of time required to grasp machine-screw
nuts from various types of bins. Averages of median time values for five male
and five female operators are shown.

parts so that they may be readily picked up with special screwdrivers
or wrenches.   Figure 104 shows how the body of the bolt drops down
between the rods in the bottom of the tray, the head remains above
the rods in position to be grasped with the special ratchet screwdriver
wrench shown in Fig. 146-*B*.   The tray shown in Fig. 105 is used to

keep nuts in position for grasping with the special screwdriver wrench shown in Fig. 146-A. An occasional jarring motion of the tray is all that is needed to cause the nuts to drop into the holes in the bottom of the tray.

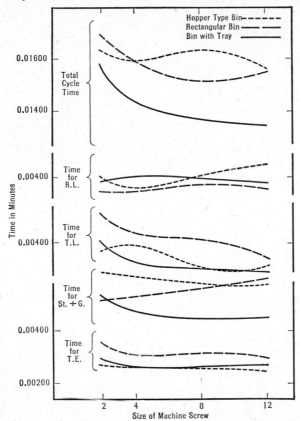

Fig. 103—Curves showing results of study of time required to grasp machine screws from various types of bins. Averages of median time values for five male operators are shown.

12. "DROP DELIVERIES" SHOULD BE USED WHEREVER POSSIBLE.

The work should be arranged so that the finished units may be disposed of by releasing them in the position in which they are completed, and delivering them to their destination by gravity. This saves the time necessary to transport the finished articles to their destination. Furthermore, the disposal of the objects by simply releasing them frees the two hands so that they may begin the next cycle simultaneously without breaking the rhythm. If a chute is used to carry the finished parts away, it should be located so that the parts can be released in the position in which they are finished, or as close to this point as possible.

FIG. 104—Tray for positioning small machine bolts for *grasping* with special screwdriver attachment.

FIG. 105—Tray for positioning nuts for *grasping* with special screwdriver attachment.

A perfect example of this is shown in Fig. 106. The operation is that of burring a hole in the end of a small angle plate. The drill is fed by means of a foot pedal, and the angle plate is held in position for burring by means of a fixture. Holes cut in the drill-press table on either side of the fixture lead to disposal chutes underneath.

The part to be burred is placed in the fixture and the drill is brought down against it. This holds the part in position while it is being burred and, when the burring is completed and the drill is raised, the burred plate drops out of the jig by gravity into the top of the disposal chute. It was economical to equip the drill press as described above because of the large quantity of burring to be done.

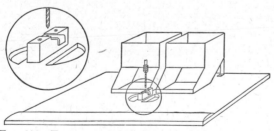

FIG. 106—Foot-operated drill press for burring small parts. Finished parts drop out of the fixture into the disposal chute by gravity.

In the bolt and washer assembly (see page 147) it was necessary to lift the finished assemblies out of the fixture and move them a few inches to one side before releasing them into the chute. A still better arrangement would have been to have had the assemblies drop through the fixture by moving some sort of a trip on the bottom of the fixture which could have been actuated by a foot pedal. This, however, would have added to the cost of the fixture and was not justified in the factory where this fixture was used.

Many people do not appreciate the amount of time that may be used in disposing of finished parts. The operation shown in Fig. 26 on page 69 illustrates this point in an excellent manner. The operation is countersinking two holes on a part for a mechanical toy. The finished part is tossed into a large tote box placed on the floor at the right of the drill press. The operator carries the part such a long distance before releasing it and the velocity of her hand is so great that it actually continues to move away from her for several inches after she has released the finished piece.

A study was recently made of gauging small pins in a fixture mounted on the front edge of the table and disposing of them by tossing them into a tote box located first at a distance of 3 inches behind the fixture, then at a distance of 10 inches, and finally at a distance of 20 inches.

The time required for the therbligs transport loaded and release load was the least when the pins were tossed into the bin nearest the fixture. Eighteen per cent more time was required for the bin at 10 inches and 34 per cent more at 20 inches.

Another example of incorrect and of correct methods of disposal of parts is shown in Figs. 115 and 116 on pages 204 and 205. The operation is inspecting metal bobbin spools. Spools that have such defects as bent ends, heavy paint, light paint, and poor weld are rejected. In the old method, trays for rejects were piled on the back of the inspection table, a separate tray being used for each kind of defective spool. In disposing of a reject, the inspector was required first to pick out the tray into which the particular reject should go, then to aim and throw the spool into it. The special table shown in Fig. 116 was designed for the improved method. Four openings for rejects are located along the edge of the table to the left of the working area. The inspector soon memorizes the location of these openings and can quickly dispose of the reject in the proper place. In an analysis of this inspection operation preparatory to redesigning the table, it was found possible to classify all rejects into four groups instead of six as was formerly thought necessary. The improved method of inspection permits the inspector to do *twice* as much work per day as was formerly possible.

13. MATERIALS AND TOOLS SHOULD BE LOCATED TO PERMIT THE BEST SEQUENCE OF THERBLIGS.

The material required at the beginning of a cycle should be placed next to the point of release of the finished piece in the preceding cycle. In the assembly of the bolt and washers, the rubber washers were in bins located next to the chute into which the assemblies were disposed as the last therblig of the previous cycle. This arrangement permitted

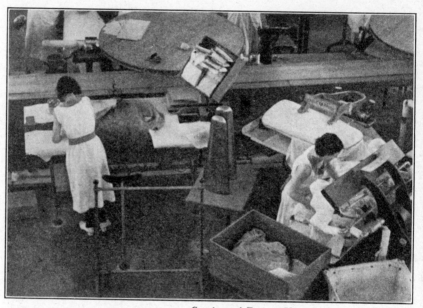

Courtesy of Factory Management and Maintenance

Fig. 107—Layout of the work place showing the position of the ironer and the finisher. This is the improved method.

the use of the two hands to best advantage at the beginning of the new cycle.

The position of the therblig in the cycle may affect the time for its performance. For example, the time for the therblig transport empty is likely to be longer when it is followed by the therblig select than when it is followed by a well-defined therblig such as a grasp of a pre-positioned part. The reason for this is that the mind begins to select during the transport empty. When the therblig transport loaded is followed by a position therblig it is slowed down by the mental preparation for the position. The time for the therblig grasp is affected by the hand velocity preceding the grasp. A satisfactory sequence of therbligs in one kind of work may aid in determining the proper sequence in other types of work.

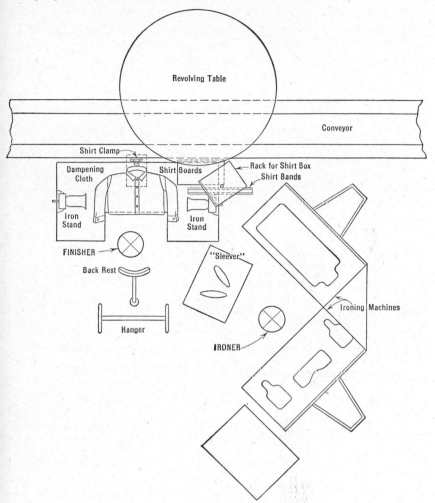

Fig. 108—Layout of the work place showing the arrangement of the finisher's table.

Since the improved method of shirt finishing in a laundry shows the application of a number of other principles of motion economy in addition to the one being described here, this operation will be presented in some detail.

Shirt Finishing in a Laundry. Ironing a shirt involves considerable hand labor and illustrates a type of work that has been considered difficult to improve. The ironing operation in a laundry is ordinarily done by two different persons, the ironer and the finisher. R. E. Smith and W. A. Reinhard of the American Institute Laundry have carefully investigated the work of the finisher and have devised a new method [7] of performing the operation with the results that the time for the complete cycle of finishing has been reduced 34 per cent and the production rate has been increased from 35 to 55 shirts per hour. Some 15,000 people are employed in the laundries of this country on this single operation.

The *ironer* operates two machines (see Figs. 107 and 108) on which she irons the collars, cuffs, fronts, and backs of the shirts. After completing this part of the work she pulls the sleeves over the steam-heated "sleever" which irons the sleeves.

The *finisher* removes the shirt from the sleever, puts it on the table, irons the yoke and the sleeves around the cuffs and shoulders, folds the shirt around a cardboard, and places a paper band around the finished shirt.

It should be remembered that it is the work of the second operator, the shirt finisher, that is being considered here.

Old Method of Shirt Finishing. The old method of finishing was done in the following manner. The operator removed the shirt from the sleever at her right (see Figs. 107 and 108), turned the collar, buttoned the collar button, and placed the shirt on the table. She then straightened the yoke of the shirt, dampened the various parts of the yoke, and ironed them. This sequence was repeated for the right shoulder and sleeve, and for the left shoulder and sleeve. The shirt was then turned over and the above process was repeated.

The shirt was then folded around a cardboard stiffener and a band placed around the shirt. The first column in Table XVIII shows the time required for each group of elements in finishing a shirt by this old method.

Improved Method of Shirt Finishing. The following changes were made in the layout of the work place before the new method was put into effect. A recess cut in the front of the table allows the tails to drop out of the way. This also permits the shirt to be placed flat on the table, front up, with the sleeves, neck, and shoulders forming a

---

[7] R. E. Smith and W. A. Reinhard, "A Shirt Finishing Method," *Laundry-owners National Association,* Service Bul. 46, pp. 1-7, March 25, 1936. Also, "Motion Camera Uncovers 34 Per cent Savings," *Factory Management and Maintenance,* Vol. 94, No. 11, pp. 46-47, November, 1936.

semicircle around the operator (see Figs. 107 and 108). The table height is adjustable and the back legs of the table are longer than the front so that the work is brought closer to the operator, thus reducing back strain. It was found impracticable to seat the operator, but a back rest was provided and may be used during part of the cycle, providing a change of position, support for the back, and rest for the operator's feet.

A 3½-pound cordless electric iron is used instead of a 6-pound one. A stand for the iron is placed on each side of the work place and special contacts on each stand allow the iron to heat between "uses." These two stands permit the operator to put down the iron on the side of the work place where she finishes with it, and from which she may take it most conveniently in beginning the next ironing operation.

A clamp located on the back of the table is dropped down on top of the shirt just below the collar, thus holding the shirt firmly in place while it is being folded around the cardboard stiffener.

The instruction sheet given below lists in sequence each step in the improved method of shirt finishing. The directions are stated in terms of the operator's left and right side as she faces the table.

1. Make one-quarter turn to right and take shirt off sleever.
2. Make one-quarter turn to left and face table.
3. Turn collar. (Bring collar to body to help curve.)
4. Button collar button.
5. Partly set collar by holding shirt away from body. (Operator uses back rest for elements 1 to 5.)
6. Grasp sleeves approximately 2 inches from each shoulder seam, take one step forward and lay shirt on table, front of shirt up (using elbows with a forward motion to make gussets fall alongside body of shirt). (See Fig. 108.) Sleeves will fall in this position approximately 50 per cent of the time.
7. Button third button.
8. Set collar and smooth shirt front if necessary.
9. Grasp dampening cloth, which is on left side of table. (Dampening cloth has remained in this position from previous operation.)
10. Dampen front of shirt from left to right at the following points:
    (a) Left gusset, shoulder seam, yoke.
    (b) Right yoke, shoulder seam, gusset. (If the sleeves do not fall in proper position on table in element 6, the operator does not correct the position of that particular sleeve until she is ready to dampen it.)
11. Drop dampening cloth on upper right side of table.
12. Grasp iron, which is on right side of table. (Iron has remained in this position from previous operation.)

13. Iron front of shirt from right to left at points previously dampened in element 10.
14. Place iron on stand on left side of table. Note: If collar support is used, it should be inserted at this point or before element 9.
15. Cross hands, grasp the left shoulder seam with the right hand and the right shoulder seam with the left hand.
16. Take a half step back from table and uncross hands, thereby turning over the shirt.
17. Take one-half step forward and lay shirt on table with back up, using same motions as described in element 6.
18. Grasp dampening cloth, which is on the right side of table.
19. Dampen from right to left the same points as were dampened on the front of the shirt; that is, right gusset, shoulder seam, etc.
20. Drop dampening cloth on left side of table.
21. Grasp iron on left stand and iron, from left to right, the same area as dampened in element 19. (Notice that motions on back of shirt are similar to those on front, thus building rhythm in operation.)
22. Place iron on right stand.
23. Grasp shirt board on right side of table and place in position on back of shirt. (Notice that shirt does not have to be moved on table for folding.)
24. Grasp left cuff in left hand and right cuff in right hand; make a half turn with each cuff to straighten out sleeves, then bring them together approximately in the center of the shirt board, about 8 to 10 inches above board.
25. Make a "Z" fold with the sleeves, keeping both cuffs together. (Notice that both hands are used in this folding operation.)
26. Bring shoulders one at a time over shirt board.
27. With left hand hold both shoulders in place, and with right pull down shoulder clamp.
28. Straighten out shirt fold on board, and bring shirt tail over board, removing clamp.
29. Reach for shirt band on upper right-hand side of table (see Fig. 108) and at the same time lift bottom of shirt up with left hand and slide shirt band under shirt with right hand.
30. Release shirt, bring both ends of shirt band together, fasten.
31. Turn shirt over for inspection. Place shirt in box on right side of table. (See Fig. 108.)

In the old method much time was used in carrying, turning, laying down, and adjusting the shirt. Also, there were many repetitions of the dampening and ironing elements. In the new method the shirt is placed on the table in the correct position for ironing the entire shirt on one side. The operator then takes the dampening cloth from its position on the left side of the table and progressing across the shirt from left to right dampens all necessary points. She releases the cloth on the right side of the table and grasps the iron. Working across the shirt from right to left she irons one entire side of the shirt, putting the iron down on the stand at the left of the work place. The operator then turns the shirt over by crossing her arms and grasping opposite shoulders of the shirt with her hands. A quick sweeping motion of uncrossing the arms turns the shirt over. The operator then repeats the dampening and ironing elements for the back of the shirt in the same manner as for the front.

Results. Table XVIII gives a detailed comparison of the two methods of shirt finishing. An analysis sheet listing individual ther-

TABLE XVIII

ELEMENTS AND TIME REQUIRED FOR SHIRT FINISHING

Time in Minutes

Elements	Methods of Shirt Finishing	
	Old	Improved
1. Reaching for shirt, turning collar, buttoning collar button, carrying shirt to table..............................	0.178	0.1357
2. Setting collar, buttoning shirt buttons, and smoothing shirt front...	0.109	0.0590
3. Picking up, laying down, or adjusting shirt in other ways to aid ironing..	0.134	0.0603
4. Reaching for and moving dampening cloth to and from shirt...	0.089	0.0357
5. Total dampening time................................	0.217	0.1798
6. Reaching for and moving iron to and from shirt.........	0.121	0.0367
7. Total ironing time..................................	0.410	0.3300
8. Folding shirt......................................	0.359	0.2130
9. Carrying shirt to box...............................	0.029	0.0310
Total Time...	1.646	1.0812
Production Rate—Shirts per Hour.......................	36.45	55.5

bligs shows that 242 therbligs were used by the right hand in finishing one shirt by the old method whereas but 114 therbligs appear on the possibility chart of the improved method.

Uniform Finishing in a Laundry. The University of Iowa Laundry processes over four million pounds of laundry per year. This includes laundry from the university hospitals, dormitories, and dining rooms.

Since nurses' and doctors' uniforms account for approximately 50 per cent of the garments that require hand finishing, these garments were the logical ones on which to make improvements in ironing methods. Roscoe C. Richards undertook to improve the method as a project in an industrial engineering course.

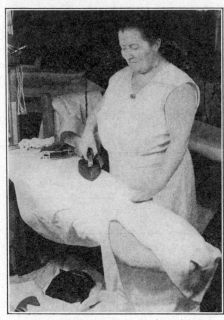

FIG. 109—Work place for old method of finishing uniforms. Conventional type of ironing board.

In the original method the conventional ironing board was used (see Fig. 109), and there was much time consumed in carrying, turning, laying down, and adjusting the uniform. Also there were many repetitions of the dampening and ironing elements.

The improved ironing table for finishing shirts described on page 194 was tried for uniforms and was found unsatisfactory. However, by using this table and by designing a small oval ironing board (see Fig. 110) which was supported on an arm attached to the main table, it was possible to improve greatly the method of finishing uniforms. The small oval ironing board was used for finishing the shoulders, waist seams, and collar.[8]

The production rate on finishing fairly simple nurses' uniforms was 15 uniforms per hour using the old method. When the improved method was used, the operator could finish 25 per hour, an increase in output of 66 per cent. The following reasons account for this increase in output:

1. Fewer lays were required to do the same work.
2. The distance that the iron was carried was reduced from 63 feet to 16 feet per uniform.

[8] Ralph M. Barnes and Roscoe C. Richards, "A New Method of Finishing Uniforms," *Laundry Age,* Vol. 19, No. 8, October, 1939.

3. The distance the operator walked was reduced from 18 feet to 6 feet per uniform.

4. The operator was trained in the correct dampening and ironing methods, eliminating patting and excessive drying time.

5. A cordless iron was used, and a definite place was provided for the iron when not in actual use.[9]

FIG. 110—Work place for improved method of finishing uniforms. Operator grasps dampening cloth with right hand from right side of table.

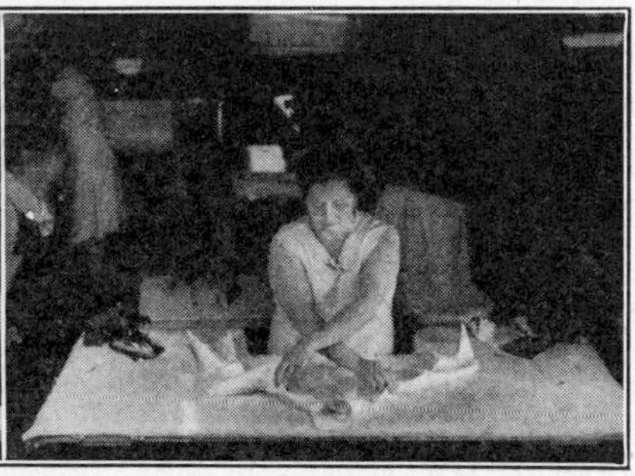

FIG. 111—Recommended method of turning over uniforms. Operator crosses arms and grasps opposite shoulders of uniform, uncrossing the arms turns over the uniform.

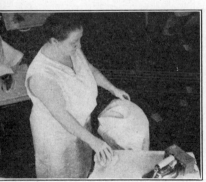

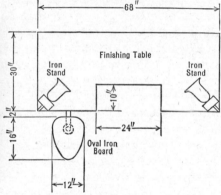

FIG. 112—Shoulders, waist seams, and collar are finished on the small oval ironing board. The stand and electric power connection for the iron are also shown. The cordless iron heats when not in use.

FIG. 113—Drawing showing dimensions of uniform finishing table.

[9] For other studies of laundry work see: David B. Porter and A. H. Mogensen, "Time and Motion Study—Its Effect on Laundry Production," *Starchroom Laundry J.*, Vol. 42, No. 4, pp. 49-52, April 15, 1936; H. G. Maule, "Time and Movement Study in Laundry Work," *The Human Factor*, Vol. 10, No. 10, pp. 351-359, October, 1936; L. A. Legros and H. C. Weston, "On the Design of Machinery in Relation to the Operator," *Ind. Fatigue Research Bd.*, Report 36, 1926; and M. Smith, "Some Studies in the Laundry Trade," *Ind. Fatigue Research Bd.*, Report 22, 1922.

14. PROVISIONS SHOULD BE MADE FOR ADEQUATE CONDITIONS FOR SEEING. GOOD ILLUMINATION IS THE FIRST REQUIREMENT FOR SATISFACTORY VISUAL PERCEPTION.

Visual perception may take place under such widely varying conditions that adequate provisions for seeing in one kind of work are not always most suitable for another. For example, the provisions for seeing on such very fine work as watch making would be different from those recommended for inspecting "leather cloth" or tin plate for surface defects. However, if adequate illumination is provided, seeing is made easier in every case although this may not be the complete solution of the problem. By adequate illumination is meant (1) light of sufficient intensity for the particular task, (2) light of the proper color and without glare, and (3) light coming from the right direction.

It should be borne in mind that the visibility of an object is determined by the following variables: [10] brightness of the object, its contrast with its background, the size of the object, the time available for seeing, the distance of the object from the eye, and other factors such as distractions, fatigue, reaction-time, and glare. These variables are so related that a deficiency in one may be compensated by an augmentation of one or more of the others, provided all factors are above certain limiting values.[11]

The intensity of illumination falling on an object and the reflection-factor of the object, or that of its background, should be considered together in providing adequate illumination. For example, the pages of a telephone directory are dark in color and the contrast between the printed letter and the page is not as great as that of printing on good book paper. The paper of the directory reflects only 57 per cent of the incident light, whereas the book paper reflects about 80 per cent. Two to three times as much light is required to read a telephone directory as is required to read with equal facility the same critical details of names and numbers printed with blacker ink on white book paper.[12] The task of sewing on very dark cloth is difficult even under the best conditions of lighting. For example, dark cloth of 4 per cent reflection-factor would require 200 foot-candles to produce the same

[10] M. Luckiesh and F. K. Moss, "The Applied Science of Seeing," *Trans. Illuminating Engg. Soc.,* Vol. 28, p. 846, 1933.
[11] M. Luckiesh and F. K. Moss, "The Human Seeing-Machine," *J. Franklin Institute,* Vol. 215, No. 6, p. 647, June, 1933.
[12] M. Luckiesh, "Seeing and Human Welfare," Williams & Wilkins, Baltimore, Md., p. 85, 1934.

brightness as 10 foot-candles on white cloth.[13]   A knowledge of this point suggests the use of greater intensity of illumination or lighter background for work with objects with a low reflection-factor or for very fine work.   The size of the image of the object falling on the retina of the eye must be sufficiently large to allow adequate discrimination of the details.   This factor requires greatest consideration in very fine work.   An increase in the illumination on the object, or an increase in the contrast between the object and its surroundings, produces the same effect, within limits, as a decrease in the distance between the eye and the object.

Relief of Eyestrain on Fine Assembly Work.   The following case [14] shows the changes that may be made to improve the seeing on fine assembly work.   The operation was assembling and adjusting the parts

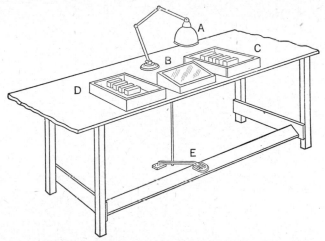

FIG. 114—Improved lighting unit. *A.* Adjustable lamp for direct light; *B.* Background light; *C.* Finished work; *D.* Work awaiting adjustment; *E.* Foot-operated switch for adjustable lamp.

of a delicate electric meter mechanism.   The task was performed by men and boys, and about three-quarters of an hour was required for each unit.   Eyestrain and fatigue were excessive, owing to the fact that on certain parts of the operation the illumination was so inadequate in relation to the smallness of the parts that the work had to be held close to the eyes.

[13] M. Luckiesh and F. K. Moss, "The Applied Science of Seeing," *Trans. Illuminating Engg. Soc.,* Vol. 28, p. 854, 1933.

[14] J. H. Mitchell, "The Relief of Eyestrain on a Fine Assembly Process," *The Human Factor,* Vol. 10, No. 10, p. 341, October, 1936.

In order to remedy this condition a rest period was introduced and improvements were made in the illumination of the work place. Figure 114 shows the improved lighting units. Because of the fact that certain parts of the operation could be done best by silhouetting the mechanism against an illuminated background, a background light was placed on the work bench and was kept "on" all of the time. When it was necessary to view the assembly under direct light the foot pedal was depressed, turning on the upper lamp. Tests showed that the best color for the background light was white or pale yellow and that it should be free from glare.

The effects of the rest period and of the improved illumination on six men in the experimental group over the period of the test were an improvement in the quality of the work and also an increase in output of 19.5 per cent. The rest period was included as working time in calculating hourly output.

Use of Special Spectacles for Very Fine Work. On certain kinds of very fine work the eye must be kept very near the object, however high the intensity of illumination may be. The constant use of the eyes on objects at such close range imposes a serious strain [15] on the muscles of convergence and accommodation.[16] Experiments show that the use of special spectacles is advisable to permit the eyes to assume their normal condition. An increase in output approximating 12 per cent has been found to result from the use of glasses on such work as mounting lamp filaments, "linking" in hosiery making, and "drawing-in" in weaving processes.[17]

Time for Seeing. Seeing can take place only after the eyes come to a stop and are focused on the object. In the process of reading a printed page, for example, the eyes do not make a continuous movement along the line, but rather move in a series of jumps or leaps. The eyes begin at the left-hand end of the printed line and progress from one fixation to the next along the line to the right-hand end of the line. The eyes then move back to the left-hand end of the next line with a single smooth sweep, during which movement the eyes see

[15] H. C. Weston and S. Adams, "On the Relief of Eyestrain among Persons Performing Very Fine Work," Ind. Fat. Research Bd., Report 49, p. iii, 1928.

[16] "When a near object is viewed, two muscular actions take place simultaneously, the one causing a slight rotation of the eyes inwards toward each other, thus allowing the image to fall on the same point of the retina in each eye, the other a change in the curvature of the lenses of the eyes, the object being thereby kept in focus. The former of these is known as *convergence*, the latter as *accommodation*. . . ." *Ibid.*, p. iii.

[17] *Ibid.*, p. 5.

nothing. The movements of the two eyes are coordinated and one cannot move voluntarily without the other. The number of movements and pauses which the eyes make in reading a line of print will vary, usually from three to seven, depending upon the length of the line, the visibility of the print, the skill of the reader, and other factors.

It is generally agreed that the optimum length of line is 3 to 4 inches and that it should not exceed 4 inches in length. Ten-point type seems to be the optimum size, although there is some evidence to show that the optimum size may cover a considerable range.[18]

Fixation pauses require on the average 0.17 second. Tests show that the shortest interval of time possible for a person to see an object to gain an adequate visual impression varies from 0.07 second to 0.30 second, the average being 0.17 second.[19] The intensity of illumination affects the time required for seeing. "If an object of 50 per cent contrast can just be seen under a certain intensity of illumination when the time available is 0.30 second, the intensity of illumination must be trebled if it is to be visible when the time is reduced to 0.07 second." [20]

INSPECTION WORK

The provision for adequate conditions for seeing is of paramount importance in inspection work. Such work is usually highly repetitive, exacting in nature, and predominantly mental in its demands. Constant attention and almost continuous use of the eyes are required in many kinds of inspection work. Perception of a defect must be followed by instant action on the part of the inspector to reject the defective part. Some individuals are able to see smaller differences than others and to perceive the same differences with greater speed. Since reaction time and visual acuity are important elements in most inspection work it is essential that persons be selected by means of suitable tests before being employed for such work.[21]

Inspection of Metal Spools. Some practical applications are included here to show how provisions were made for adequate conditions for seeing. The first case is the inspection of metal bobbin spools for dents, scratches, heavy paint, light paint, and bent flanges. Since the improved method of inspection employs a number of principles of

[18] M. D. Vernon, "The Experimental Study of Reading," pp. 165-166, Cambridge University Press, London, 1931.

[19] M. Luckiesh, "Seeing and Human Welfare," p. 96, Williams & Wilkins, Baltimore, Md., 1934.

[20] *Ibid.*, p. 96.

[21] S. Wyatt and J. N. Langdon, "Inspection Processes in Industry," *Ind. Health Research Bd.,* Report 63, p. 46, 1932.

motion economy in addition to those for adequate seeing, this operation will be presented in some detail.

Original Method of Inspection. The inspector was seated at a table as shown in Fig. 115. The spools to be inspected were placed at the inspector's left in a large steel tote box *A*. The good spools were arranged in order in the small metal tray *B* at the inspector's right. Defective spools were tossed into trays at the back of the table and directly in front of the inspector. They were classified as *C*—bent ends, *D*—light paint, *E*—overlap barrels, *F*—off-center flanges, *G*—culls, *H*— heavy paint.

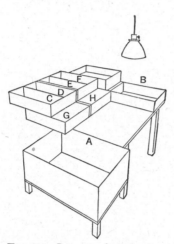

Elements of the Operation. The inspector, turning to the tote box (previously positioned by the supply man) at her left, grasped spools with both hands and carried them to the table in front of her where she deposited them. This was repeated until a pile had been accumulated. The inspector procured an empty tray for the good spools from a pile at her right. She also positioned empty trays for various kinds of defects.

The inspector then proceeded with the inspection of the spools in the following manner:

FIG. 115—Layout of work place for inspection of metal spools— old method. *A*. Supply of spools to be inspected; *B*. Good spools; *C-D-E-F-G-H*. Rejected spools.

1. She picked up one spool from the pile with the thumb and index finger of each hand, inspected the outside of flanges by looking straight down on them, tipped spools slightly, and then, by turning spools, inspected for bent ends. She turned spools end for end and repeated the above elements for the other flanges. Then she tipped spools back horizontally and by turning spools around inspected for defects on the inside of flanges. If the spools were good she flipped them back into the palm of her hand; if a defect was found she disposed of the spool in the proper defect tray.

The above elements were repeated until three or four spools (depending upon the size of the spools) had been accumulated in each hand.

2. The inspector placed the spools held in her right hand in the tray of good spools at her right. She then transferred the spools

accumulated in the left hand to the right hand and placed these in the tray with her right hand. During this time the left hand was idle. The inspector then moved both hands to the pile in front of her and repeated the elements in 1.

3. As tiers of good spools were built up in the tray the operator jogged the spools into position, pushing the tier over against the preceding one; or, if it was the first tier, she pushed it over against the side of the tray.

4. When a tray was filled the inspector made out a ticket and placed it in the end of the tray. She then placed the tray on the back of the table where it was picked up by the supply man.

Improved Method of Inspection. The inspector is seated at a table as shown in Fig. 116. The spools to be inspected are placed in the hopper *A*, Fig. 116, by the supply man and they are fed by gravity down on the inspection table. The good spools are placed in order in the tray *B* at the inspector's right. This tray is tipped up at an angle and is placed at the correct height for disposing of the spools with least effort. When a defective spool is found it is disposed by the left hand into one of the four openings in the top of the table at the inspector's left.

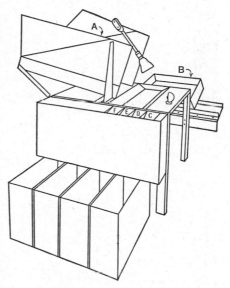

Fig. 116—Layout of work place for inspection of metal spools—improved method. *A*. Supply Hopper—spools to be inspected; *B*. Good spools; *C-D-E-F*. Rejected spools.

These go by chute to trays on the floor. Defective spools are classified as *C*—bent ends, *D*—light paint, *E*—heavy paint, or *F*—culls.

Elements of the Operation

Elements for Good Spools

Left Hand	Right Hand
1. Pick up two spools	1. Pack good spools in tray
2. Transfer one spool to right hand	2. Receive one spool from left hand

Elements for Good Spools—(Continued)

Left Hand	Right Hand
3. Inspect upper flange under upper light.	3. Inspect upper flange under upper light
4. Turn spool 60°	4. Turn spool 60°
5. Inspect other flange in front of lower light	5. Inspect other flange in front of lower light
6. Inspect barrel while spool is rotated between thumb and index finger (under upper light)	6. Inspect barrel while spool is rotated between thumb and index finger (under upper light)
7. Flip spool to palm of hand	7. Flip spool to palm of hand
8. Pick up one spool	8. Pick up one spool

Repeat elements 3, 4, 5, 6, 7, and 8 until there are three or four spools in each hand.

9. Transfer spools to right hand	9. Grasp spools from left hand

Elements for Defective Spools

1. When heavy paint, bent ends, or "jams" are found in elements 3, 5, or 6, reject spools to disposal chute. When light paint is found in element 3, inspect spool (elements 5 and 6) for other defects before rejecting	1. Pick up another spool
2. Grasp spool from right hand and reject it	2. When a defective spool is found in right hand transfer it to left hand and get new spool

Auxiliary Elements

1. Procure empty tray from pile behind inspector and position tray on table at right

2. When tray is full make out ticket and place in end of tray

3. Push finished tray of work to back of table ready for collection by the supply man

Comparison of the Two Methods of Inspection. The improved method of inspection is superior to the old method in the following ways:

1. Two lights on the new table furnish illumination for inspection so that it is necessary only to turn the spools 60 degrees to inspect both ends. In the old method, using but one light, it was necessary to turn

the spools end for end or 180 degrees. The intensity of illumination has been greatly increased so that now at the point of inspection there is 150 foot-candles. The bulbs are completely shielded to prevent glare.

2. The work of the two hands has been so arranged that neither hand has practically any idle time during the cycle.

3. The supply of spools is placed in the hopper by the supply man and they are fed by gravity (occasionally pulled down by the inspector with a hook) down to the inspection table. This saves the time of lifting the spools from the tote box to the table as required in the old method.

4. The rejected spools are dropped in openings located conveniently near the working position of the hands. In the old method the inspector had to toss the spools into trays piled in front of her. This required more time and more physical effort than the new method.

5. The tray for receiving good spools is located at the proper height and is tipped up at a convenient angle.

6. The tray of finished work rests on a metal track and may be easily shoved to the back of the table, from which the supply man removes it. The inspector is not required to lift full trays of work.

7. Inspectors are now given a five-minute rest period at the end of each hour, and they are enthusiastic about them. Formerly one five-minute rest period was provided in the morning and one in the afternoon. The inspectors are paid at their regular hourly base rate for the rest periods. For the remainder of the day they are paid a wage incentive in the form of a premium for all production above standard.

8. Arm rests on the front of the table tend to steady the hands and reduce fatigue. Chairs are carefully adjusted to fit the individual inspector.

Training Inspectors. Considerable study was required in designing the new table and in determining the proper procedure for the inspection elements themselves. After the most satisfactory method was worked out the inspectors were carefully trained. Slow-motion pictures were used to show the sequence of motions, and only after very careful and persistent training were the inspectors able to do the work in the proper manner and thus accomplish the expected amount of work per day.

Savings. The inspectors can now inspect *twice* as many spools per day as formerly and they apparently do it with less eyestrain and fatigue. Less than one half the floor space is required for the inspection work and the department has a neater appearance than formerly. The quality of inspection has not suffered by the increased output per inspector. The new tables cost less than $25 each.

Inspection of Polished Surfaces. The inspection of highly polished surfaces for surface defects cannot be done under ordinary artificial lighting systems because the glare produced on the shiny surfaces reflects the light into the eyes of the inspector. The special lighting booth shown in Fig. 117 was devised for such work.[22] The curved background is painted a dull white with black parallel stripes running vertically at one end. This lighting unit serves two purposes. The reflection of the stripes on sheet material that is supposed to be smooth and flat aids in revealing uneven or irregular surfaces, and the portion of the lighting unit having no stripes gives a high-intensity indirect light which is effective for disclosing scratches, holes, thin plating, and other similar surface defects. Dents and rough spots also show up well in reflected light.

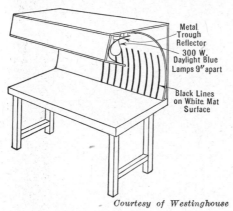

Metal
Trough
Reflector

300 W.
Daylight Blue
Lamps 9″ apart

Black Lines
on White Mat
Surface

Courtesy of Westinghouse

FIG. 117—Special lighting booth for the inspection of products with polished surfaces.

Inspection by Transmitted Light. Products made of transparent or translucent material may be inspected by transmitting the light through the product. Broken fibers, knots, and other defects in cloth are easily detected; bubbles, cracks, and foreign material in glass and cellulose show up when transmitted light is used for inspection.

Figure 118 shows an example of transmitted light for inspecting milk bottles for dirt, cracks, grease, and pieces of broken glass. In a trough just above the moving belt on which the washed bottles pass on their way to the bottling machines, 200-watt bulbs are installed base to base. Approximately 150 foot-candles of light is present on the belt surface. The back portion of the inspection surface is painted white in order to reveal black defects, and the conveyor belt is black in order to aid in detecting pieces of broken glass which might be rest-

[22] J. J. McLaughlin, "Tailor-Made Local Lighting," *Mill and Factory*, Vol. 19, No. 5, p. 56, November, 1936.

ing on the bottom of the bottle. An operator can inspect bottles at the rate of 128 per minute as they pass by on the conveyor.

Adjusting Electric-Fan Blades. After the blades for an electric fan have been formed and assembled to the hub it is necessary to bend or adjust the blades until they are true. The original method of doing this was to mount the fan blade unit on a vertical spindle attached to the work bench and then twist each blade until the two edges just cleared pins or gauges mounted on the bench.

Courtesy of Westinghouse

Fig. 118—Inspection of milk bottles by transmitted light.

An improved method was developed by which a beam of light was passed over one blade and onto a white screen on which were placed black lines to indicate the correct position of the top and bottom edges of the fan blade. The operator merely twisted the blade until the shadow came within the two black lines on the screen and then proceeded to adjust the next blade. A booth with three sides and a top was placed on the work bench so that a dark shadow would be cast on the screen by the fan blade. An operator using this improved method can now do five times as much work as formerly.

15. THE HEIGHT OF THE WORK PLACE AND THE CHAIR SHOULD PREFERABLY BE SO ARRANGED THAT ALTERNATE SITTING AND STANDING AT WORK ARE EASILY POSSIBLE.

The worker should be permitted to vary his position by either sitting or standing as he prefers.[23] Such an arrangement enables the individual to rest certain sets of muscles, and a change of position always tends to improve the circulation. Either sitting or standing for long periods of time produces more fatigue than alternately sitting or standing at will. In many kinds of work provision can easily be made for this sitting-standing combination.

So important is this from the point of view of health that some states have laws requiring that the work place be arranged to permit either sitting or standing.

SEATS AND WORK TABLES. As far as, and to whatever extent, in the judgment of the commission, the nature of the work permits, the following provisions shall be effective: Seats shall be provided at work tables or machines for each and every woman or minor employed, and such seats shall be capable of such adjustment and shall be kept so adjusted to the work tables or machines that the position of the worker relative to the work shall be substantially the same whether seated or standing. Work tables, including cutting and canning tables and sorting belts, shall be of such dimensions and design that there are no physical impediments to efficient work in either a sitting or a standing position, and individually adjustable foot rests shall be provided. New installations to be approved by the commission.[24]

Although it would be preferable to have the height of the work place and the chair fit the particular operator who has to use it, this cannot always be done. It may be necessary in many cases to make the benches of such height that they will be most suitable for the average worker.

The height of the worker's elbow above the standing surface is commonly taken as the starting place for determining the proper height of the work place and the chair. The Industrial Welfare Commission of California has found that the height of the average worker's elbow above the standing surface is 40 inches for women (for men this would be two or three inches higher) and that a large percentage

---

[23] "First Principles of Industrial Posture and Seating," N. Y. Dept of Labor Special Bul. 141, p. 2, January, 1926.

[24] "Seating of Women and Minors in the Fruit and Vegetable Canning Industry," California Ind. Welfare Commission, Bul. 2a, p. 3, February, 1928.

of the workers will not vary 1½ inches from this measurement.[25] A study [26] of 200 factory girls made in England shows that the mean height for the group was 39.5 inches and 70 per cent of the group fell within 1.5 inches variation.

With 40 inches taken as the average elbow height of the female workers in this country (the range being from 34 to 45 inches) and with the hand allowed to work 1 to 3 inches lower than the elbow, the average height of the working surface should be 37 to 39 inches. The chair should be 25 to 31 inches high, depending upon the proportions of the individual. With such table and chair heights the worker is permitted either to stand or sit at work, with the elbow and the hand maintained at the same position relative to the work place.

Space between Top of Seat and Under Surface of Bench Top. The work place should be constructed to permit plenty of leg room for the worker. Braces, shafts, and other obstructions under the work place often interfere with the natural position of the worker and so cause poor posture and discomfort. Such obstructions should not be permitted. The work bench should preferably be not over 2 inches thick and there should be 6 to 10 inches of space between the top of the chair seat and the under surface of the bench.

A bench 37 inches high will be too high for the short person but this can be corrected by placing a rack of the proper height on the floor for the worker to stand on. For the tall worker a small rack or platform can sometimes be placed on top of the bench to raise the height of the work place. Where this cannot be done the tall worker is handicapped while standing at work but, of course, this is not necessarily true when she is seated.

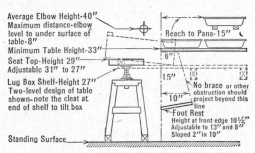

Fig. 119—Cutting table dimensions—table designed by the Industrial Welfare Commission of California.

In some kinds of work it is necessary to have equipment or material containers mounted on top of the work bench. This has the

[25] *Ibid.,* p. 3.

[26] L. A. Legros and H. C. Weston, "On the Design of Machinery in Relation to the Operator," *Ind. Fat. Research Bd.,* Report 36, p. 9, 1926.

effect of adding to the "thickness" of the bench. A work place more than 5 inches thick cannot ordinarily provide a comfortable sitting-standing position for the worker. The Industrial Welfare Commission of California was confronted with the problem of specifying a standard work place for their fruit and vegetable canning industries where a pan 3 inches high was placed on top of the work table. The work place [27] which their studies led them to recommend is shown in Fig. 119. Considering the average elbow height as 40 inches above the floor and allowing for the hands to work at a position 1 inch lower than the elbow, and further allowing 3 inches for the height of the ordinary fruit pan, we see that the top of the work bench should be about 36 inches above the standing surface in this case.

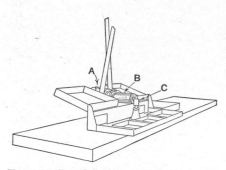

FIG. 120—Bench lathe cut in half to permit sitting or standing at work. This lathe is used for the assembly of hard rubber syringe parts.

As Fig. 119 shows, a foot rest is attached to the bench, and a chair that can be adjusted for height is specified. This arrangement permits the worker to sit or stand while working and still maintain the same relative position of the elbow.

The minimum table height for a comfortable position is determined by another limiting factor. A distance of not more than 8 inches between the elbow height and the under side of the table can be permitted if a restful position is to be maintained. A distance much greater than this interferes with the natural position of the knee. Using this distance of 8 inches as the limiting factor and allowing 1 inch for the thickness of the bench, we find the minimum height of the top of the bench to be 33 inches.

In some plants bench lathes have been cut in half (see Fig. 120) and mounted on the bench with the axis of the spindle perpendicular to the front edge of the bench. This arrangement permits sitting-standing and facilitates working with both hands.[28]

Arm Rest. Occasionally the work is of such a nature that it is desirable to have arm rests provided at the work place. Arm rests are most effective on work that requires little movement of the forearms

[27] California Ind. Welfare Commission Bul. 2a, p. 10.
[28] W. R. Mullee, "Motion Study Is Safety's Partner," *Nat. Safety News,* Vol. 34, No. 5, p. 23, November, 1936.

with the hands working at approximately the same position, often at some distance from the body, for long periods of time. Light drilling, tapping, and reaming operations are frequently of this type. On such work it is restful to have padded, metal, or wood arm rests placed on top of, or at the edge of, the work bench in a position to support the forearm. The arm rests need not interfere with the necessary working movements of the arms or hands. Figure 106 on page 190 shows such an arm rest.

Foot Rest. When high chairs are used a foot rest should be provided. This foot rest should preferably be attached to the floor or the bench but, even though less desirable, it may be fastened to the chair. The foot rest should be of ample width and depth to permit the entire bottoms of both feet to rest on it and allow for some movement. This usually requires a depth of 12 inches or more. The absence of a foot rest forces the worker to hook the heel of his shoe over the rung of the chair (see Fig. 80), or else let the feet dangle in the air, both of which positions are uncomfortable.

16. A CHAIR OF THE TYPE AND HEIGHT TO PERMIT GOOD POSTURE SHOULD BE PROVIDED FOR EVERY WORKER.[29]

The following statements are included here to explain clearly just what is meant by good posture.

Good standing posture is one in which the different segments of the body—head, neck, chest, and abdomen—are balanced vertically one upon the other so that the weight is borne mainly by the bony framework and a minimum of effort and strain is placed upon the muscles and ligaments. In this posture under normal conditions the organic functions—respiration, circulation, digestion, etc.—are performed with least mechanical obstruction and with greatest efficiency.

[29] New York State Labor Law, Section 146, Subdivision 3: "No female under sixteen years of age shall be employed in any capacity which compels constant standing."

Section 150: "A sufficient number of suitable seats, with backs where practicable, shall be provided and maintained in every factory, mercantile establishment, freight or passenger elevator, hotel and restaurant for female employees who shall be allowed to use the seats to such an extent as may be reasonable for the preservation of their health. In factories, female employees shall be allowed to use such seats whenever they are engaged in work which can be properly performed in a sitting posture. In mercantile establishments, at least one seat shall be provided for every three female employees and if the duties of such employees are to be performed principally in front of a counter, table, desk or fixture, such seats shall be placed in front thereof, or if such duties are to be performed principally behind such counter, table, desk or fixture they shall be placed behind the same."

Good sitting posture. The thing which should always be insisted upon in the use of the body in any way is that the body should be kept straight from the hips to the neck and should not be allowed to flex or bend at the waist line. Any position which allows this lowers the vitality of the individual, leads to strain of the back, and naturally lessens the efficiency of the worker.

The most frequent violation of the good sitting posture occurs when the individual slumps in his chair or assumes a sideways slouch, both of which are fatiguing and impair the health.

When the worker is seated, the chair should aid and not hinder him in maintaining good posture. A good chair should have the following features:

1. The chair should be adjustable in height so that it may be readily fitted to the particular individual who is to use it. Non-adjustable chairs may be obtained in different sizes and issued to the workers according to their height. Such chairs are not generally considered as practical as the adjustable type. The chair should be adjusted to a height that permits the worker to sit comfortably with both feet resting on the floor or the foot rest. (See Fig. 121.)

2. The chair should be rigidly built, preferably of steel frame with wood seat and back. It is important that a wood seat and back be provided since wood is more comfortable than metal. The edges of the seat and back should be rounded so that no sharp edges can cause discomfort and impede the circulation. Swivel chairs and chairs with casters are not recommended for factory work unless absolutely necessary. The easy movement of such chairs tends to cause unsteadiness while being used. This is particularly noticeable if the work requires some muscular effort. The chair may be provided with smooth metal "sliders" which permit the operator to shove it back out of the way without disturbing his work when he wishes to work standing.

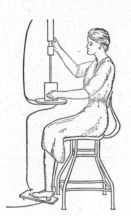

Fig. 121—A well-designed and properly adjusted back rest helps to hold the spine erect by relieving the strain on the back muscles.

3. The chair seat should be form fitting. A saddle seat permits the weight of the body to be evenly distributed and so promotes comfort. The front edges of the seat should be well rounded. (See Fig. 122.) For normal work the front edge of the

chair should be approximately 1 inch higher than the back edge. When the person works leaning forward, the seat of the chair should be approximately flat. The seat should be of sufficient width to accommodate the body—16 to 17 inches is none too wide. However, the seat should not be over 13 or 14 inches in depth. The shallow seat permits the body to bend at the hip when leaning forward, whereas a deep seat tends to prevent this and to cause the body to bend at the waist line, putting a curve in the spine and disturbing the posture. The deep seat also tends to cut off the circulation of the blood through the underside of the thighs near the knee.

Fig. 122—The chair seat should be form fitting and the front edges should be well rounded.

4. A back rest should be provided to support the lower part of the spine. (See Fig. 121.) To do this the chair should not have a horizontal cross slat or bar lower than 6 inches above the seat. The body should sit well back on the seat so that the back rest can support the small of the back. The lower edge of the back should be 6 to 7 inches above the seat, depending upon the individual. The back rest may be 3 to 4 inches wide and 10 to 12 inches broad. The back rest may be small and yet give satisfactory support. It can be so designed that it will not interfere with the movements of the individual's arms while working. It is important that the back rest be adjustable so that it may be fitted to the worker's body. When the worker leans forward while working, the chair back is of no use; however, the worker can use it while resting and it serves a very valuable purpose in being there for momentary relaxation.

In the finishing of shirts in the laundry it was found to be impracticable for the operator to work seated; however, a back rest was provided and could be used by the operator during a part of each cycle. (See page 194.)

CHAPTER 14

PRINCIPLES OF MOTION ECONOMY AS RELATED TO THE DESIGN OF TOOLS AND EQUIPMENT

17. THE HANDS SHOULD BE RELIEVED OF ALL WORK THAT CAN BE PERFORMED MORE ADVANTAGEOUSLY BY THE FEET OR OTHER PARTS OF THE BODY.

From an observation of the tools and fixtures usually found in the factory one is convinced that most tool designers do not give much thought to the principles of motion economy when they design them.[1] In most cases the fixtures are made for hand operation only, whereas foot-operated ones would more advantageously permit the operator to have both hands free to perform other motions.

Foot-Operated Tools and Fixtures. Figure 123 shows an ordinary

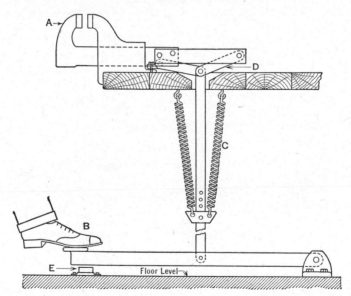

Fig. 123—Foot-operated bench vise.

[1] A. H. Mogensen, "Motion Study in the Design of Production Equipment," *Product Engg.*, Vol. 3, No. 8, pp. 313-316, August, 1932; also "Motion Study: Why Has the Designer Ignored It?," *Mech. Engg.*, Vol. 55, No. 12, pp. 727-731, December, 1933.

bench vise converted into a foot-operated one.   Depressing the foot pedal *B* opens the vise jaw *A*, and then the piece to be held is placed in the vise and the pedal is released.   The heavy coil springs *C* close the vise, and the toggle joint *D* holds the vise in the closed position while the operation is being performed on the piece. One end of the toggle joint is linked to the stationary vise jaw and the other end is connected to an extension of the movable jaw. This type of vise was developed at the Cadillac factory and it is used in a number of places in that plant. Where greater gripping power is needed a special vise may be built with a compressed-air-operated piston to actuate the vise jaws, the air being controlled by a foot-operated valve.

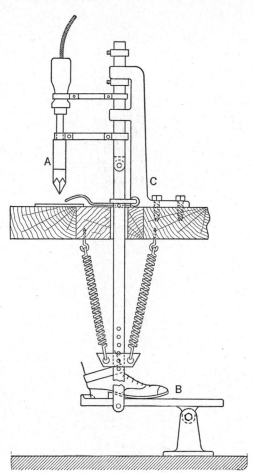

Hand tools can often be attached to or incorporated with a simple foot press or a modified arbor press in such a way that the tool is manipulated entirely by the foot. The electric soldering iron *A* in Fig. 124 is raised and lowered by the foot pedal *B*. After the soldered joint is made and as the iron is raised and

Fig. 124—Foot-operated soldering iron.

valve *C* on the compressed air line opens, a stream of air cools the soldered joint.   One company saved 50 per cent in time on the operation of soldering a wire to the end of a flat metal electric static shield by the use of this foot-operated soldering iron.

The electric motor-driven screwdriver shown in Fig. 125 has made possible a 50 per cent saving in time on several short assembly operations. The assembly fixture, material bins, and drop-delivery chute have been omitted from the figure in order to show more clearly the linkage which permits the foot operation of the screwdriver.

Although the foot pedals shown in Figs. 123, 124, and 125 are satisfactory for manipulating most devices, they are not satisfactory when greater control is required, such as in feeding a small drill press. This is particularly true when very small drills are used and the problem of excess drill breakage becomes important. The pedal shown in

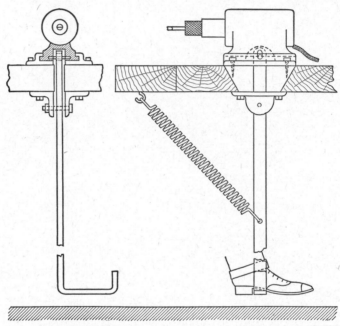

Fig. 125—Motor-driven screwdriver—foot-operated.

Figure 126 gives the operator almost as much control with the foot as with the hand in feeding the drill. The pedal, of course, frees both hands for other useful work. The linkage is clearly shown in the figure—the operator lowers the drill by moving the pedal away from him, the weight at A acting to return the pedal and thus permitting the drill to rise. The roller B attached to the bottom of the pedal moves on the flanged metal track C attached to the floor. Since the weight of the foot is carried entirely by the roller and since the movement of the drill is affected only by the motion of the pedal in the horizontal plane, very accurate control is possible. The whole linkage is quite stable, enabling the operator to manipulate the drill press with ease and precision.

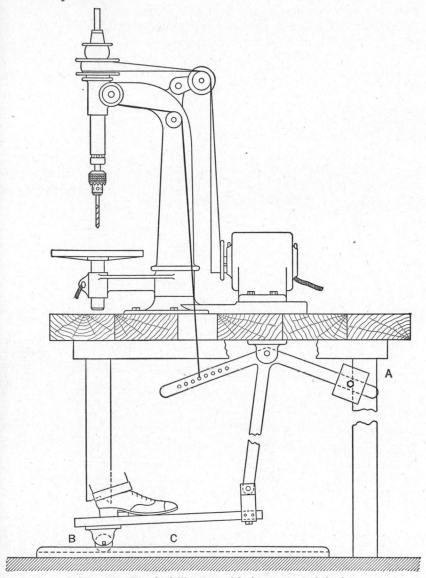

FIG. 126—Bench drill press with foot-operated feed.

It is sometimes possible to use two foot pedals to actuate different parts of a jig, fixture, or machine. Such a setup should cause no difficulty for the operator. We are all familiar with the fact that the automobile has three and often more pedals which the driver manipulates with ease and often while traveling at high speed.

Refrigerator Door-Knob Assembly. The assembly shown in Fig. 127 is a knob for a refrigerator compartment door. The parts consist

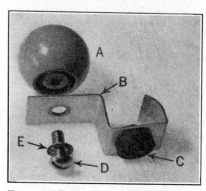

of a plastic molded knob, A, a stamped aluminum bracket, B, containing a rubber bumper, C, a No. 8-32 machine screw, D, and a lock washer, E.

The rubber bumper was attached to one end of the bracket and a hole was drilled in the other end for the machine screw. The hole in the molded knob was threaded to receive the screw. Figure 127 shows the parts in position for assembly.

Fig. 127—Refrigerator door-knob assembly. A. Plastic molded knob; B. Aluminum bracket; C. Rubber bumper; D. Machine screw; E. Lock washer.

Old Method. The work place was arranged with the screws and washers dumped in piles on top of the table at the left of the operator. The plastic knobs were placed in a carton in front of the operator, the brackets were placed in a tote box at the right of the operator, and the finished assemblies were placed on the table beyond the box of

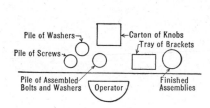

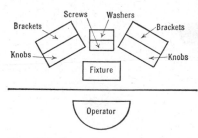

Fig. 128—Layout of work place for refrigerator door-knob assembly—old method.

Fig. 129—Layout of work place for refrigerator door-knob assembly—improved method.

brackets. Figure 128 shows the arrangement of the work place for the old method of assembly.

The procedure for assembling the parts was as follows: A number of screw and washer assemblies were made and placed on the table in front of the operator. A knob was then picked up with the left hand and held while the right hand picked up a bracket and placed it in position over the knob; the left hand held the knob and bracket while the right hand picked up a screw and washer and placed the screw through the hole in the bracket and into the tapped hole in the knob. The right hand then turned the screw down a few turns with a screwdriver, which was held in the palm of the right hand during the whole operation. The finished assembly was placed on the table to the right of the operator by the right hand.

Improved Method. The work place was rearranged with bins for the parts conveniently located as shown in Fig. 129. A special holding fixture operated by two foot pedals was placed in the table top and directly in front of the operator. Two stacked bins were placed on either side of the center bins. The top bin on each side contained the brackets and the bottom bins contained the knobs. The finished assemblies were dropped down out of the fixture into a tote box under the table by means of a foot pedal which tilted the whole fixture downward.

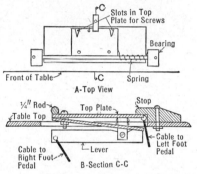

Fig. 130—Fixture used for refrigerator door-knob assembly. *A.* Top view; *B.* Cross section through center of fixture.

The jig consisted of two steel plates approximately 3 inches × 5 inches in size, as Fig. 130 shows. The top plate had two tapered slots or notches in the edge away from the operator into which the screws were placed head down. The bottom plate was clamped against the heads of the screws by a lever mechanism actuated by a foot pedal. A ¼-inch rod was welded to the back edge (nearest the operator) of the top plate and was supported at each end by bearings screwed fast to the table top. Another foot pedal connected by a cable to the front edge of the top plate served to tip the jig downward, thus dumping the finished assemblies into a chute. A coil spring on the ¼-inch rod returned the jig to the horizontal position after dumping the assemblies.

The assembly cycle for the improved method was as follows: A screw was picked up in each hand, placed head down in the slots of the jig, and clamped in place by depressing the right foot pedal. A washer was picked up in each hand and placed over the screws, likewise a bracket was placed over the screws, and a knob was picked up in each hand and placed over the screws and turned down two turns. The right foot pedal was released which released the assemblies from the clamping action of the fixture, and then the left foot pedal was depressed which dropped the two assemblies into the chute under the table. The two hands then reached for screws to begin the next cycle.

The improved method described above was worked out by James A. Hardy and resulted in an increase in output of 143 per cent.

Rethreading Machine. The rethreading machine shown in Fig. 131, built at a cost of $786, produces 1100 parts per hour.[2] It replaced a standard two-spindle threading machine which cost $1356 and produced 600 parts per hour.

The improved machine, incorporating a number of principles of motion economy, was built under the direction of O. W. Habel, Factory Manager of Saginaw Steering Gear Division, General Motors Corporation.

Some of the reasons why the new machine enabled the operator to double his output are given here:

1. Hand motions were replaced by foot and mechanical movements. The operator, seated at the machine, picks up a blank with each hand, from a convenient position on the table, and places them in the two-station fixture. Pressure of the right foot on the air valve operates the clamping fixture. Pressure on the left foot pedal brings the die head down.
2. Work does not pass from one hand to the other, and the finished work is dropped down a chute into a tote box.
3. Hand and eye motions are kept within the normal working space.
4. The hands are not used for holding or for manipulating any machine parts. There are no small controls to hunt for and manipulate.
5. Clamping fixtures are provided with bell mouths to facilitate the positioning of the blanks.

It is scarcely necessary to cite further illustrations of foot-operated apparatus, for their use is so common. In fact the question might properly be asked about almost any kind of bench or machine work, "Can a foot-operated device of some kind be used to facilitate the work?"

Design of Foot Pedals. Although the foot pedal is one of the most common devices for freeing the hands for productive work, most pedals are very poorly designed.

[2] O. W. Habel and G. G. Kearful, "Machine Design and Motion Economy," *Mech. Engg.*, Vol. 61, No. 12, p. 897, December, 1939.

FIG. 131—Machine for rethreading ball studs—production rate 1100 per hour.

Pedals might be classified as (1) those requiring considerable effort for manipulation and (2) those requiring little effort. The first-named class is well illustrated by the garment press and by certain foot-operated punch presses and shears. The second class is illustrated by the trip on the power punch press, the control on the electric sewing machine, and the pedals shown on pages 216-219.

Particularly in the first class, where considerable force is required for manipulation, the pedal should be of sufficient width to permit its operation by either foot. Some pedals are placed across the entire front of the machine in order to facilitate this. The pedal should also be designed so that the operating foot can carry part of the body weight. Poorly arranged pedals, such as the one shown in Fig. 132, tend to put all of the body weight on one foot, throwing the body out of its normal position and resulting in excessive strain and fatigue for the operator.[3]

FIG. 132—Poorly designed pedal.

Where the operator is seated and where little effort is required to manipulate the pedal there should be a "steady rest" or a suitable support for one side of the foot or for the heel. The foot throttle or accelerator on the automobile is a good illustration of this. The accelerator pedals on most cars are well designed. The pedals shown in Figs. 123 and 125 are poorly designed; those in Figs. 124 and 126 are quite satisfactory.

It is essential that a cushioning device be incorporated into the design of the pedal in order to check the swing gradually and prevent a sudden stop at the end of the swing. The pedal on some sheet metal shears and foot presses strikes the floor when it is depressed to its full extent, causing a sudden jar or shock which is transmitted to the operator. A rubber or felt pad, a spring, or a dash pot might be used to prevent the sudden stopping of the pedal stroke. (See soft rubber pedal stop E in Fig. 123.)

Hand Tools Permanently Positioned for Using. It is frequently possible to mount hand tools such as power-driven wrenches, screw-

[3] L. A. Legros and H. C. Weston, "On the Design of Machinery in Relation to the Operator," *Ind. Fatigue Research Bd.*, Report 36, p. 13, 1926. Figure 132 reproduced by permission of the Controller, H. M. Stationery Office, London.

drivers, and electric soldering irons on fixed brackets in a suitable position for using.

For example, two small copper parts were soldered together in the following manner. An ordinary vertical liquid-soap dispenser with an outlet valve in the bottom was mounted rigidly above the bench and in front of the operator. Beside it was also mounted an electric soldering iron. Liquid flux was placed in the soap dispenser and was applied to the copper parts by merely touching the parts up against the valve. The copper parts were then moved a short distance and brought up against the tip of the soldering iron. Solder from the tip of the iron flowed in between the two parts completing the operation. The operator supplied solder to the iron from a coil of wire solder which she carried in the palm of her hand.

In another case, that of assembling set screws in a small collar, an electric motor-driven wrench was mounted under the work bench. The chuck of the wrench projected up through a hole in the bench. The set screw was assembled into the collar by using one hand to place the screw in the wrench chuck while the other hand brought the collar into position for receiving the screw.

18. TWO OR MORE TOOLS SHOULD BE COMBINED WHEREVER POSSIBLE.

It is usually quicker to turn a small "two-ended" tool end for end than it is to lay one tool down and pick up another. There are many examples of the two-tool combinations—tack hammer and tack puller, two-ended wrench, pencil, and eraser—and the designer of the "hand-set" telephone used this idea when he incorporated the transmitter and the receiver in one unit.

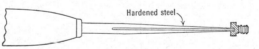

FIG. 133—Combination screwdriver and tweezers.

Two very convenient tools which have been developed at a midwestern electrical-equipment company are illustrated in Figs. 133 and 134. The first one replaces the screwdriver and tweezers—it holds the screw while it is being assembled. The second tool replaces a wrench and a screwdriver. This device permits the bolt to be set to the proper position and at the same time allows the operator to lock the nut in place by means of the "sleeve wrench" which slips over the screwdriver.

The attachments for spiral screwdrivers shown in Fig. 146 are also combination tools.

The practice of using only the thumb, first, and second fingers is so common that attention is called to the fact that the third and fourth fingers and the palm should also be used wherever possible. The combination screwdriver and wrench shown in Fig. 134, for example, permits the entire hand to be used.

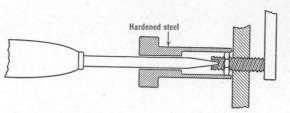

Hardened steel

FIG. 134—Combination screwdriver and wrench.

The thumb, first, and second fingers manipulate the wrench while the palm, third, and fourth fingers manipulate the screwdriver.

Small tools should be kept in the hand during the operation provided they do not interfere with the motions of the hand. It is frequently possible for the operator to hold a small tool in the hand constantly and still be able to use the thumb, first, and second fingers without any loss in efficiency. In the operation of folding and creasing paper the operator held the bone in her hand continuously. See page 166.

19. TOOLS AND MATERIALS SHOULD BE PRE-POSITIONED WHENEVER POSSIBLE.

Pre-positioning refers to placing an object in a predetermined place in such a way that when next needed it may be grasped in the position in which it will be used. For pre-positioning tools, a holder in the form of a socket, compartment, bracket, or hanger, should be provided into which or by which the tool may be returned after it is used and where it remains in position for the next operation. The tool is always returned to the same place. The holder should be of such design that the tool may be quickly released into its place from the hand. Furthermore, the holder should permit the tool to be grasped in the same manner in which it will be held while being used. The most familiar example of pre-positioning is the fountain-pen desk set where the pen is held in writing position even when not in use, and from or to which it may be easily and quickly removed or returned.

There are innumerable devices which aid in pre-positioning tools and materials and only a few typical examples can be shown here. Since the spiral screwdriver is one of the most common small tools for assembly work, some devices for pre-positioning it will be described.

Figure 135 shows a funnel-shaped holder set at an angle with the bench top. The holder illustrated in Fig. 136 permits the screwdriver

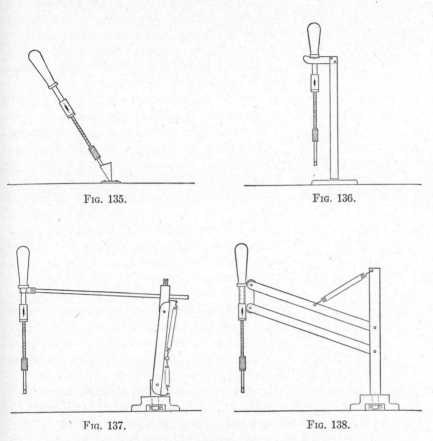

FIG. 135.   FIG. 136.

FIG. 137.   FIG. 138.

Devices for pre-positioning spiral screwdrivers.

to be dropped into place between two curved prongs. The screwdriver in Fig. 137 is clamped to the end of the swinging arm of the holder. The spring at the back of the vertical member automatically draws the screwdriver up and back out of the way after it has been released by the operator.

The holder in Fig. 138 is a form of a pantograph and was developed in Professor Porter's laboratory at New York University. The arm swings horizontally about the vertical axis and because of the pantograph action reduces the time required for positioning the screwdriver on screws or nuts to be assembled onto parts held in a jig.

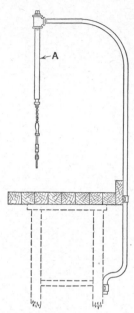

The screwdriver in Fig. 139 is suspended from above the work place. A coil spring inside the vertical arm A pulls the screwdriver up out of the way when it is released.

Screwdriver Work with Varying Degrees of Pre-positioning. The results of a study [4] of the time required to use a spiral screwdriver when completely pre-positioned, partially pre-positioned, and when lying flat on the bench are shown in Fig. 140 and Table XIX.

The operation consisted of grasping the screwdriver, carrying it to a screw which had already been started, positioning the screwdriver on the screw, and driving the screw down one-half inch until tight. The screwdriver was then disposed of, and the wheel containing the screws was indexed to bring up the next screw into position for assembly.

Fig. 139—Device for pre-positioning spiral screwdrivers.

The total time of *screwdriver usage* (the time from the instant the hand grasped the screwdriver until the instant it released it after running down a screw) was a minimum when the completely pre-positioned screwdriver was used. The partially pre-positioned screwdriver required on the average 23 per cent more time, and the screwdriver when not pre-positioned at all required 46 per cent more time for this part of the total cycle.

The special trays shown on page 190 may be used to advantage with screwdrivers mounted as illustrated in Figs. 137, 138, and 139. Special screwdriver attachments such as those shown on Fig. 146 would be required. The funnel-shaped guide in front of the chuck in Fig. 120 on page 212 assists in positioning hard-rubber parts.

20. WHERE EACH FINGER PERFORMS SOME SPECIFIC MOVEMENT, SUCH AS IN TYPEWRITING, THE LOAD SHOULD BE DISTRIBUTED IN ACCORDANCE WITH THE INHERENT CAPACITIES OF THE FINGERS.

The normal right-handed person performs work with less fatigue and greater dexterity with the right hand than with the left. Although

[4] *Univ. Iowa Studies in Engg.,* Bul. 16, p. 60, 1939.

TABLE XIX

SCREWDRIVER WORK WITH VARYING DEGREES OF PRE-POSITIONING

	Screwdriver Completely Pre-positioned	Screwdriver Partially Pre-positioned	Screwdriver Not Pre-positioned At All
Time in Minutes	0.0417	0.0511	0.0610
Time in Per Cent (Shortest Time = 100%)	100	123	146

SCREWDRIVER USAGE
Time to grasp screwdriver, carry it to screw, position and assemble bit, run down No. 8 machine screw one-half inch in nut, remove screwdriver, and dispose.

most people can be trained to work equally well with either hand on most factory operations, the fingers have unequal inherent capacities for doing work. The first and second fingers of the two hands are ordinarily superior in their performance to the third and fourth fingers.

A study made to determine the ideal arrangement of the keys of

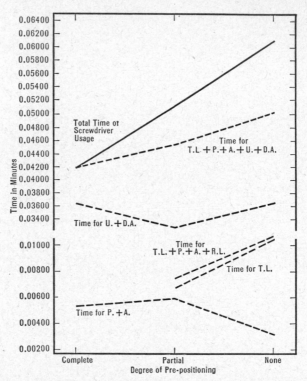

Fig. 140—Curves showing results of a study of screwdriver work with varying degrees of pre-positioning of the screwdriver. Averages of median time values for five male operators are shown.

the typewriter for maximum efficiency also illustrates this difference in the capacities of the fingers.[5]   First, an analysis was made of the frequency of occurrence of the twenty-six letters of the alphabet in several lists of the most commonly used words of the English language.   Then a large number of typical business letters were analyzed to determine the frequency of occurrence of punctuation marks, capital letters, and other characters.   Studies were conducted to determine the

[5] R. E. Hoke, "Improvement of Speed and Accuracy in Typewriting," *Johns Hopkins Studies in Education*, No. 7, pp. 1-42, 1922.

abilities of the eight fingers of the two hands for typewriting. This was done by means of tapping tests made for each finger, both on a typewriter and on a desk. With all of this information, together with data on the errors made by the different fingers, it was possible to determine the ideal arrangement of the keys of the typewriter.

That part of the study which is of most interest here revealed that the ability of the right hand as compared to that of the left was as 100 to 88.87, or approximately as 10 to 9. This agrees with the findings of another investigator already cited.[6] The data in Table XX show the ideal load, in strokes, based on the abilities of the fingers. The finger loads required by the present typewriter keyboard are shown for comparison.

These data show that the first and second fingers of the right hand should carry the greatest load, whereas the fourth finger of the left hand should carry the smallest load. They also show that the total load of the right hand using the present typewriter is 3422, and of the left hand 4488, or a ratio of 100 to 131.25 when it should have been as 100 to 88.87. Thus there is an overload of the left hand of 47.7 per cent as compared with the load of the right hand.

It was suggested from the analysis of the data secured in this investigation that the keys of the typewriter should be so arranged that the letters occurring most frequently should be typed with the fingers capable of carrying the greatest load. In fact, many

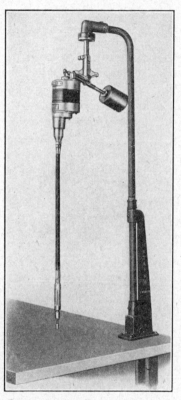

Fig. 141—Electric motor-driven screwdriver.

investigators in this field have proposed new keyboards. The one shown in Fig. 142 is the Dvorak-Dealey "simplified" keyboard [7] tested

[6] Wm. L. Bryant, "On the Development of Voluntary Motor Ability," *Am. J. Psychol.*, Vol. 5, No. 2, p. 123, November, 1892.

[7] A. Dvorak, N. I. Merrick, W. L. Dealey, and G. C. Ford, "Typewriting Behavior," p. 219. Copyright, 1936, by American Book Co., New York, and used by their permission.

TABLE XX

RELATIVE FINGER LOADS ON THE "IDEAL" AND ON THE PRESENT KEYBOARD

	Left Hand				Right Hand			
Finger....................	4	3	2	1	1	2	3	4
Ideal load.................	855	900	975	1028	1097	1096	991	968
Present keyboard load.......	803	658	1492	1535	1490	640	996	296

over a period of years at the University of Washington. Researches conducted under a grant from the Carnegie Foundation for the Advancement of Teaching seem to indicate that the simplified typewriter

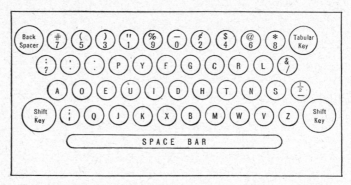

FIG. 142—Dvorak-Dealey "Simplified" typewriter keyboard.[7]

keyboard eliminates many of the defects of the universal keyboard and that it is:

1. Easier to master in that it requires less time to attain any particular level of typing speed.
2. Faster, since it makes higher net rates possible for average typists.
3. More accurate, since fewer typing errors are made.
4. Less fatiguing through simplifying the stroking patterns and through adapting the hand and finger loads to the relative hand and finger abilities.[8]

[8] Dwight D. W. Davis, "An Evaluation of the Simplified Typewriter Keyboard," *The J. of Business Education*, Vol. 11, No. 2, p. 21, October, 1935.

21. HANDLES SUCH AS THOSE USED ON CRANKS AND LARGE SCREWDRIVERS SHOULD BE DESIGNED TO PERMIT AS MUCH OF THE SURFACE OF THE HAND TO COME IN CONTACT WITH THE HANDLE AS POSSIBLE. THIS IS PARTICULARLY TRUE WHEN CONSIDERABLE FORCE IS EXERTED IN USING THE HANDLE. FOR LIGHT ASSEMBLY WORK THE SCREWDRIVER HANDLE SHOULD BE SO SHAPED THAT IT IS SMALLER AT THE BOTTOM THAN AT THE TOP.

Two studies have been made which furnish results that have a bearing on the shape and size of handles that are most effective. One study gives results on four different shapes of handles used in turning a crank. The subject grasped the handle and turned the crank at a uniform speed against a brake, the load being applied in known amounts. The grip of the operator's hand was measured before and after turning the crank. It was assumed that the least effective handle caused greatest decrease in the pressure that the operator could exert in gripping the hand dynamometer. The most effective handle by this test was one with the main part straight (handle *C* in Fig. 143) except that there was a slight indentation near the tip of the forefinger. Handles *B* and *D* in Fig. 143 were the poorest of the four.[9]

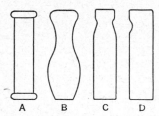

Fig. 143—Types of crank handles tested.

Another study was made to determine the most effective large screwdriver handle. A number of different types of screwdriver handles were made in different diameters ranging from approximately

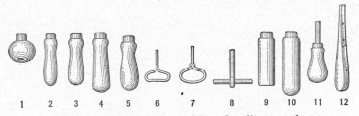

Fig. 144—Types of screwdriver handles tested.

¾ of an inch (18 mm.) to 1½ inches (40 mm.) and tests were made on each type, varying the diameter. Handle 10 (Fig. 144), which has a straight shank with a rounded end, was most efficient of all.

[9] O. Klemm and F. Sander, "Experimentelle Untersuchungen über die Form des Handgriffes an Drehkurbeln" (Experimental Research on the Shape of Handles for Cranks), *Praktische Psychologie*, Vol. 4, pp. 300-302, 1923.

This handle had the same general shape as the most effective crank handle shown in Fig. 143. The relative efficiencies of the other handles are shown in Fig. 145.

The object of the first test of the screwdriver handles was to determine the handle with which the operator could exert the maximum force in turning it through 6/10 of a revolution. Another set of tests was made in which the operator used the screwdriver to lift a weight by turning a screw for a half minute and the amount of work done was computed. In both parts of this study, handle 10, Fig. 145, was most effective. The results also showed that within the range tested, 18 mm. to 40 mm., the larger the diameter the more effective it was.[10]

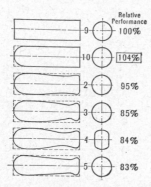

FIG. 145—Types of screwdriver handles that were most effective.

All information on this subject seems to show that where the hand carries a load, as in carrying a pail, turning a crank or screwdriver, the maximum efficiency results when the unit pressure on the hand is lowest. This means that the largest surface of the hand possible should be used in grasping the handle. The two investigations described above did not cover the use of screwdrivers for light work, such as the assembly of small screws or nuts.

Plain Screwdrivers for Light Work. Most of the assembly work in the shop and factory requires the use of a light or medium-sized screwdriver rather than a large one. In many cases operators use screwdrivers that are too large for this light class of work. Tests show that the best plain screwdriver for such work is a short one, small in diameter near the blade and with a rotating finger rest on the top. The screwdriver handle should be large in diameter near the top and should be completely knurled from top to bottom. By pressing the index finger on the rotating top and gripping the thin knurled part of the stem between the thumb and second finger the screwdriver may be rotated very rapidly for assembling the screw. By using the upper part of the handle with the large diameter the screw may be properly driven home.

[10] B. Rubarth, "Untersuchung zur Bestgestaltung von Handheften für Schraubenzieher und ähnliche Werkzeuge" (Investigation Concerning the Best Shape for Handles for Screwdrivers and Similar Tools), *Industrielle Psychotechnik*, Vol. 5, No. 5, pp. 129-42, 1928.

Tests [11] show that the use of such a screwdriver will result in an increase in output of 15 to 25 per cent over that produced with a larger one of the conventional type.

In preparing to use a screwdriver many people make the mistake of grasping it at the top, then by resting the blade against the bench they slide the hand down to the bottom of the handle. Instead, they should grasp the lower end of the screwdriver with the thumb and

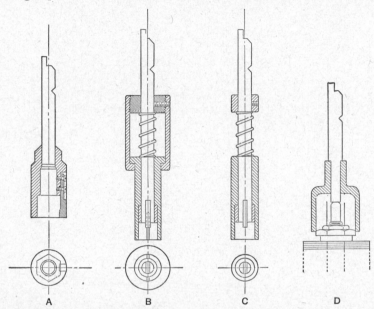

FIG. 146—Spiral screwdriver attachments. *A.* Wrench for picking up hexagon nut and positioning it for assembly. *B.* Screwdriver blade for picking up machine screw from special tray and positioning it for assembly; *C.* Self-centering screwdriver blade; *D.* Hexagon socket wrench for assembling nut on end of armature shaft. Wrench automatically slips off nut after it has been assembled a predetermined distance.

index finger and move it to the screw, the other hand helping to position it into the screw slot.

Spiral Screwdrivers. The spiral screwdriver is often superior to the plain screwdriver for light and medium work. It may be used for assembling nuts and bolts as well as for screws. Perhaps the best type is the "quick return" model with a spring in the handle, causing the handle to come back automatically for the next stroke.

[11] L. I. Hunt, "A Study of Screwdrivers for Small Assembly Work," *The Human Factor,* Vol. 8, No. 2, pp. 70-73, February, 1934.

There are many time-saving devices which may be used with the spiral screwdriver. A special wrench for picking up a hexagon nut is shown in Fig. 146-*A* and a

similar device for picking up a round-head machine screw is shown in Fig. 146-*B*. Special trays for holding the nuts and machine screws are used in connection with these two attachments. One study showed that the time required

Fig. 147—Phillips recessed head self-centering screw, and screwdriver bit.

to insert an ordinary screwdriver bit in the slot of a No. 8 machine screw with a round head was 194 per cent more than when a bit with a self-centering attachment, similar to that shown in Fig. 146-*C*, was used. Such a bit may be used to advantage with such pre-positioning devices as those shown on page 227. Figure 146-*D* shows a hexagon socket wrench for assembling a nut onto the end of an armature shaft. The wrench automatically slips off the top of the nut after it has been assembled onto the end of the shaft a predetermined distance.

The screwdriver bit shown in Fig. 148 is used by thrusting it into a container which is well filled with nuts. The split pilot projecting through the middle of the hexagon wrench picks up the nut by penetrating through the threaded hole in it. When the wrench with the nut is placed on the bolt, the pilot withdraws from the nut and the nut is assembled onto the bolt by means of the hexagon wrench. This special tool was developed by the Colonial Radio Corporation, and many of these tools are in constant use by this company.

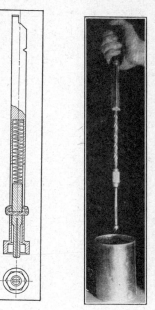

Fig. 148—Special screwdriver attachment for picking up hexagon nut and positioning it for assembly.

Figure 147 shows a Phillips recessed head self-centering screw, and screwdriver bit.

22. LEVERS, CROSSBARS, AND HAND WHEELS SHOULD BE LO-CATED IN SUCH POSITIONS THAT THE OPERATOR CAN MANIP-ULATE THEM WITH THE LEAST CHANGE IN BODY POSITION AND WITH THE GREATEST MECHANICAL ADVANTAGE.

Some machine-tool manufacturers understand that it is possible to build a machine that will perform its functions satisfactorily and at the same time will be easy to operate.

Unless a machine is fully automatic, the amount of work that it will produce depends to some extent upon the performance of the

FIG. 149—Speed selector for universal turret lathe. This device simplifies the operation of changing spindle speeds—eliminates many motions and saves time.

operator. The more convenient the machine is to operate, the greater the production is likely to be.

The Gisholt Machine Company, for example, has incorporated a speed selector in their new universal turret lathes. (See Fig. 149.) This device enables the operator to obtain easily and quickly any one of the several available spindle speeds. It is power-operated—the operator simply sets a dial, and the machine automatically makes the shift to give the correct spindle speed.

The operator standing or sitting in a normal working position should not be required to leave his place of work to operate his machine. The levers should be placed in such a way that he need not

FIG. 150—Control levers are conveniently located on this universal turret lathe.

A—Lever control for collet chuck and stock feed; B—Start-Stop-Reverse lever; C—Single lever dial speed selector; D—Coolant distributor control; E—Carriage stop bar; F—Carriage feed lever; G—Feed reverse lever; H—Carriage binder; J—Cross slide turret clamping lever; K—Single lever dial feed selector.

bend over or twist his body in an uncomfortable manner when manipulating them. Where this ideal condition cannot be provided the nearest approach to it should be adopted. (See Fig. 150.)

It is well known that levers can be operated more effectively in certain positions and at certain heights than at others. A very exhaustive study was made to determine the effectiveness of levers, crossbars, and hand wheels located in both horizontal and vertical planes, and at three different heights from the floor.[12] These devices were arranged so that the force of the push or pull was indicated in

[12] W. P. Kühne, "Studien zur optimalen Kraftreaktion an Maschinenbedienungselementen" (Studies on the Optimum Force Exerted on Machine Controls), *Industrielle Psychotechnik*, Vol. 3, No. 6, pp. 167-172, June, 1926.

kilograms by means of a dynamometer. It was the object in these tests to determine the maximum strength that could be exerted in each case. Each of the three devices was tested in the several positions shown in Figs. 151, 152, and 153.

The vertical scale represents the force in kilograms exerted by the subject and the horizontal scale shows the particular position of the device being tested. The three sets of curves on each chart represent the three different heights at which the devices were tested, namely 580 mm. (22.8 inches), 780 mm. (30.7 inches), and 1080

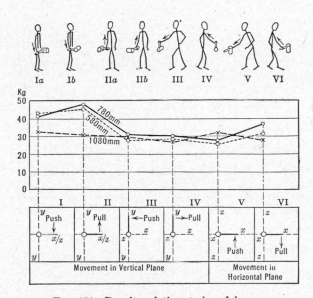

FIG. 151—Results of the study of levers.

mm. (42.5 inches). For example, in Fig. 151 the lever was most effective at the medium height, 780 mm. above the floor, and position II on the horizontal scale which represents the position where the lever was horizontal and the operator pulled up on it.

The hand wheel was most effective when placed at the 1080-mm. height and in the vertical plane, position IV in Fig. 153. The operator, standing off to one side of the wheel, pushed with his right hand and pulled with his left.

Maximum Pull and Height above Floor Level. In a series of carefully conducted tests, Vernon determined the maximum strength which could be exerted in pulling at various heights above the floor level.[13]   The pull was made in the vertical direction and its extent was measured by a dynamometer.   The curves in Fig. 154 show the results.   The lower set of curves show trials made on three different days.   In this test the subject grasped a handle with the two hands.

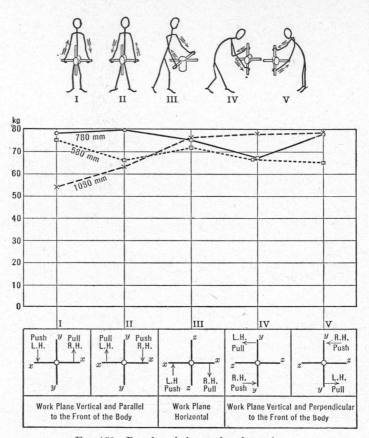

FIG. 152—Results of the study of crossbars.

The handle was shaped much like a lawn-mower handle and was held close to the body and directly in front of the subject.   The upper curves were plotted from results obtained by pulling vertically upward as before but in this test the hands grasped the two sides of a rectangular frame made of iron pipe.   The subject stood inside the

[13] E. M. Bedale and H. M. Vernon, "The Effect of Posture and Rest in Muscular Work," *Ind. Fatigue Research Bd.*, Report 29, p. 32, 1924.   Figure 154 reproduced by permission of the Controller of H. M. Stationery Office, London.

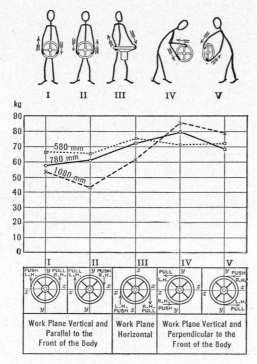

FIG. 153—Results of the study of hand wheels.

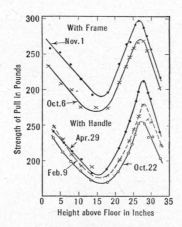

FIG. 154—Maximum pull at various heights above floor level.

frame and could grip the pipes which formed the ends of the rectangle. The hands, then, were in their normal position at either side of the body and not in front as in the test made using the handle. As the curves in Fig. 154 show, the frame made it possible for the subject to lift a greater load.

The results shown in Table XXI and by the curves might be summarized as follows. The strength of a pull or its equivalent, lifting a weight, varies considerably at different heights above the floor level. The strength is lowest when the height is 15 to 17 inches above the floor and reaches a maximum at a height of 28 inches above

TABLE XXI

RELATIVE STRENGTH OF PULL

Conditions	Subject I	Subject II
Standing on both feet and using both hands...	100	100
" " right foot " " "	98	96
" " left foot " " "	98	98
" " both feet " right hand..............	55	49
" " " " " left hand..............	52	54

the floor. The curves fall off rapidly at greater heights. The data in the table show that the lifting power falls off about 2 per cent when the subject is standing on one leg instead of two. However, the lifting power is but one-half as great when one hand is used instead of two.

Cost Reduction Report. It is essential that an estimate be made of the expected savings resulting from improvements in methods before they are made and also that a report be made after the project is finished and in effect.

The Cost Reduction Report shown in Fig. 155 has been developed by Ivan C. Lawrence and Lee S. Whitson and is used at the Minnesota Mining and Manufacturing Company for presenting proposed changes to the plant superintendent and also for reporting the savings from new methods after they are installed.

This company bases unit operation times for the old and new methods on time studies or on overall production rates, whichever gives the most representative results for the particular project. Labor costs are based on the average base rate for the particular job plus the average bonus for the department and a percentage to cover com-

MINNESOTA MINING & MFG. CO.
COST-REDUCTION REPORT

FILE 12-RM Belts
REPORT NO. 12 DATE 9/30/37

DESCRIPTION OF ITEM INVOLVED:
GROUP: Specialty   PRODUCT: Three-M-Ite Cloth Belts
OPERATION: Mark with grit number and direction to run.
OBJECT OF ANALYSIS:

COMPARISON

PRESENT METHOD	PROPOSED METHOD
MACHINE:	MACHINE:
TOOLS: Stencil brush	TOOLS: Rubber stamp
DESCRIPTION:	DESCRIPTION:
Stencil with white paint.	Stamp with white ink.

COST OF OPERATIONS INVOLVED:	$ PER belt	COST OF OPERATIONS INVOLVED:	$ PER belt
LABOR:		LABOR:	
0.00125 man-hr. per belt		0.000313 man-hr. per belt	
@ $0.54 per man-hr.	0.0068	@ $0.54 per man-hr.	0.0017
MATERIALS:		MATERIALS:	
MISC:		MISC:	
TOTAL OF ABOVE ITEMS:	$0.0068	TOTAL OF ABOVE ITEMS:	$0.0017

ESTIMATE OF SAVING:
SAVING WITH PROPOSED CHANGE: ($0.0068–$0.0017) $0.0051 PER belt.
YEARLY REQUIREMENTS, past 12 mo., 250,000 belts REPORTED BY Sales Dept.
PROBABLE REQUIREMENTS, next 12 mo., 300,000 belts ESTIMATED BY Bert Cross
ESTIMATED SAVINGS PER YEAR (BASED ON 300,000 belts PER YEAR) $ 1530.00

ESTIMATED COST OF CHANGE:			
		DEDUCT 20% FOR SAFETY,	$ 306.00
DESIGN	$ EST. BY	PROBABLE SAVINGS PER YEAR $	1224.00
EQUIPMENT	$ " "	LESS TOTAL COST OF CHANGE $	————
INSTALLATION	$ " "	NET SAVINGS FIRST YEAR $	1224.00
	$ " "	NEW METHOD WOULD PAY FOR ITSELF IN 0 MO.	
	$ " "	NOTE:	
	$ " "		
TOTAL	$ COST OF CHANGE	SUGGESTED BY: Art Rutscher, Lee Whitson	
		REPORT PREPARED BY: Lee S. Whitson	

CC TO:	ATTACHED ARE:		DATE		DATE
	SHEETS DRAWINGS	FIRST CONSIDERED	9/27/37	EXP. APPR.	
	SHEETS PRINTS	INVEST'G'N STARTED	9/27/37	INSTALLED	9 30 37
	SHEETS DETAILS	REP'T SUBMITTED	9/30/37	FINAL REP'T	
	(FOR EFFECT ON FACTORY BONUS, SEE OTHER SIDE.)				

FIG. 155—Cost-reduction report form, size 8½ × 11 inches.

pensation insurance, federal pension, old age insurance, and other costs that are directly related to labor cost.

In calculating savings this company does not include fixed overhead costs such as supervision, machine burden, etc., since the annual expenditure for these items would not necessarily be lessened by reducing the labor requirements of a particular job. If a proposed change would increase machine capacity, and if the additional capacity might forestall having to buy more equipment, this fact would be brought out in a note attached to the Cost Reduction Report.

CHAPTER 15

STANDARDIZATION
WRITTEN STANDARD PRACTICE

After finding the most economical way of performing an operation it is essential that a permanent record be made of it. This record is frequently called a "standard practice." In addition to serving as a permanent record of the operation the standard practice is often used as an instruction sheet for the operator or to assist the foreman or instructor in training the operator.

The Standard Practice as a Permanent Record. Once the improved method is standardized and put into effect, constant vigilance on the part of management is necessary in order to maintain this standard. Often tools and equipment get out of adjustment, belts become loose, and materials vary from specifications. When such conditions exist, standard performance cannot be expected from the operator. Only by rigid maintenance of standard conditions can there be reasonable assurance of standard performance as to output and quality.

Since most time standards are used as the basis for wage incentives and since most incentive plans either imply or specifically state that time standards, or rates, will not be changed [1] unless there is a change in the method of performing the work, it is essential that an accurate and complete record be made of the method at the time it is put into effect, or at the time the rate is set for the operation. If no such record is kept it will be almost impossible in the future to tell whether the method then being used is the same as that in effect at the time the standard was originally set.

One company uses the forms shown in Figs. 156 and 157 as a permanent record of each operation. This standard practice is ordinarily prepared by the person making the motion and time study or by the person in charge of the investigation if several men are engaged in the work. These two forms are prepared after the correct method has been established and put into effect and before the stop-watch time study of the operation has been made and the time standard has been determined. The "Standard Job Conditions" and the "General Job

[1] *Methods of Wage Payment,* Publication of National Metal Trades Assoc., Chicago, Ill., p. 15, 1928. Also, J. O. P. Hummel, "Motion and Time Study Today," *Mill and Factory,* Vol. 19, No. 2, p. 42, August, 1936.

STANDARD JOB CONDITIONS

BASE RATE NO. 27112   CODE NO. ___—___

DATE 12/18/39   STUDY NOS. 32906-32909   SYM. NO. ___—___   BINDER NO. 27

BLDG. 148A   DEPT. No. 17   DIVISION Eastern   OBSERVER Davis, W.T.

OPERATION Label 4-oz. Bottles   Hardening Solution

SKETCH OF WORK PLACE

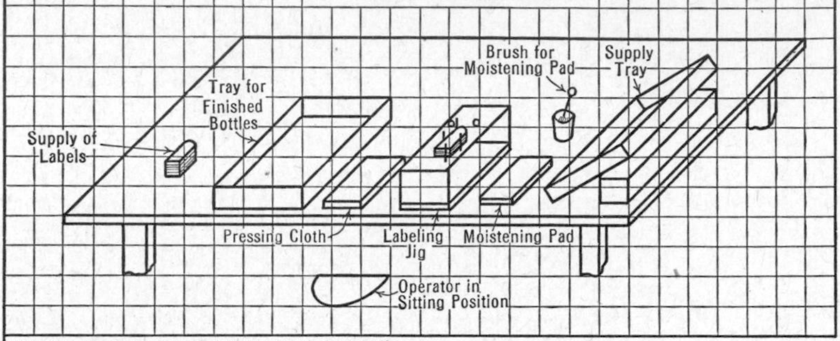

SPECIAL TOOLS, JIGS OR FIXTURES   Labeling Jig

JOB ELEMENTS

1. Moisten pad with brush.	
2. Insert labels in jig.	
3. Procure bottle from supply tray, moisten bottle on moistening pad, label, using jig, press smooth on pressing cloth.	AUXILIARY
	Set up and clean up by
	handler or operator. No allow-
4. Dispose bottle to wooden tray.	ance in standard.
5. Upon completion of tray, make out ticket and place in tray as check against quality of labeling. Foreman can determine responsibility if labels are not up to standard.	Handler supplies bottles and disposes of finished tray.

AUDIT   Production can be checked by order number. Foreman checks time turned in.

FIG. 156—Standard Job Conditions form, size 8½ × 11 inches.

GENERAL JOB CONDITIONS

DATE OF ISSUE___12/18/39___ BASE RATE NO.___27112_____CODE NO._____

BLDG.____148A____ DEPT. ___No. 17___ DIVISION ___Eastern___ OBSERVER_____Davis, W.T.____

TYPE OF OPERATION____Fill and Pack Bottles of Liquid

LAYOUT OF OPERATION OR LOCALITY

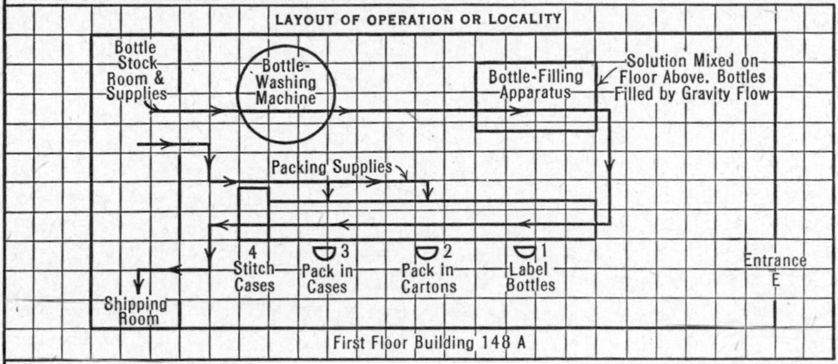

Bottle Stock Room & Supplies

Bottle-Washing Machine

Bottle-Filling Apparatus

Solution Mixed on Floor Above. Bottles Filled by Gravity Flow

Packing Supplies

4 Stitch Cases — 3 Pack in Cases — 2 Pack in Cartons — 1 Label Bottles

Entrance

Shipping Room

First Floor Building 148 A

RANGE OF APPLICATION Unit designed for handling bottles of liquid product from 4-oz. to 32-oz. size.

DESCRIPTION OF STANDARD EQUIPMENT Balanced production line from supply room through to finished product in shipping room. Equipment consists of: bottle-washing machine No. 3712-A, bottle-filling apparatus No. 2192-O, battery of work places on long bench for labeling, packaging, and packing, and stitching machine No. 3127-C. Bottles handled in wooden trays to prevent accidents due to broken glass.

DESCRIPTION OF WORKING CONDITIONS Regular working hours 8-12, 1-5. Jobs performed in large airy room under daylight conditions. Artificial light available if necessary. Bottle washer wears rubber apron and gloves. Filling operator wears goggles, rubber apron and gloves, and cloth sleeves.

FLOW OF MATERIAL OR SUPPLIES Bottles supplied to washing machine from stock room. Washed bottles then moved to filling apparatus. Moved by truck from filling apparatus to labeling work place. Labeled bottles are then packed in cartons, cartons are packed in cases. Finished case is stitched on stitching machine, and then flows to shipping room. Packing supplies and labels are sent from supply room to position on work place.

Fig. 157—General Job Conditions form, size 8½ × 11 inches.

Conditions" forms used by this company are printed on bond paper, the first in yellow color and the latter in salmon color. An original and one carbon copy of each of these forms are made out in pencil. The original is placed in the folder with the original time studies of the operation and filed in the Wage Standards Department office. The carbon copy is filed in a loose-leaf binder in the office of the foreman of the department in which the operation is performed. This is used by the operator, foreman, and time keeper.

The "Standard Job Conditions" form contains complete details of the specific operation; and the "General Job Conditions" form, as the name indicates, contains more general information about the operation and the location of the work place relative to the rest of the department or building, information about the flow of material to and from the work place, working conditions, and other similar matters.

Some classes of work are relatively simple and written standard practices can be quickly prepared. On machine tool work, for example, the speed and feed, shape and size of tools, coolant used, and the method of chucking the piece are the important factors. The form in Fig. 191 on page 360, developed by one company primarily as instructions for the operator, also serves as the basis for their permanent record of the operation.

In some plants where many operations are similar, methods are

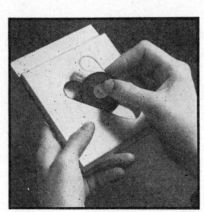

FIG. 158—Loop of film, and container card for filing.

frequently developed for a whole class of work, and time standards are determined from tables of standard data or formulas. In such cases similar operations can be grouped into classes for which one master standard practice can be prepared. For example, all sizes of gear blanks turned on the J and L Flat Turret Lathe (Operation 5TR, Case D) follow the same sequence of motions of the operator and machine although the speeds, feeds, and the sizes of the tools vary with the size of the blank.

Motion-Picture Records. Some complicated manual operations can be recorded best by motion pictures. In fact, it may be more economical in certain cases to make the record in this manner than to rely entirely on a written description of the job.   On important operations "before" and "after" motion pictures are frequently made for other purposes and of course may also serve as a supplement to the written standard practice.   Figure 158 shows a loop of 8-mm. film and the filing card with the auxiliary data pertaining to the operation recorded at the appropriate places.   Few companies as yet have seen fit to use motion pictures for standard-practice records in a general way.

CHAPTER 16

THE RELATION OF TIME STANDARDS TO WAGE INCENTIVES

During the past 50 years the emphasis in motion and time study application has been on the setting of time standards for use with wage incentives. Of course, motion and time study has been used for improving methods and for standardization of conditions but greatest interest and most extensive use has been for rate setting. However, the present trend is toward a more nearly balanced program. Motion study is receiving considerable attention at the present time and there is much evidence to show that this phase of motion and time study is as valuable if not more so to the manager than the use of time study for rate setting. Also, employees are more likely to react favorably to this broader program of motion and time study, particularly since motion study has as its primary object finding the easiest and most satisfactory way of doing work which usually increases output without requiring the employee to increase his effort.

Necessity for Measuring Labor Accomplishment. Labor is an important factor in the cost of producing manufactured goods and it must be bought and paid for much like materials, supplies, and other elements which enter into the cost of production. No attempt is being made here to class labor as a commodity. In fact, there is plenty of evidence to show that the worker's mental attitude, morale, "will to work," and enthusiasm for the job and for the company are of real value to the management; and wages alone, however large they may be, will not necessarily produce these desirable attributes in a working force.

Most things of value are purchased by measure, that is, a price is paid for a number of units of a given commodity of a specified quality. For example, sugar is bought by the pound, cloth by the yard, and energy by the kilowatt-hour. When a single factor is to be measured, the unit of measurement deals only with that factor. Thus, distance may be measured by units of length and contents by units of volume. However, when two factors are involved, as in electrical energy, both time and power must be included in the unit of measurement.

All work is largely a combination of mental and manual effort expended in a given period of time. Seldom is work entirely manual or entirely mental, although one or the other may predominate. Most factory work and much office work are largely manual in nature and it is this type of labor which is being considered in this volume.

The results of work determine its value rather than the effort exerted. It is the operator's productivity, his accomplishment, that largely measures his worth to his employer. Since accomplishment results from the application of effort and since accomplishment is influenced by both the duration and the intensity of effort, the unit of measurement of work done must therefore include both quantity and time. Accomplishment can usually be measured most effectively in terms of quantity of work done per unit of time, that is, pieces per hour, or tons per day. Ordinarily a standard of quality is specified, and only those units that meet the quality standard are considered as finished units.

Although much criticism has been directed at the principle of payment of labor in proportion to its productivity, there is much in favor of such a plan if properly administered. The greatest difficulty in the application of such incentives is in the determination of the standard task. The answer to the question "What constitutes a day's work?" is very important, indeed.

Motion and time study is the most accurate system known for measuring labor accomplishment. Although not a perfect tool it will, if applied by well-qualified and properly trained persons, give results that are satisfactory to both the employee and to the employer.

In past years, and to some extent today,[1] rates have been set on the basis of (1) past performance of operators, (2) overall time for a trial lot, and (3) estimate by the supervisor or by an "estimator." These methods of measuring what should constitute a day's work are never satisfactory and should not be used. An elemental stop-

---

[1] In a survey made of the members of the National Metal Trades Association, definitely established methods of setting standards or rates were reported by 256 members as follows:

112—or 43.3 per cent by time study exclusively.

79—or 30.8 per cent by a combination of time study and some other means.

43—or 16.8 per cent by a study of past performances only.

22—or 8.5 per cent by estimating, process used ranging from careful calculations based on previously prepared tables and charts of weights, dimensions, and values, down to the more or less accurate guess.

"Methods of Wage Payments," published by the Metal Trades Assoc., Chicago, Ill., p. 11, 1928.

watch study carefully made by a competent analyst should be used in setting time standards.

Effects of Motion and Time Study Applications on the Worker. The two phases of motion and time study that concern the worker most are (1) improving the method of doing the work, and (2) setting a time standard as the basis for a wage incentive. These two functions affect the operator in distinctly different ways. Both tend to reduce the labor cost to the employer mainly by reducing the man-hours required; consequently both tend to displace labor on a given operation. That is, if windows in the factory and office buildings can be washed in one-half the time formerly taken, through the use of a carefully planned method and the use of a wage incentive, then only half as many window washers will be required on the payroll of the company as would otherwise be the case. No further discussion of this point is needed here, for in this respect motion and time study falls into the same category with tools and machinery which displace labor because of their greater efficiency.

By the improvement of methods alone production is often made sufficiently easy so that with the same expenditure of energy the operator is able to produce more work. Thus through the use of duplicate bins and the simple fixture for the assembling of the bolt and washers described on page 147 the operator was able to do a half more work in the same time. This phase of motion and time study permits the operator to do more work without asking that he use more energy.

In contrast, the second phase of motion and time study, that of setting a time standard to be used with a wage incentive, reduces man-hours by offering to pay the operator more wages if he will do more work in a given period of time. To earn this extra reward the operator must produce more mainly through greater concentration on the job and through greater expenditure of energy.

Perhaps the use of an example is the best way to show the whole picture. This case will not only indicate how these two phases of motion and time study affect the employee through increase in earnings, but it will also show how it affects the employer through a decrease in the direct labor cost of the product. It will be assumed that no increase in wages is given to the operator when improvements in methods alone are made.

The operation is that of assembling a work-rest bracket for a bench grinder. The data in Fig. 159 show that a 40 per cent saving in time resulted from an improvement in the method of assembling the bracket. The operator worked without incentive in both Case I and Case II. That is, she was paid a flat day wage irrespective of her output. She exerted approximately the same physical effort and gave approximately the same mental attention in both cases. However in Case I she made 720 assemblies per day whereas in Case II she made 1200 assemblies per day. This increase in output resulted,

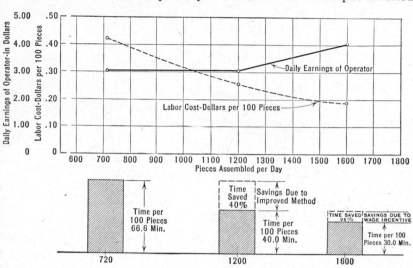

CASE I

Method: Assemble one piece at a time. Left hand holds bracket while right hand assembles parts.

Supervision: Poor.

Performance of Operator: Poor.

Method of Wage Payment: Day wage. Hourly rate = $0.38. Daily earnings of operator = $3.04.

Average Production taken from past records is 720 pieces for an 8-hr. day. Average time per 100 pieces = 66.6 minutes.

Average Labor Cost per 100 pieces = $0.422.

CASE II

Method: Assemble two pieces at one time using special fixture.

Supervision: Poor.

Performance of Operator: Poor.

Method of Wage Payment: Day wage. Hourly rate = $0.38. Daily earnings of operator = $3.04.

Average Production taken from past records = 1200 per 8-hr. day. Average time per 100 pieces = 40.0 minutes.

Average Labor Cost per 100 pieces = $0.253.

CASE III

Method: Assemble two pieces at one time using special fixture.

Supervision: Good.

Performance of Operator: Good—operator now on piece work.

Method of Wage Payment: Straight piece rate with guaranteed minimum rate of $0.38 per hour. Standard time per 100 pieces set by time study = 30.0 min. Piece rate per 100 pieces = $0.19. Standard output per day = 1600 pieces. Average number of pieces actually produced per day by this operator = 2133. Average daily earnings of this operator = $4.05.

Average Labor Cost per 100 pieces = $0.19.

OPERATION: Assemble Work Rest Bracket for Bench Grinder
OPERATOR: Helen G. Meyers, No. 746231
BASE WAGE: 38 cents per hour—8-hr. day—40-hr. week

FIG. 159—The relation of time standards to wage incentives.

not from "speeding up" or working faster, but from a better arrangement of the work place and from the use of a special fixture which enabled the operator to use her hands and arms to better advantage. She could do more work in the same time and with the same expenditure of energy because she could assemble a bracket with fewer motions, with no tiring holding of parts, and with an easy rhythm which was not possible in Case I.

In Case III a time standard was set by means of a stop-watch study and a piece rate was established for the operation. The operator now had the opportunity of earning more than her guaranteed base wage of $3.04 per day. In fact, she was easily able to do 33⅓ per cent more work than the standard, and in return for this extra performance she earned $4.05 per day.

The increased output resulting from the application of the piece rate came because the operator "worked harder" than she did in Case II. That is, she worked more consistently through the day, eliminated idle time, took less personal time, and visited less frequently with her neighbors. She was at her bench ready to start work when the whistle blew and worked until quitting time, concentrating on the work she was doing during the entire day. Although it is likely that the operator used approximately the same motions in completing a cycle in Case III as in Case II, it is certain that she moved faster in Case III than in Case II. The incentive of greater pay for greater output was responsible for this. It is also likely that the operator was more fatigued at the end of the day in Case III than in Case II.

It is, therefore, apparent that increased output through improved methods ordinarily causes the operator no increase in fatigue. In fact, the improved method is usually easier, more satisfying, and less fatiguing than the original method. On the other hand, the application of a wage incentive does cause the operator to work harder. The extent of the operator's exertion will depend upon her own inclination and her fitness for the job. With straight piece rate the reward is in direct proportion to the output.

For the employer the application of motion study reduced the direct labor cost 40 per cent and the setting of the rate and the wage incentive reduced it another 25 per cent. The direct labor cost per piece in Case I was $0.422, in Case II $0.253, and in Case III $0.19. This is shown graphically by the curve at the top of Fig. 159.

CHAPTER 17

MAKING THE STOP-WATCH STUDY

Stop-watch time study is the most commonly used method of measuring labor accomplishment in industry today although there is a movement toward making greater use of standard time values for carefully defined elements, therbligs, and combinations of therbligs.

The various methods of determining the time required to do a given task are presented in the following seven chapters. This chapter describes the equipment used and explains how a stop-watch time study is made. Chapter 18 shows how the rating factor, allowances, and the time standard are determined. Chapters 19, 20, and 21 deal with elemental time data and formulas for setting time standards; and Chapters 22 and 23 show how time values for combinations of therbligs may be used for obtaining the standard time for an operation.

EQUIPMENT FOR MAKING STOP-WATCH STUDIES

In contrast to the equipment required for full micromotion studies, that needed for stop-watch studies is simple and inexpensive. In making stop-watch studies, as in all phases of motion and time study work, successful results depend mostly upon the abilities of the analyst rather than upon the equipment he uses.

The ordinary equipment for stop-watch studies consists of a decimal stop watch, observation sheets, and a board for holding the watch and these data sheets. On machine work a speed indicator and a slide rule are also required.

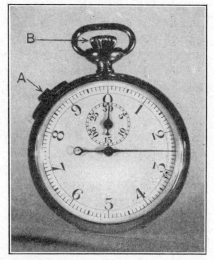

Fig. 160—Minute-decimal stop watch.

The Decimal Stop Watch. The minute-decimal stop watch is most commonly used (see Fig. 160) for stop-watch studies. It has the dial divided into 100 equal spaces, each of which represents 0.01 minute, the hand making one complete revolution per minute. A smaller dial on the watch is divided into 30 spaces, each of which represents 1 minute, the hand making one complete revolution in 30 minutes. The hands of the watch are controlled by the slide A and the winding stem B as shown in Fig. 160. The starting and stopping of the watch are controlled by the slide. It is possible to stop the hand at any point and then start it again from that position. Pressure on the top of the stem B returns the hand to zero, but it starts off immediately upon releasing the stem. The hand may be held at zero either by holding the stem down or by pushing the slide A away from the stem.

The hour-decimal stop watch is like the minute-decimal watch in design and operation. However, it has the dial divided into 100 spaces, each of which represents 0.0001 hour, the hand making 100 revolutions per hour. The small dial on the watch is divided into 50 spaces, each of which represents 0.01 hour, the hand making 2 revolutions per hour. The principal advantage of this watch is that the readings are made directly in fractions of an hour, which is the common unit of time measurement in industry.

The split-second stop watch is not recommended and is seldom used for stop-watch study work.

Time-Recording Machines. For some years machines have been used in this country and abroad for recording time on paper moving through the machine at uniform velocity. The earlier machines were operated by a clock mechanism whereas an electric motor is now used.

The most effective machine for time-study purposes uses the principle of the kymograph, that is, as paper tape is drawn through the machine at uniform and known velocity by the motor, keys, operated by the thumb and fingers, are used to actuate pencils or other marking devices which record the time on the moving tape.

Mechanical timers are sometimes connected either mechanically or electrically to machines to measure idle time or to record the time for various phases of an operation.

The time-recording machine when used instead of a stop watch for making a time study enables the analyst to measure shorter elements than he could with a stop watch and to measure them more accurately.

The machine seems to be most useful where short cycles are to be timed and where operators follow a given routine without the introduction of many foreign elements. It is also necessary to have access to electric power or lighting circuits which have the correct voltage to operate the recording machine motor.

Stop-Watch Board.   A light-weight board, slightly larger than the observation sheet, is used to hold the paper and the watch.   There are many different arrangements in use but it seems best to have the watch mounted rigidly somewhere near the upper right-hand corner of the board and the observation sheets held in place by some form

FIG. 161—Stop-watch study board with observation sheet for recording data taken by the continuous method.

of clamp at the side or top of the board.   The stop-watch board shown in Fig. 161 is a form that is commonly used.   Since the analyst, in most cases, must take down the data while standing, it is desirable to have his watch and paper arranged as conveniently as possible.

While taking a stop-watch study the observer should hold the board against his body and the upper left arm in such a way that the watch can be operated by the thumb and index finger of the left hand. The observer holds the board with his left hand and arm, leaving his right hand free to record the data.

By standing in the proper position relative to the work being observed, and by holding the board so that the dial of the watch falls in the line of vision, the observer can more easily concentrate on the three things demanding his attention, namely, the operator, the watch, and the observation sheet.

Other Equipment. Observation sheets for recording stop-watch data differ widely as to size and arrangement but they should at least have the following features. There should be adequate space for identification information; the ruling should be conveniently arranged; and the sheet should be of such size as is convenient to use and file. A sheet 8½ inches × 11 inches is a size that is widely used mainly because of the ease of binding and filing. Additional features often included on the observation sheet are a ruled space for a sketch of the piece and of the work place and space for a summary of the data.

Although it is impossible to design a single observation sheet that would be suitable in every type of industry, those shown in Figs. 161, 163, and 164 have proved to be satisfactory in industries manufacturing a diversified line of products.

A speed indicator, or a tachometer, is required where machine-tool operations are studied. It is a very good rule for the analyst to check speeds and feeds in making a stop-watch study even though the machine has a table attached which gives this information for each setting of the speed and feed-control levers. Experience has shown that actual machine speeds do not always correspond with those on the manufacturer's tables because of variations in line-shaft speeds, changes in gearing, and other alterations of the machine that may have been made after the machine left the factory. If many different studies of the equipment are to be made it is best to check all speeds and feeds and prepare a new chart to replace the one on the machine if it is not correct.

The ordinary slide rule is recommended as a valuable aid and time saver to every motion and time study analyst. Special slide rules may be purchased or constructed and used to advantage in connection with certain kinds of work. For example, the simple rule shown in Fig. 162 permits the conversion to be made from revolutions per minute to surface velocity in feet per minute, or vice versa, with one setting of the rule. Such a rule is invaluable to any one studying lathe, milling-machine, or drill-press operations.

Selecting the Operator. Although the best operator available is the most desirable subject for micromotion studies, there are some objections to using the best operator for stop-watch studies. Since a rating factor is used to evaluate the operator's performance as to skill and effort and to standardize it at that of the average operator, it theoretically makes little difference whether the best or the poorest operator is timed. However, it is admittedly difficult to evaluate correctly the skill and effort of a very poor operator. Usually such performance occurs only with a beginner before he has learned the work, and it is seldom advisable to take a study of such an operator.

The fact that it is important to maintain the good will and cooperation of the employee in motion and time study work should not be overlooked. For psychological reasons it is often better to time an average operator rather than the best one. Workers, not fully understanding the process of rating operator performance, are likely to feel that time standards will be set directly on the output of the person timed and, if that person is the best one on the job, then they may think that the standard time will be so low that it will be very difficult or impossible for the average operator to meet it.

Since full micromotion studies are seldom used in industry for improving methods, the improvement of the job will, in most cases, tie in with the stop-watch study so that the same operator will serve as the subject for the entire procedure. Frequently there is but a single person on the job; consequently there is no choice of operator.

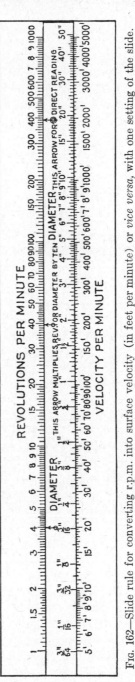

FIG. 162—Slide rule for converting r.p.m. into surface velocity (in feet per minute) or *vice versa*, with one setting of the slide.

THE TECHNIQUE OF STOP-WATCH STUDIES

The exact procedure used in making stop-watch studies may vary somewhat depending upon the nature of the work and the type of motion and time study being made (see Table I on page 18); yet the following steps are usually required:

1. Securing necessary information.
2. Dividing the operation into elements.
3. Taking and recording the data.
4. Rating the skill and effort of the operator.
5. Determining the allowances.
6. Determining the time standard.

Standardization of the work has been discussed at length in the preceding chapters and it has been emphasized that all of this should precede the actual setting of the time standard. The extensiveness of this work has been indicated in Table I on page 18 as ranging from the very elaborate Type A investigation requiring much time and considerable expense to the Types D and E requiring but a cursory analysis and a general check for methods. Attention again is called to the fact that never should a stop-watch study be made without at least this minimum of preliminary work.

Where a standard procedure has been determined for performing a general class of work such, for example, as light drill-press work using simple fixtures, and where there is but little variation in the size, shape, weight, or length of the piece, it is apparent that the methods work would consist of little more than determining the proper speed and feed to be used, the proper kind and grind of drill, and ascertaining that the material is arranged as prescribed for this kind of work. With these things satisfactory, the observer is then ready to proceed with the study.

In the past, stop-watch studies were too often considered as separate and distinct from motion studies. Today we realize that motion study and stop-watch study for rate setting must be considered together.

Making the Stop-Watch Study. Those phases of stop-watch study that can be carried out at the time and place of the performance of the operation will be described in this chapter. They are: obtaining and recording necessary information, dividing the operation into subdivisions or elements, listing these elements in proper sequence, timing them with the stop watch and recording the readings, noting and recording the skill and effort of the operator's performance, and making a sketch of the piece and of the work place.

Securing Information. All information asked for in the heading of the observation sheet should be carefully recorded. This is important because stop-watch studies hastily and incompletely made are of little use. The first place to practice thoroughness is in filling in all necessary information for identification. A study may be practically worthless as a record or as a source of information for formula construction a few months after it has been made because the person who made the study has forgotten the circumstances surrounding it. Ordinarily, the necessary information concerning the operation, part, customer, order number, lot size, etc., can be obtained from the route sheet, bill of material, or drawing of the part.

A sketch of the part should be drawn at the bottom or on the back of the sheet if a special place is not provided. A sketch of the work place should also be included showing the position of the operator, location of the tools, fixtures, and materials. Specifications of the materials being worked upon should be given and a description of the equipment being used should be recorded on the sheet in the space provided. Ordinarily the trade name, class, type, and size of the machine are sufficient description. If the machine has an identification number assigned to it this should be included. Accurate record should be made of the number, size, and description of tools, fixtures, gauges, and templets.

Division of the Operation into Elements. All manual work may be divided into eighteen subdivisions or therbligs, as has already been explained. These minute subdivisions are too short in duration to be timed by a stop watch, therefore, a number of them must be grouped together into elements of sufficient length to be conveniently timed.

Three general rules should be borne in mind in dividing an operation into elements:

1. The elements should be as short in duration as can be accurately timed.
2. Handling time should be separated from machine time.
3. Constant elements should be separated from variable elements.

To be of value a stop-watch study must be a study of the elements of the operation and not merely a record of the total time required per cycle to do work. However, if elements are too short it is impossible to time them accurately. Elements of 0.03 or 0.04 minute in length are perhaps as short as can be conveniently measured with a stop watch.

In machine work it is desirable to separate the machine time, that is, the time that the machine is doing work from the time during which the operator is working. There are several reasons for this. Where power feeds and speeds are used on the machine it is possible to calculate the time required for the cut and thus check the actual stop-watch data when the machine time is kept separate. Also, the beginning and the end of a "cut" are excellent beginning and ending points for an element. Where elemental time standards and formulas are to be developed it is essential that machine time be separated from handling time. The reasons for this will be explained in Chapter 19.

The elements of a cycle that are constant should be separated from those that are variable. The term constant elements refers to those elements that are independent of the size, weight, length, and shape of the piece. For example, in soldering seams of tin cans made by hand, the time to touch the iron to the bar of solder is a constant whereas the time to solder the side seam on the can is a variable, varying directly with the length of the seam.

The analyst trained in the micromotion study technique will find it relatively easy to decide upon the elements of the operation because they are merely combinations of therbligs. The analyst without such training should see that the elements begin and end at well-defined points in the cycle. These points will have to be memorized by the analyst so that he will always read his watch at exactly the same place in the cycle; otherwise the time for the elements would be incorrect.

Each element should be concisely stated and recorded on the sheet in the space provided. It is sometimes advisable to use symbols to represent elements that are often repeated. In fact, in some industries a standard code of symbols is prepared and used by all time study observers. In either case the meaning of the symbols should appear on each observation sheet.

Taking and Recording the Data. Four of the more or less commonly used methods of reading the stop watch are: (1) continuous timing, (2) repetitive timing, (3) accumulative timing, and (4) cycle timing. The first two are generally used and the last two are adapted to special cases and are therefore only occasionally used.

Continuous Timing. The continuous method of timing is generally considered the most accurate one and it gives very satisfactory results on most kinds of work.. The watch is permitted to run con-

SHEET NO. 1	OF	1 SHEETS		DATE 1/20/37		
SKILL		EFFORT				
POOR 45-55		POOR 45-55		OPERATION Drill ¼" Hole		OP. NO. D-20
AVG. 55-65		AVG. 55-65				
GOOD 65-75	60	GOOD 65-75	60	PART NAME Motor Shaft		PART NO. MS-267
EXC. 75-85		EXC. 75-85				
SUPER 85-		SUPER 85-		DEPT. DL 21	FOREMAN	H. Miller
AVG. OF SKILL AND EFFORT		60			MCH. NAME &	
PERSONAL & FATIGUE ALLOW.		5%		MATERIAL S A.E. 2315	MCH. NO.	2174 Avey.
DELAY ALLOWANCE		%				
		%		REG. NO. 1347	OPERATOR S.K.Adams	
TOTAL ALLOWANCE		5%		EXPERIENCE	MALE ✔	NO. PCS.
TOTAL RATING WITH ALLOW.		63%		ON JOB 18 Mo. on Sens. Drill	FEMALE	ON ORDER 100
BEGIN 10:15	FINISH 10:38			ELAPSED 23	UNITS FINISHED 20	ACTUAL TIME PER 100 115 / NO. MACHINES OPERATED 1

ELEMENTS	SPEED	FEED		1	2	3	4	5	6	7	8	9	10	SELECTED TIME
1. Pick Up Piece and Place in Jig			T	.12	.11	.12	.13	.12	.10	.12	.12	.14	.12	
			R	.12	.29	.39	.54	.66	.77	.92	8.01	.14	.32	
2. Tighten Set Screw			T	.13	.12	.12	.14	.11	.12	.12	.13	.12	.11	
			R	.25	.41	.51	.68	.77	.89	7.04	.14	.26	.43	
3. Advance Drill to Work			T	.05	.04	.04	.04	.05	.04	.04	.04	.03	.04	
			R	.30	.45	.55	.72	.82	.93	.08	.18	.29	.47	
4. DRILL ¼" HOLE	980	H	T	.57	.54	.56	.51	.54	.58	.52	.53	.59	.56	
			R	.87	.99	3.11	4.23	5.36	6.51	.60	.71	.88	11.03	
5. Raise Drill from Hole			T	.04	.03	.03	.03	.03	.03	.03	.03	.04	.03	
			R	.91	2.02	.14	.26	.39	.54	.63	.74	.92	.06	
6. Loosen Set Screw			T	.06	.06	.07	.06	.06	.06	.06	.06	.07	.08	
			R	.97	.08	.21	.32	.45	.60	.69	.80	.99	.14	
7. Remove Piece from Jig			T	.08	.09	.08	.08	.09	.08	.07	.08	.09	.07	
			R	1.05	.17	.29	.40	.54	.68	.76	.88	10.08	.21	
8. Blow Out Chips			T	.13	.10	.12	.14	.13	.12	.13	.12	.12	.11	
			R	.18	.27	.41	.54	.67	.80	.89	9.00	.20	.32	
9.			T											
			R											
10. (1)			T	.12	.11	.13	.14	.12	.12	.11	.13	.12	.12	.12
			R	11.44	.56	.69	.82	.87	17.01	18.09	.21	.31	.42	
11. (2)			T	.12	.14	.12	.11	.12	.10	.13	.15	.12	.11	.12
			R	.56	.70	.81	.93	.99	.11	.22	.36	.43	.53	
12. (3)			T	.04	.04	.04	.03	.04	.04	.04	.04	.04	.04	.04
			R	.60	.74	.85	.96	16.03	.15	.26	.40	.47	.57	
13. (4)			T	.54	.53	.55	.52	.57	.54	.50	.53	.55	.54	.54
			R	12.14	13.27	14.40	15.48	.60	.69	.76	.93	21.02	22.11	
14. (5)			T	.03	.03	.03	.03	.03	.03	.03	.03	.03	.03	.03
			R	.17	.30	.43	.51	.63	.72	.79	.96	.05	.14	
15. (6)			T	.06	.06	.06	.07	.06	.05	.06	.06	.05	.06	.06
			R	.23	.36	.49	.58	.69	.77	.85	20.02	.10	.20	
16. (7)			T	.08	.08	.09	.08	.08	.07	.08	.06	.08	.08	.08
			R	.31	.44	.58	.66	.77	.84	.93	.08	.18	.28	
17. (8)			T	.14	.12	.10	.09	.12	.14	.15	.11	.12	.12	.12
			R	.45	.56	.68	.75	.89	.98	19.08	.19	.30	22.40	
18.			T											1.11
			R											

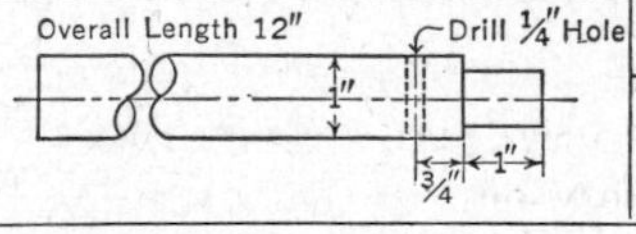

Overall Length 12" Drill ¼" Hole

BASE TIME PER PIECE 1.11   STANDARD TIME PER PIECE 1.17

TOOLS, JIGS, GAUGES: Jig No. D-12-33
Use H.S.Drill ¼" Diam.
Hand Feed
Use Oil - S4

TIMED BY J.B.Mv.

Fig. 163—Stop-watch study of a drill-press operation made by the continuous method.

tinuously during the period of the study. The observer notes the reading of the watch at the end of each element and records this reading on the observation sheet opposite its name or symbol.

Figure 163 illustrates the continuous method of timing. The operation of drilling the ¼-inch hole in the shaft was divided into 8 elements. The observer started his watch at the beginning of the first element, read it at the end of the first element, and recorded the reading in the vertical column 1 in the space opposite R and also opposite element 1. In a similar manner the watch was read at the end of each element and the readings for the first cycle were recorded in column 1. The second cycle was then timed and the data recorded in the second vertical column, etc.

The time for each element was later determined by subtraction. Thus, for the first element, $0.12 - 0 = 0.12$ was placed in the first column opposite the T (time). In a similar way for the second element $0.25 - 0.12 = 0.13$ minute was placed in the first column opposite the second element.

The watch may be permitted to run for the entire study or it may be snapped back to zero at the end of each cycle. The former practice is the better.

Repetitive Timing. In the repetitive or snap-back method the hands of the watch are snapped back to zero at the end of each element. At the beginning of the first element the operator snaps the hand back to zero by pressing the stem of the watch. The hand moving forward instantly begins to measure the time for the first element. At the end of the first element the observer reads the watch, snaps the hand back to zero, and then records this reading. In a like manner he times the rest of the elements. This method of timing gives the direct time without subtractions and the data are recorded on the observation sheet as read from the watch.

Perhaps the greatest disadvantage of this method of timing is the tendency for the observer to neglect to time and record delays, foreign elements, or false motions of the operator by simply holding down the stem of the watch. Thus, the sum of the elements timed will not equal the elapsed time for the study and there is no record of what took place during the missing intervals. This inaccuracy does not appear in studies made by the continuous method. Other inaccuracies of the repetitive method are: loss of time due to snapping back the watch hand, and the possibility that the observer will read the hand too early or too late. Some plants forbid the use of repetitive studies; others permit them only in special cases.

Accumulative Timing. The accumulative method of timing permits the direct reading of the time for each element by the use of two stop watches. These watches are mounted close together on the stop-watch board and are connected by a lever mechanism in such a way that, when the first watch is started, the second watch is automatically stopped. When the second watch is started the first is stopped. The watch may be snapped back to zero immediately after it is read, thus making subtractions unnecessary. The watch is read with greater ease and accuracy since the hands of the watch are not in motion at the time it is read.

Cycle Timing. It is difficult to time very short elements with a stop watch. When an operation is composed of a series of elements of 0.03, 0.04, or 0.05 minute each, the cycle method of timing is suggested unless there are too many elements. Of course, the most accurate method of timing such an operation is the full micromotion study which has already been described.

The cycle method consists of taking the time of the sum of all elements in the cycle less one element. The observer times as many cycles as there are elements, omitting a different element each time. By means of a simple calculation [1] it is possible to find the times for each element of the cycle.

Recording the Stop-Watch Readings. To the uninitiated it may seem difficult for the observer to do the several things required of him in such quick succession, viz., observe the operator, read the watch, and record the data on the observation sheet; but it is easily possible after a little experience.

A distinctive sound frequently accompanies the beginning and the ending of the element and assists in dividing the operation into elements for the study. Thus, in the study of the drilling operation (Fig. 163), as the shaft is dropped into place in the jig there is a metallic click which denotes the end of the first element. Such sounds aid the observer in taking his readings and he soon learns to make use of them.

The general policy of carefully timing every part of the operation should be insisted upon. If, for example, every fifth or every tenth piece is gauged, such information should be included on the observation sheet and a sufficient number of readings of this element should be made to include it in the time for the operation. The time for the element would, of course, be divided by 5 or 10, as the case might be, in order to prorate the gauging time.

[1] F. W. Taylor, "Shop Management," p. 173, Harper & Bros., New York, 1919.

When foreign elements occur they should be timed and recorded on the observation sheet. These may or may not be included in the time standard, depending upon their nature. By foreign elements is meant elements that do not regularly occur in the cycle, such as accidentally dropping a wrench or piece of material on the floor, tightening the belt on the machine, breaking a tool, placing oil on a tight screw in a jig, etc.

Such elements as "change tools," "blow chips out of jig," "replace tote box," "lubricate die," and the like should be considered specific parts of the operation and should be timed as such. The policy of timing only those elements that occur in each cycle and then placing all other elements in the allowances shows very poor training or laziness on the part of the observer. Such practice will result in inaccurate time standards.

Number of Cycles to Be Timed. The number of cycles to be timed will depend upon the nature of the work but should be sufficient to give a true sample. The following are some of the factors that affect this problem: the length of the cycle, the number of elements in the cycle, possible variation in the length of the cycle, consistency and skill of operator, and the relation of the machine time to the handling time. A skilled operator working in a consistent and uniform manner will enable the observer to make a satisfactory study with fewer observations than will one who is erratic. Also, when an operation consists largely of machine time fewer observations are required than when it is entirely controlled by the operator. In any case, it is better to have taken too much data than too little.

Rating Factor. As the observer makes the study he will also determine the level of skill and effort, or the rate of speed at which the operator is working.

There are a number of different "systems" or methods of arriving at this rating factor although they all depend upon the judgment of the analyst.

One of the most common methods is for the analyst to determine a rating factor for the operation as a whole. At the beginning and at the end and perhaps at intervals throughout the study the observer concentrates on making skill and effort ratings of the operator. It is his object to determine the average level of performance at which the operator was working while the study was being made. Such a rating is recorded on the observation sheet in the form of a rating or leveling factor.

Another method is for the analyst to determine a rating factor for each element of the operation. Still a more refined rating plan requires the analyst to rate each element when it is timed, recording the rating factor for the element on the observation sheet when the stop-watch reading is recorded. Using this method there would be a rating factor recorded for each stop-watch reading.[2]

The use of the rating factor will be explained more fully in the next chapter.

Steps in Making Stop-Watch Observations:

1. Secure the cooperation of the operator. Explain to him what you are going to do.
2. Obtain all necessary information and record it on the observation sheet.
3. Make a sketch of the piece and of the work place.
4. Divide the operation into its elements and list these on the observation sheet. If symbols are used give the meaning of each on the sheet.
5. Record the time of day as the study is begun.
6. Start the decimal stop watch at the beginning of the first element of the cycle. Read and record the time for each element of the cycle.
7. When the study is completed and when the stop watch is read at the end of the last element, read and record the time of day on the sheet.
8. Rate the skill and effort of the operator and record these on the observation sheet.
9. Sign and date the study.

[2] R. E. Green, "Leveling the Time Study," *Proceedings 1939 Conference,* Industrial Management Society, Chicago, Illinois.

CHAPTER 18

DETERMINING RATING FACTOR, ALLOWANCES, AND TIME STANDARD

After the stop-watch study has been taken the next step is to subtract successive watch readings in order to get the time for each element. It is advisable to record these subtracted times in ink in order to make them stand out from the rest of the data and also to insure permanence.

Selecting Time Values. As the study on page 263 shows, there are twenty time values for each of the eight elements. It now becomes necessary to select from these data a time value for each of these eight elements.

Occasionally there may be an abnormally high or low element due to an error in reading the stop watch; such readings should not be considered in selecting the time value for the elements. However, the fact that there is considerable variation in successive times for certain elements does not mean that all high and low elements should be thrown out. In many cases there are good reasons for such data— an occasional hard casting may require longer drilling time, or a piece with a fin or a burr may take longer to place in the jig, etc. If such time values are typical or representative of what may be expected on the job, they should not be eliminated from the study even though they happen to be abnormal.

There are four methods commonly used in arriving at the selected time for each element of a stop-watch study. They are: (1) average, (2) modal, (3) "good time," and (4) minimum.

The average method of determining the selected time value is widely used and simply consists of taking the arithmetical average of the data for each element.

The modal method, also widely used, consists of taking the time that recurs most frequently for the element. High or low time values will have less effect upon the selected time by this method than by the average method. The selected time values in the stop-watch study shown on page 263 were determined by the modal method.

The "good time" method consists of selecting a representative time value even though it is not the one that occurs most frequently. This method gives the analyst some leeway for the use of his judgment in selecting time values for an element. A time value that occurs with reasonable frequency may be more representative than one that occurs most frequently.

The minimum time is the lowest time value for the element occurring in the study. This method probably is used less than any of the three methods previously described, although the minimum time is claimed by some to form the most definite basis for establishing a standard time.[1]

In micromotion study work it is the very fastest time for an element that is of greatest concern. However, in setting a time standard the situation is somewhat different in that the level of operator performance must be evaluated and a standard time set on the basis of average performance.

Having selected the time value for each element, the next two steps in determining the standard time are first to apply the rating factor, and then to add the allowances.

DETERMINATION OF RATING FACTOR

Individual Differences. From our own observations and experience we know that there are wide differences in capacities and abilities of individuals in every activity of life. We have seen champion athletes run the mile in 4 minutes and 8 seconds, the 10,000 meter race in 30 minutes and 18.8 seconds, and we have heard of such physical feats as one man's lifting 1384 pounds unaided.[2] These, however, are rare exceptions. Wechsler shows that the range of most physical and mental activities vary as 2 to 1, if the rare exceptions are not considered. That is, the best has roughly twice the capacity of the poorest.

In industry the working force is a selected group so the range might be expected to be smaller than would be found among a similar group of individuals taken at random. At the time of employment the worker is carefully selected for the particular job he is to do. Moreover, on some kinds of work the cycle is machine-paced, which tends

[1] L. P. Alford, Ed., "Cost and Production Handbook," p. 556, Ronald Press Co., New York, 1934.
[2] David Wechsler, "The Range of Human Capacities," p. 73, Williams & Wilkins, Baltimore, Md., 1935.

to bring the output of all individuals to one level. Then, too, poor operators become discouraged and transfer to other work or quit, and often supervisors give special attention to the poorer workers until they reach satisfactory performance. Although these influences tend to bring the performance of operators to a much more uniform level, there is still considerable variation in output per unit of time.

Table XXII shows the average performance for one day of 121 girls operating semi-automatic lathes, the work being identical for all operators. These were all experienced operators, they worked under the point system of wage payment,[3] and they were paid a 75 per cent premium for all work produced above 60 points per hour, this being the performance expected of the average operator. As the record shows, the five poorest operators averaged approximately 55 points an hour; the five best operators averaged approximately 95 points an hour.

Although this variation in performance may be caused by many different things, the experienced motion and time study analyst would note two main factors which affect the output of the operator. These are his skill and his productive effort or effective speed. Thus, of two people exerting the same productive effort one may accomplish more in a given time because he possesses greater skill than the other. One has only to compare the clumsy way an apprentice handles a tool with the smooth easy manner of the experienced tool maker to see extremes in skill. In a like manner, of two people possessing the same skill, one might do more work in a given time because of his greater physical exertion. More work is accomplished by moving at a faster pace. In such therbligs as transport empty and transport loaded, the average velocity in feet per minute may vary widely. This is illustrated by the greater speed in feet per minute shown by operator A2 over operator A1 in the therbligs transport loaded and transport empty in the link-forming operation described on page 96.

The data obtained by a stop-watch study show the actual time taken by the operator to perform a series of consecutive cycles of work. It tells nothing of the skill and the effort at which the operator worked while the study was being made. The operator might have been working at a level similar to that of the operator at the top of the column in Table XXII or he might have been working at a level similar to that of the operator at the bottom of the column. It is necessary to consider the degree or extent of the operator's skill and

[3] Ralph M. Barnes, "Industrial Engineering and Management," pp. 220-245, McGraw-Hill Book Co., Inc., New York, 1931.

TABLE XXII
DIFFERENCE IN THE PERFORMANCE OF OPERATORS WORKING ON SEMI-AUTOMATIC LATHES

Average Performance of Operators for Friday, Dec. 11, 1936

Number of Operators	Av. Point Hour for the Day (av. output)	Distribution	
		No.	Range
1	104	1	100 to 109
2	98	5	90 to 99
1	91		
2	90		
2	89		
2	87		
1	86		
2	85		
6	84	25	80 to 89
2	83		
1	82		
1	81		
8	80		
4	79		
1	78		
3	77		
4	76		
4	75		
1	74	40	70 to 79
2	73		
4	72		
3	71		
14	70		
3	69		
2	68		
3	67		
4	66		
3	64	45	60 to 69
6	63		
4	62		
6	61		
14	60		
1	58		
1	55		
1	54	5	50 to 59
1	52		
1	51		
Total 121	Av. 71.8		

effort in order that a standard may be determined that will permit the average operator to do the work in the time set for the job.

Methods of Determining Level of Performance.   There is only one way of determining the level of skill and effort at which the operator is working and that is by the judgment of the time study analyst. There are, however, a number of different methods of expressing this level of performance and of applying this leveling factor to the selected stop-watch time in order to have it represent the amount of work that is expected of the average operator.

Perhaps the oldest method is selecting the time for each element in such a way as to give proper weight to the skill and effort of the operator.   Thus, if an operator exhibiting excellent skill and effort were timed, the analyst would scan the data on the observation sheet, taking each element individually, and he would select a time value longer than the average; whereas, if the operator were poor in skill and effort, he would select a time value shorter than the average. The analyst would, in all cases, try to select time values which the average operator would have taken had he been timed.   The greatest difficulty with this method of rating or leveling is that the analyst must not only judge the level of the operator's skill and effort but he must also use his judgment in scanning the data in selecting a time value that seems to him to represent the time which the average operator would have taken for the element.   Experience shows that this method is less likely to produce satisfactory results than one that requires the analyst to make a specific quantitative rating of skill and of effort and then to apply these ratings as a percentage to the selected time in arriving at the base time for the job.

Leveling Method.   Westinghouse, through many years of experience, has developed a method of leveling [4] by using descriptive words to denote the various levels of skill and effort.   They have assigned numerical values to each of these for use in adjusting the selected time.[5]   Thus, skill is classified as either poor, fair, average, good, excellent, or super and operator effort is similarly classified.

Other organizations use percentage as the index factor.   Thus, 70 per cent might represent average performance, and 100 per cent might

[4] S. M. Lowry, H. B. Maynard, and G. J. Stegemerten, "Time and Motion Study," p. 139, McGraw-Hill Book Co., Inc., 1932.

[5] The leveling factor used in calculating the standard (allowed) time for the turret lathe operation in the stop-watch study shown in Figures 164 and 165 on pp. 274 and 275 was determined by the use of the performance rating table (from Lowry, Maynard, and Stegemerten's "Time and Motion Study," McGraw-Hill Book Co., Inc., and used by their permission) shown on the next page.

represent the highest continuous output expected from any person working over a long period of time.

PERFORMANCE RATING TABLE

Skill			Effort		
+0.15 +0.13	A1 A2	Superskill	+0.13 +0.12	A1 A2	Killing
+0.11 +0.08	B1 B2	Excellent	+0.10 +0.08	B1 E2	Excellent
+0.06 +0.03	C1 C2	Good	+0.05 +0.02	C1 C2	Good
0.00	D	Average	0.00	D	Average
−0.05 −0.10	E1 E2	Fair	−0.04 −0.08	E1 E2	Fair
−0.16 −0.22	F1 F2	Poor	−0.12 −0.17	F1 F2	Poor
Conditions			Consistency		
+0.06	A	Ideal	+0.04	A	Perfect
+0.04	B	Excellent	+0.03	B	Excellent
+0.02	C	Good	+0.01	C	Good
0.00	D	Average	0.00	D	Average
−0.03	E	Fair	−0.02	E	Fair
−0.07	F	Poor	−0.04	F	Poor

Rating Method. Of the several methods of measuring operator performance in use today perhaps the most easily understood and one of the most widely used is that based on the point as the unit of labor accomplishment and 60 points per hour as the level of performance expected of the average operator. Any of the terms—"point," "productive minute," or "standard minute"—may be used, for they all have a common meaning.

This method of rating would probably not result in a more accurate time standard than some other method if used by equally competent analysts. However, this method has the advantage of using a single numerical factor to express the level of operation performance or rate of output. The definition of a 60-point hour is relatively easy to grasp and the exact relation of a 50-point hour or a 70-point hour, for example, to the 60-point hour standard appeals to those who use the plan. In fact, when this method of rating is introduced into a plant it is but a short time before all members of the organization, employees and supervisors alike, understand the meaning of the term

Sheet 1 of 1 sheets

Number / Line	1 Get stud from table and place in chuck		2 Tighten chuck with socket wrench		3 Start machine		4 Face stud		5 Turn turret one position		6 Point stud		5		7 Turn stud		8 Turn turret two positions		9 Chamfer head		5		10 Thread stud		5		11 Stop machine		12 Remove stud and place in tote pan	
	T	R	T	R	T	R	T	R	T	R	T	R	T	R	T	R	T	R	T	R	T	R	T	R	T	R	T	R	T	R
1	18	18	19	37	3	40	38	78	14	92	10	102	10	12	40	52	12	64	14	78	14	92	18	210	10	20	14	34	13	47
2	21	68	20	88	4	62	34	326	12	38	11	49	12	61	45	406	12	18	17	35	11	46	26	72	10	82	13	95	13	508
3	20	28	20	48	4	52	48	600	10	10	10	20	12	32	46	78	12	90	13	703	11	14	21	35	11	62/57	16	57/35	15	27/62
4	25	802	16	18	3	21	45	66	12	78	9	87	11	98	50	948	11	59	16	75	10	85	28	1013	11	24	18	42	12	54
5	19	73	20	93	3	96	–	M	–	M	–	M	–	1184	41	1225	12	37	11	48	12	60	19	79	11	90	17	1307	11	18
6	25	43	19	62	4	66	46	1412	11	23	11	34	9	43	41	84	11	95	11	1506	11	17	25	42	10	52	14	66	(34)	1600
7	23	23	(10)	33	3	36	40	76	11	87	12	99	9	1708	46	54	13	67	(7)	74	10	84	28	1812	–	–	–	–	–	–
8	A 18	2330	15	45	4	49	47	96	14	2410	8	18	12	30	38	68	14	82	12	94	10	2504	24	28	16	44	18	62	12	74
9	20	94	20	2614	3	17	30	47	10	57	9	66	10	76	41	2717	11	28	15	43	12	55	23	78	11	89	16	2805	13	18
10	18	36	19	55	3	58	34	92	10	2902	10	12	11	23	51	74	15	89	15	3004	12	16	32	48	12	60	(22)	82	10	92
11	18	110	17	27	(2)	29	31	60	12	72	10	82	11	93	46	239	11	50	14	64	10	74	29	303	12	15	18	33	(8)	41
12	B 25	430	(43)	73	3	76	38	514	13	27	9	36	11	47	46	93	11	604	9	13	11	24	22	46	14	60	11	71	C 12	792
13	21	813	14	27	3	30	46	76	11	87	10	97	9	906	42	48	11	59	(21)	80	12	92	20	1012	12	24	16	40	12	52
14	28	80	D 19	1137	3	40	33	73	11	84	(6)	90	12	1202	45	47	11	58	–	M	–	M	–	1301	14	15	18	33	11	44
15																														
16																														
17																														
18																														
19																														
20																														

Summary

	1	2	3	4	5	6	5	7	8	9	5	10	5	11	12
Totals "T"	0299	0218	0043	0510	0590	0119		0618	0167	0147		0315		0189	0134
No. Observations	14	12	13	13	52	12		14	14	11		13		12	11
Average "T"	00214	00182	00033	00392	00116	00099		00442	00119	00134		00242		00158	00122
Minimum "T"	0018	0014	0003	0030	0009	0008		0038	0011	0009		0018		0011	0010
Maximum "T"	0028	0020	0004	0048	0016	0012		0051	0015	0017		0032		0018	0015
Rating (S E C Act.)	CICIBD														
Leveling Factor	1.15														
Standard Time	00246	00209	00038	00451	00133	00114		00508	00137	00154		00278		00182	0014
% Allowance	25	20	20	10	20	20		10	20	20		10		20	25
Time Allowed	0031	0025	0004	0050	0016	0014		0056	0016	0018		0031		0022	0018

Foreign Elements

Sym.	R	T	Description
A	2312/1812	500	Break Stud
B	405/341	64	Get 14 Studs
C	780/671	109	Get Drink
D	1123/1085	38	Drop Wrench Wipe off Hands
E			
F			
G			
H			
I			
J			
K			
L			
M			
N			
O			

Skill		Effort	
A1, A2	Super.	A1, A2	Killing
B1, B2	Excellent	B1, B2	Excellent
✓ C1, C2	Good	✓ C1, C2	Good
D	Average	D	Average
E1, E2	Fair	E1, E2	Fair
F1, F2	Poor	F1, F2	Poor

Conditions		Consistency	
A	Ideal	A	Perfect
✓ B	Excellent	B	Excellent
C	Good	C	Good
D	Average	✓ D	Average
E	Fair	E	Fair
F	Poor	F	Poor

General rating for study	Skill	Effort	Cond	Consy
	+.06	+.05	+.04	.00

Study started	Study finished	Overall time
8:46 A.M.	9:12 A.M.	.433 hrs.

FIG. 164—Stop-watch study of a turret-lathe operation made by the continuous method using a decimal-hour stop watch. The Westinghouse leveling method was used in determining the standard (allowed) time. From Lowry, Maynard, and Stegemerten, "Time and Motion Study," McGraw-Hill

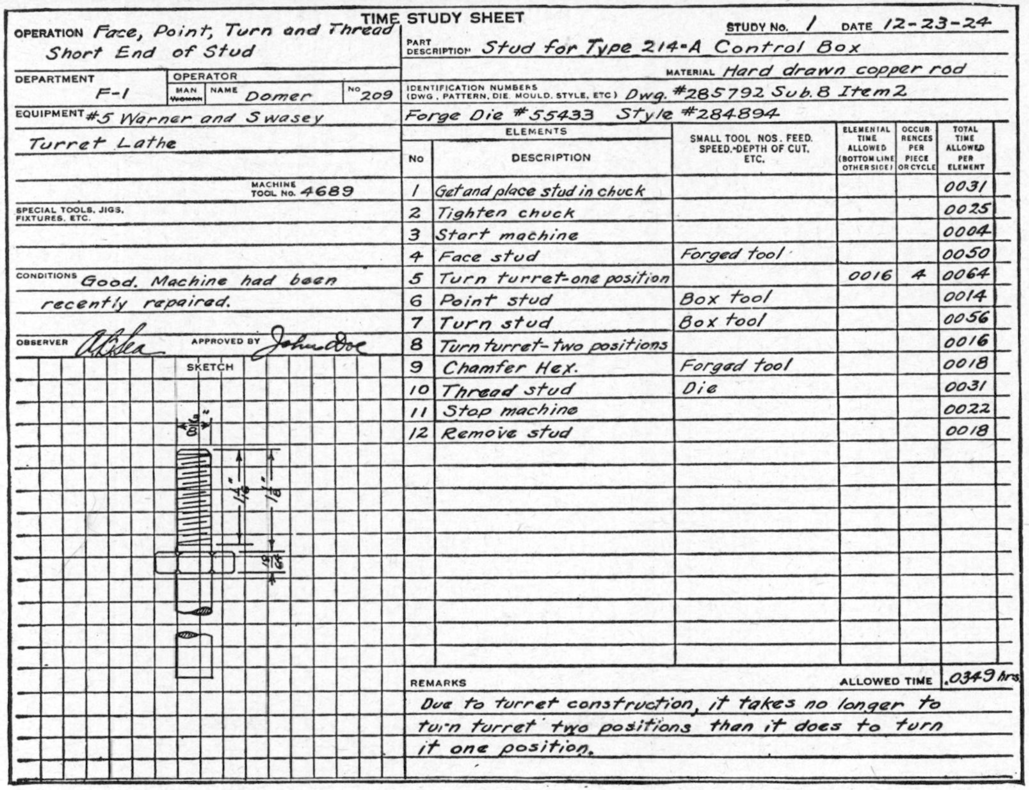

TIME STUDY SHEET

OPERATION Face, Point, Turn and Thread Short End of Stud   STUDY No. 1   DATE 12-23-24

PART DESCRIPTION Stud for Type 214-A Control Box

DEPARTMENT F-1   OPERATOR MAN No. Webman   NAME Domer   No. 209

MATERIAL Hard drawn copper rod

IDENTIFICATION NUMBERS (DWG., PATTERN, DIE, MOULD, STYLE, ETC.) Dwg. #285792 Sub 8 Item 2

EQUIPMENT #5 Warner and Swasey Turret Lathe   Forge Die #55433 Style #284894

MACHINE TOOL No. 4689

SPECIAL TOOLS, JIGS, FIXTURES, ETC.

CONDITIONS Good. Machine had been recently repaired.

OBSERVER (signed)   APPROVED BY (signed)

ELEMENTS		SMALL TOOL, NOS., FEED. SPEED-DEPTH OF CUT. ETC.	ELEMENTAL TIME ALLOWED	OCCUR. PIECE OR CYCLE	ELEMENTAL TIME ALLOWED (BOTTOM-LINE OTHER SIDE)	OCCUR. PIECE OR CYCLE	RENCES PER PIECE	TOTAL TIME ALLOWED PER ELEMENT
No	DESCRIPTION							
1	Get and place stud in chuck							0031
2	Tighten chuck							0025
3	Start machine							0004
4	Face stud	Forged tool						0050
5	Turn turret-one position		0016	4				0064
6	Point stud	Box tool						0014
7	Turn stud	Box tool						0056
8	Turn turret-two positions							0016
9	Chamfer Hex.	Forged tool						0018
10	Thread stud	Die						0031
11	Stop machine							0022
12	Remove stud							0018

REMARKS Due to turret construction, it takes no longer to turn turret two positions then it does to turn it one position.

ALLOWED TIME .0349 hrs

FIG. 165—Back of observation sheet completely filled out.

and find it useful whenever it is necessary to refer to rate of labor accomplishment.

The point is a unit of measurement of work. The amount of useful work in a point is based upon the performance of an average operator working without incentive at a preconceived maintainable speed at which he will produce 60 points per hour. This average operator would possess that amount of skill that would be expected of a man who knew his job well. He should be able to do accurate work, know how to handle his tools, and work to specifications. He would have to be more than a beginner, although he would not be expected to have that super skill which comes only from many years of experience in a special field, or because he is especially well adapted to the particular work. This average operator would be expected to exhibit an average amount of effort or speed. That pace used by operators working without incentive (that is, paid by the day) with reasonably good supervision is what is meant by average effort. The operator using average skill and effort would produce 60 points or standard minutes of work in one hour. It should be within possibility for every employee to reach this 60-point hour level of performance. In fact, a majority of the workers should be able to do considerably more than this average. Of the 121 semi-automatic lathe operators (see Table XXII on page 271) more than half were able to make a 70-point hour average or above for the week, and six averaged 90 points per hour or better for the week. Only five fell below the 60-point hour level.

Applying the Rating Factor. If this method of rating is used, a chart similar to that at the upper left-hand corner of the observation sheet on page 263 might be used as a guide in rating. The analyst would note in the appropriate square his estimate of the skill of the operator and in a like manner the effort of the operator. In all cases he is comparing the performance of the worker being studied with the mental picture of the "average operator" which has just been described. In a given case, for example, if the analyst rated the operator's skill at 85 and his effort at 75 the average of these two ratings would be 80. This would indicate that this operator was doing $33\frac{1}{3}$ per cent more than that expected of an average operator. In other words, at the time the study was made the analyst believed that the operator was doing 80 points of work in an hour and therefore this rating factor would be used to correct the data recorded on the observation sheet in order to determine a time value that would represent the time that an average operator would have taken had he been studied.

Assume that in a particular operation of assembling an electric meter the operator gave a consistent performance throughout the entire cycle and throughout the entire study and that the sum of the selected times was 2.20 minutes per cycle. With 80 as the average rating for skill and effort, the application of the rating factor to the selected time would be as follows:

$$\frac{80}{60} \times 2.20 = 2.93$$

This value of 2.93 represents the time that the average operator would need in order to complete one cycle of the operation. This value is not the time standard for the job since allowances must be added. The determination and the application of allowances will be explained later.

Accuracy of Rating. This method, like any other method of rating operator performance, starts with the "average operator." It is not only necessary for the analyst to maintain a mental picture of this average operator as his standard against which to judge the performance of all others, but also he must prevent this picture's varying from day to day and he must keep his ratings in line with those of the other members of the time study department who are engaged in making stop-watch studies. The questions, "How accurate is this rating factor?" and "How consistent are stop-watch study observers in rating skill and effort?" might properly be asked,[6] for a time standard is no more accurate than these factors. Unfortunately there is little published data available relating to these questions. It is generally agreed that competent motion and time study analysts are able to rate operator performance, determine allowances, and establish time standards for most kinds of manual work that are sufficiently accurate to be satisfactory both to the employee and to the employer.

Time standards set by any one of a group of competent and well-trained analysts or by the same one on different days should fall within 5 to 7 per cent of the average of the group. That is, no one should differ more than 10 or 15 per cent from any other. Some motion and time study analysts claim that they can consistently do this within 2 or 3 per cent but this is doubtful.

We need to analyze the work of large numbers of time study men in order to evaluate their ability in recording data, rating operator performance, determining fatigue allowances, and performing the

[6] R. S. Uhrbrock, "A Psychologist Looks at Wage-Incentive Methods," *Am. Management Assoc. Bul.*, Inst. of Management 15, 1935.

necessary computations in arriving at a time standard for a task. It seems certain that with sufficient thought and energy directed toward the problem even the best stop-watch time study techniques in use today could be greatly improved.

Methods of Improving Rating Ability. A well-managed motion and time study department will provide definite means of checking and improving the rating ability of the members of the department. There are two common ways of doing this. The usual method is for several analysts to rate the same operator simultaneously and compare their ratings. The other method requires that a motion picture be made of an operation with a camera at constant speed, usually at 1000 exposures per minute. This film is then spliced into a loop and projected at exactly the same speed at which it was taken. The time study analysts of the department then rate the performance of the operator on the screen. From these ratings it is possible to know how each person compares with the average for the entire group. This procedure may be used for a number of different operations. By repeating the rating of a given operation at intervals it is possible to determine the consistency of the rating ability of the men.

DETERMINATION OF ALLOWANCES

Since the time standard for an operation should permit the average employee to work on that operation indefinitely without undue fatigue and perform the task easily in the standard time, it is evident that this standard must include all the elements that enter into the operation plus time for personal needs, rest, and delays. Instead of arbitrarily combining all allowances, the operation should be carefully studied over a sufficiently long period to enable the allowances to be classified at one of the following: (1) personal allowance, (2) fatigue allowance, or (3) delay allowance.

Personal Allowance. Personal allowance will be considered first because every worker must be allowed time for his personal needs. The amount of this allowance can be determined by making all day stop-watch studies of various classes of work. For light work where the operator works 8 or 9 hours per day without rest periods, 2 to 4 per cent (10 to 25 minutes) per day is all that the average worker will use for personal time. The results of a series of studies made in one plant gave 21 minutes as the average time used by women and this included two 7-minute rest periods, one in the morning and one in the afternoon. The men used 8 minutes per day, there being no rest periods for them in this factory. This plant uses a 3 per cent

Management sets up 5% Personal allow
(24 min & 03 min per hour)

personal allowance for both men and women and pays the women for the two 7-minute rest periods at their base wage rate.

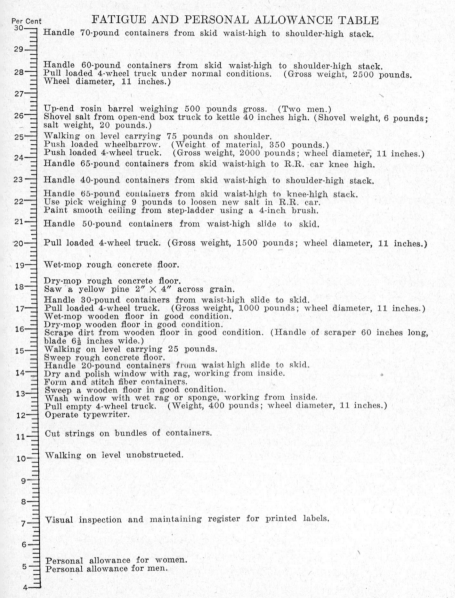

Per Cent   FATIGUE AND PERSONAL ALLOWANCE TABLE

30 — Handle 70-pound containers from skid waist-high to shoulder-high stack.

29 —

28 — Handle 60-pound containers from skid waist-high to shoulder-high stack.
Pull loaded 4-wheel truck under normal conditions.   (Gross weight, 2500 pounds.
Wheel diameter, 11 inches.)

27 —

26 — Up-end rosin barrel weighing 500 pounds gross. (Two men.)
Shovel salt from open-end box truck to kettle 40 inches high. (Shovel weight, 6 pounds;
salt weight, 20 pounds.)

25 — Walking on level carrying 75 pounds on shoulder.
Push loaded wheelbarrow. (Weight of material, 350 pounds.)
Push loaded 4-wheel truck. (Gross weight, 2000 pounds; wheel diameter, 11 inches.)
24 — Handle 65-pound containers from skid waist-high to R.R. car knee high.

23 — Handle 40-pound containers from skid waist-high to shoulder-high stack.

Handle 65-pound containers from skid waist-high to knee-high stack.
22 — Use pick weighing 9 pounds to loosen new salt in R.R. car.
Paint smooth ceiling from step-ladder using a 4-inch brush.

21 — Handle 50-pound containers from waist-high slide to skid.

20 — Pull loaded 4-wheel truck. (Gross weight, 1500 pounds; wheel diameter, 11 inches.)

19 — Wet-mop rough concrete floor.

Dry-mop rough concrete floor.
18 — Saw a yellow pine 2″ × 4″ across grain.
Handle 30-pound containers from waist-high slide to skid.
17 — Pull loaded 4-wheel truck. (Gross weight, 1000 pounds; wheel diameter, 11 inches.)
Wet-mop wooden floor in good condition.
Dry-mop wooden floor in good condition.
16 — Scrape dirt from wooden floor in good condition. (Handle of scraper 60 inches long,
blade 6½ inches wide.)
15 — Walking on level carrying 25 pounds.
Sweep rough concrete floor.
Handle 20-pound containers from waist high slide to skid.
14 — Dry and polish window with rag, working from inside.
Form and stitch fiber containers.
13 — Sweep a wooden floor in good condition.
Wash window with wet rag or sponge, working from inside.
Pull empty 4-wheel truck. (Weight, 400 pounds; wheel diameter, 11 inches.)
12 — Operate typewriter.

11 — Cut strings on bundles of containers.

10 — Walking on level unobstructed.

9 —

8 —

7 — Visual inspection and maintaining register for printed labels.

6 —

5 — Personal allowance for women.
Personal allowance for men.

4 —

Fig. 166—Personal and fatigue allowances used by one company having mainly handling and hand-truck operations. The allowances given include personal time.

Although the amount of personal time required will vary with the individual rather than with the kind of work, it is a fact that employees need more personal time when the work is heavy and done under unfavorable conditions, particularly in hot humid atmosphere. Under such conditions studies would undoubtedly show that more than 2 or 3 per cent allowance should be made for personal time.

Fatigue Allowance. In the modern well-managed plant in this country so many steps have been taken to eliminate fatigue that it is not of as great concern as formerly. In fact, fatigue is of such little consequence on some kinds of work that no allowance is required at all. There are many reasons for this. The length of the working day and the length of the working week have been shortened; machinery, mechanical handling equipment, tools, and fixtures have been improved so that the day's work is more easily done and the employee works in greater physical comfort than formerly. Accident hazards have also been reduced so that the fear of physical injury is of less importance.

Professor Anderson of the University of Illinois recently spent a year studying the effect of fatigue upon the worker in a large midwestern factory. He states: "The general and final conclusion of this study of human fatigue is, then, to the effect that industrial operations as carried on in a modern, progressively managed manufacturing plant do not subject the workers to undue fatigue, either physical or mental, and that fatigue is not a factor tending to limit production." [7]

Of course, there are some kinds of work that still involve heavy physical exertion and are performed under adverse conditions of heat, humidity, dust, and accident hazards and, therefore, require rest for the operator. Fatigue results from a large number of causes, some of which are mental as well as physical. There is at the present time no satisfactory way of measuring fatigue except in terms of reduced output resulting from work. Therefore, all-day studies of the operation made over a period of time would be the only way to determine the allowance that should be made on jobs that involve considerable fatigue.

Delay Allowance. Delays may be avoidable or unavoidable. Those delays that the operator makes intentionally will, of course, not be considered in determining the time standard. Unavoidable delays do occur from time to time and are caused by the machine, the operator, or by some outside force.

[7] A. G. Anderson, "A Study of Human Fatigue in Industry," an abstract of a thesis, p. 22, Univ. of Illinois, 1931.

It is expected that machines and equipment will be kept in good repair. However, when there is a breakdown or when repairs are necessary, the operator is usually taken off the job and such delays do not enter into the time standard. Sometimes there are minor adjustments, breakage of tools such as drills and taps, lost time due to occasional variation in material and interruptions by supervisors, and these must be included in the standard. Each unavoidable delay should be considered as a challenge by the analyst and every reasonable attempt should be made to eliminate these delays.

Applying the Allowances. Personal allowance is applied as a percentage of the base time and affects both handling time and machine time alike. For convenience fatigue allowance is usually applied in the same way, although some believe that this allowance should apply only to those elements during which the operator works and not to the machine time during which the machine works. Delays are applied as a percentage of the base time, or, if entirely a machine-delay allowance, then only on the machine clements. If these three allowances are applied uniformly to all elements, then they may be added together and applied together, necessitating but a single computation.

DETERMINATION OF THE TIME STANDARD

In the preceding chapter the explanation was made of the method of determining the selected time for a stop-watch study. The rating factor is applied to this selected time value to give the base time, and the standard time is then determined by adding the allowances to the base time. This is shown by the following example:

Selected time. 2.20
Skill and effort rating. 80
Base time = $\frac{80}{60} \times 2.20$. 2.93
Personal and fatigue allowance = 5 per cent. 15

Total time standard for the operation. . . . . 3.08 use 3.1 minutes

The above computations might be simplified by applying the allowances as a percentage of the rating factor. For example:

Selected time. 2.20
Skill and effort rating. 80
Personal and fatigue allowance in per cent. 5

Total rating including allowances = $\dfrac{80 \times 105}{100}$ . . . . = 84

Total time standard for the operation = $\frac{84}{60} \times 2.20 =$ 3.08 use 3.1 minutes

Stop-Watch Time Study of a Core-Making Operation. The study shown in Fig. 163 on page 263 is perhaps typical of stop-watch time

OBSERVATION SHEET

STUDY NO. 8765

SHEET 1 OF 1 SHEETS

ELEMENTS	SPEED	FEED	UPPER LINE: SUBTRACTED TIME / LOWER LINE: READING																MIN. TIME	AV. TIME	SELECT-ED TIME	OCC. PER CYCLE	SKILL & EFFORT RATING	NORMAL TIME
			1	2	3	4	5	6	7	8	9	10	11	12	13	14	15						
1. Fill core box with 3 handfuls of sand. Press sand down each time.			.09	.09	.09	.08	.08	.08	.10	.07	.08	.08	.09	.07	.08	.09	.06	.06	.081	.08	1	70	.093
			.09	.41	.71	1.07	.38	.67	.98	.28	.57	.87	.18	.46	.76	4.05	.32						
2. Press sand down with one trowel stroke. Strike off with one trowel stroke.			.06	.05	.08	.06	.05	.05	.06	.05	.05	.06	.06	.05	.05	.06	.06	.05	.059	.06	1	75	.075
			.15	.46	.79	.13	.43	.72	2.04	.33	.62	.93	.24	.51	.81	.11	.38						
3. Get and place plate on core box, turn over, rap, and remove box.			.13	.13	.15	.14	.13	.13	.14	.13	.14	.13	.12	.14	.12	.13	.13	.10	.126	.13	1	80	.173
			.28	.59	.94	.27	.56	.85	.18	.46	.76	3.06	.36	.65	.93	.24	.51						
4. Carry plate with core 4 feet. Dispose on oven truck.			.04	.03	.04	.03	.03	.03	.03	.03	.03	.03	.03	.03	.02	.02	.03	.20	.032	.03	1	75	.038
			.32	.62	.98	.30	.59	.88	.21	.49	.79	.09	.39	.68	.96	.26	.54						
(1)			.07	.10	.08	.08	.08	.08	.07	.08	.08	.08	.07	.07	.08	.09	.09						
			.61	.95	.25	.53	.83	.12	.41	.71	7.01	.28	.55	.84	.16	.48	.77						
(2)			.05	.05	.05	.05	.06	.06	.06	.06	.05	.06	.06	.07	.06	.05	.05						
			.66	5.00	.30	.58	.89	.18	.47	.77	.06	.34	.61	.91	.22	.53	.82						
(3)			.14	.13	.12	.13	.12	.13	.13	.12	.11	.12	.13	.13	.14	.13	.13						
			.80	.13	.42	.71	6.01	.31	.60	.89	.17	.46	.74	8.04	.36	.66	.95						
(4)			.05	.04	.03	.04	.03	.03	.03	.04	.03	.02	.03	.04	.03	.02	.03						
			.85	.17	.45	.75	.04	.34	.63	.93	.20	.48	.77	.08	.39	.68	.98						
(1)			.07	.07	.08	.08	.07	.08	.07	.08	.09	.08	.08	.08	.08	.08	.09						
			9.05	.34	.64	.93	.21	.50	.78	11.07	.39	.69	.99	.29	.59	.89	.19						
(2)			.05	.06	.05	.06	.06	.07	.06	.07	.08	.07	.06	.06	.07	.06	.08						
			.10	.40	.69	.99	.27	.57	.84	.14	.47	.76	12.05	.35	.66	.95	.27						
(3)			.14	.13	.13	.11	.12	.11	.11	.12	.10	.12	.12	.13	.12	.12	.11						
			.24	.53	.82	10.10	.39	.68	.95	.26	.57	.88	.17	.48	.78	13.07	.38						
(4)			.03	.03	.03	.04	.03	.04	.04	.04	.04	.03	.03	.03	.03	.03	.03						
			.27	.56	.85	.14	.42	.71	.99	.30	.61	.91	.20	.51	.81	.10	.41						

FOREIGN ELEMENTS:

Talley-by elements

No. 1	No. 2	No. 3	No. 4
.06-ɪ	.05-卌卌	.10-ɪ	.02-卌
.07-卌卌	.06-卌卌卌ɪ⋁	.11-卌	.03-卌卌卌卌
.08-卌卌卌卌ɪ⋁⋁	.07-卌	.12-卌卌	.04-卌卌
.09-卌卌ɪ	.08-卌	.13-卌卌卌卌ɪ	.05-ɪ
.10-卌		.14-卌卌	
		.15-ɪ	

TOOLS, JIGS, GAUGES, PATTERNS, ETC. √

Core box No. C-1D-7253, Size 1⅞" x 3½" x8½"; Wt. 1 lb.; 5"Molder's trowel

Plates 4 x 9"; weight with core 3½ lb.

OVERALL SKILL & EFFORT RATING		
75		

BEGIN	END	ELAPSED
9:18	9:32	14:00

UNITS FINISHED	ACTUAL TIME PER PIECE
45	0.31 Min.

FIG. 167—Front of observation sheet—core-making operation, size of form 8½ × 11 inches.

SUMMARY

NO.	ELEMENTS	NORMAL TIME	FATG. & PERS'L. ALLOW.	OTHER ALLOW.	STD. TIME
1.	Fill core box with 3 handfulls of sand. Press sand down each time.	.093	12	—	.104
2.	Press sand down with one trowel stroke. Strike off with one trowel stroke.	.075	15	—	.086
3.	Get and place plate on core box, turn over, rap, and remove box.	.173	15	—	.199
4.	Carry plate with core 4 feet. Dispose on oven truck.	.038	12	—	.042
					.431

TOTAL STD. TIME PER CYCLE: .431

NO. PIECES PER CYCLE 1

STD. TIME PER PIECE .431

DRAWING OF PART:

Core:

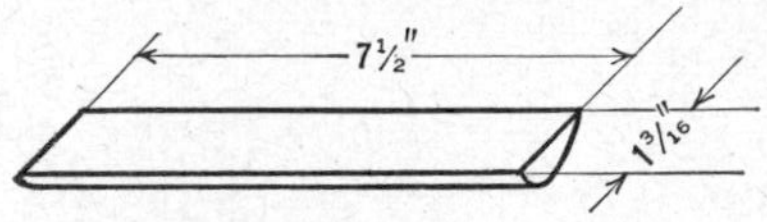

One half of cylinder $1 \tfrac{3}{16}'' \times 7\tfrac{1}{2}''$

Wt. of core before baking = 1/4 lb.

$7\tfrac{1}{2}''$ $1\tfrac{3}{16}''$

OPERATION: Make Core for Crank Frame No. 7253   OP. NO.: C-10-A

PART NAME: Core for Crank Frame No. 7253   PART NO.: —

MACH. NAME: Bench No. 62   MACH. NO.: —

OPERATOR'S NAME & NO.: S.R. Martin   MALE ☒ FEMALE ☐

EXPERIENCE ON JOB: Six months   FOREMAN: M.L. Ray

NO. MACHINES OPER'D: —   MACH. SPEED —   DEPT. NO. 17

MATERIAL: Dry core sand- Specification No. A16

SKETCH OF WORK PLACE   SCALE: One square = 4 inches

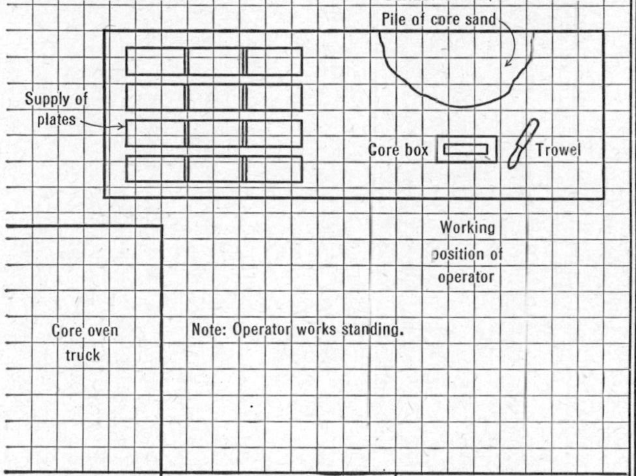

Pile of core sand

Trowel

Core box

Working position of operator

Supply of plates

Core oven truck

Note: Operator works standing.

DATE OF STUDY 1-11-40   OBSERVER C.A. Clark   APPROVED J.S.R. 1-13-40

FIG. 168—Back of observation sheet—core-making operation.

study practice today although some organizations rate each element separately instead of making an overall rating for the study, and also determine and apply a fatigue and personal allowance factor for each element. Figures 167 and 168 show such a study.

The operation studied was the making of a dry sand core in a wood core box. The core was 7½ inches long and 1³⁄₁₆ inches in diameter, taking the general shape of one-half of a cylinder.

A full description of the operation is given in the left-hand column below and the abbreviated description recorded on the observation sheet is given in the right-hand column below. The end points used in reading the watch are also given.

Detail Description of the Operation	Condensed Description of the operation as recorded on the observation sheet. The end points for reading the watch are also given.
1. Walk 4 feet from core-oven truck to bench, pick up core box with both hands, push loose sand on front edge of bench back against pile with edge of core box. Hold core box with left hand and fill core box with three handfuls of sand, pressing sand down in core box each time.	1. Fill core box with 3 handfuls of sand. Press sand down each time. *End of element* as right hand begins to grasp trowel.
2. Pick up trowel with right hand, press sand down with one stroke of trowel across top of box, strike off (draw edge of trowel across top of box), removing excess sand with edge of trowel. Dispose of trowel on bench at right of core box.	2. Press sand down with one trowel stroke. Strike off with one trowel stroke. *End of element* as trowel is dropped on bench (hits bench).
3. Get plate and carry from pile on bench 3 feet to left of core box, turn plate upside down, and place on top of core box. Turn plate and core box over. Pick up trowel with right hand and rap core box twice with handle of trowel, and dispose of trowel on bench to right of core box. Using both hands, carefully lift core box upward from plate, allowing core to remain on plate. Place core box on bench to right of plate.	3. Get and place plate on core box, turn over, rap and remove box. *End of element* as core box is placed on bench (hits bench).
4. Walk, carrying plate and core, 4 feet to left and place on shelf of core-oven truck.	4. Carry plate with core 4 feet. Dispose on oven truck. *End of element* as plate is placed on (touches) shelf of core-oven truck.

Before recording stop-watch readings the back of the observation sheet (Fig. 168) was filled out, a drawing of the layout of the work place was made, and a sketch of the core was placed in the lower right-hand corner of the sheet. The continuous method of timing and a decimal stop-watch were used. As the analyst made the study he evaluated the skill and effort of the operator for each element of the operation. The method of rating used here combines skill and effort ratings into a single index number. In making studies such as this one the analyst may occasionally record a skill and effort rating value above the stop-watch reading as the study progresses. Then, after the study is completed, he will record the skill and effort for each element of the study. These values are recorded on the front of the observation sheet in the vertical column headed "Skill and Effort Rating." An overall rating factor for the entire study is also recorded in the space provided in the lower right-hand section of the observation sheet. This may be used in connection with the elapsed time and the number of pieces finished, to check the time standard after it has finally been determined.

The selected time value for each element is determined by tallying the data as shown on the bottom of the observation sheet. If there is not space on this sheet the tally is made on a plain sheet of paper and attached to the observation sheet. The tally shows that, for Element 1, 0.06 is the minimum time value, 0.08 is the time value that occurs most frequently, and 0.081 is the average. In a similar manner values are determined for the other three elements of the study. The number of times that the element occurs in the study is recorded in the column marked "Occurrence per Cycle."

The normal or base times are then calculated in the following way:

$$(\text{Selected Time}) \times \frac{(\text{Skill and Effort Rating})}{60} = \text{Normal Time}$$

For Element 1 this is $0.08 \times \dfrac{70}{60} = 0.093$ minute.

Time Study Summary. After the normal time values are calculated for each element a summary is made on the back of the observation sheet in the space provided. A fatigue and personal time allowance is determined for each element and recorded in the appropriate column. Twelve per cent is allowed for the first and fourth elements and 15 per cent for the second and third elements. These allowances are obtained from a table similar to the one shown in Fig. 166. No other allowances are made.

The standard time is determined for each element in the following manner:

Normal Time + [(Normal Time) × (Fatigue and Personal Allowances)] = Standard Time

For Element 1 this is 0.093 + (0.093 × 0.12) = 0.093 + 0.011 = 0.104 minute.

In a like manner the standard time is determined for each of the four elements. Then these are added together to give the standard time for the cycle. Since one piece is produced per cycle, the standard time per piece is the same as the standard time per cycle.

A helper supplies the core maker with core sand and plates, and provides empty core-oven trucks; therefore no time is included in the standard for this work. Had this been part of the core maker's job this would have been timed and included as additional elements in the operation.

Production Studies. Although a motion and time study may be made with care and the instruction card for the operation prepared and given to the operator, there is sometimes a complaint made by the operator that he is unable to perform the task in the time called for on the instruction card. If, after a preliminary check, it appears that the inability to do the task in the time set is not the fault of the operator, it is essential that a new study be made to check the original stop-watch study. This new study is sometimes termed a "production study" in that it covers a longer period of time than the original study —sometimes as long as a day or two.

The inability of the operator to perform the task in the time specified may be due to any one or a combination of the following causes: conditions of material, tools, or equipment that are different from those existing at the time the original study was made; lack of skill on the part of the operator; or errors in the stop-watch study itself.

The production study should be made in such detail as to permit the checking of elemental times. This study, covering a long period of time as it does, may show the effect of fatigue by a decrease in the rate of output toward the end of the day.

Although every effort should be made to prevent errors in setting the original time standard, it is essential that the management be willing at all times to rectify errors or to demonstrate the correctness of the time standard. The workers must have confidence in the standards and in the men who set them.

Recording and Filing. When a stop-watch study is to be made of a series of similar operations it is desirable to define carefully each of the elements in order that standard-time data for each element may finally be determined. For example, in the operation "solder side seam of rectangular can" the elements are defined (see page 312) and irrespective of the person making stop-watch studies of soldering work this uniform division of the operation into elements will be made. A master form is prepared and the essential data from each stop-watch study of soldering side seams are recorded on this sheet. After sufficient data have been accumulated they will be used for setting up formulas for synthetically determining time standards on soldering operations as illustrated in Chapter 20.

Stop-watch studies together with other data and information concerning the operation should be filed in such a way that they may be readily located when needed. Cross indexing is often worth while. Too many stop-watch studies are independently made and the study filed never to be used again. The following chapters show how motion and time study data may be used for determining standard elemental data and for constructing formulas.

CHAPTER 19

DETERMINING TIME STANDARDS FROM ELEMENTAL TIME DATA AND FORMULAS

Many stop-watch studies are made of a single operation with little or no idea that the data taken will be of value on any other operation. There are, however, some kinds of work that have certain elements which are alike. For example, in a given class of machine-tool work all elements may be virtually alike except for the machine time or the cutting time. Thus, the same jig used for drilling the ¼-inch hole in the end of the shaft (see Fig. 163 on page 263) might also be used for drilling many other sizes of shafts. If the length and the diameter of the shafts fall within a limited range, handling time for drilling all shafts would be practically constant and the only variable in the operation would be the time required to drill the hole, which would vary with its diameter and depth. Other operations using jigs similar to this one would have certain elements in common such as "tighten set screw," "lower drill to work," etc.

Where motion and time studies are to be made of many different operations of a similar class of work, such as that on sensitive drill presses, lathes, gear hobbers, etc., it is best to consider the entire class of work as a unit, working out such improvements in methods as seem advisable, and standardizing all factors for the entire class of work. When the stop-watch studies are begun on this work, the elements should be selected in such a way as will make it possible eventually to construct tables of standard-time data that may be applied to all elements that are likely to appear continually in that particular class of work.

Use of Time Values for Constant Elements. The data shown in Tables XXIII to XXV were obtained from a sufficient number of stop-watch studies of representative kinds of work to guarantee their being reliable. With such data available in the time study department,[1] it is possible to set time standards for the handling elements of any job

---

[1] For other elemental time data for drilling see: Ralph M. Barnes, "Industrial Engineering and Management," pp. 134-135, McGraw-Hill Book Co., New York, 1931.

TABLE XXIII

Time-Setting Data for Sensitive Drills

Setup Time

Description of Work	Time, Minutes
1. Small work held in jig which can be handled very easily by hand....	15.00
2. Small work held in vise..	15.00
3. Small work held to table by one or two straps...................	15.00
4. Small work held in jig having a number of drilled, tapped, and reamed holes...	30.00
5. Small work held in jig and jig held in vise.....................	30:00
6. Work of medium size held by one or two straps..................	30.00
7. Work of medium size prevented from turning on table by a stop in T-slot...	15.00
8. Work of circular type such as washers, collars, bushings, and sleeves held to table by a draw bolt through center....................	15.00

on a sensitive drill falling within the classes listed in Tables XXIV and XXV. These data do not give the time required to drill the hole in the piece and consequently this information must be obtained by means of a stop-watch study of this element.

Assuming that Tables XXIII, XXIV, and XXV were available and that it was necessary to determine the standard time to drill the $\frac{1}{4}$-inch hole in the end of the shaft (Fig. 163 on page 263), the procedure would be as follows:

Chuck and remove piece (from Table XXIV) 0.50
  (Class B, work held by set screw)
Machine manipulation (from Table XXV) 0.07
  (Class A, drilling, one drill and no bushing)
DRILL $\frac{1}{4}$-INCH HOLE (stop-watch data obtained as in Fig.
  163) 0.54
                                                         ————
  Total base time per piece 1.11
  5 per cent allowance 0.06
                                                         ————
  Total standard time per piece .... 1.17 minutes
Setup time (from Table XXIII) = 15.00 minutes

The value of standard-time data such as that illustrated above is evident. It reduces the number of stop-watch studies needed, shortens

TABLE XXIV

Elemental Time Data for Sensitive Drills

Chucking and Removing Time

1. Work Held in Jig

    Classes:

        A. Held by thumb screw
        B. Held by set screw
        C. Held by thumb and set screw
        D. Held by cover strap and thumb screw
        E. Held by cover strap and set screw
        F. Held by cover strap, thumb screw, and set screw

Elements	Time, Hundredths of a Minute					
	A	*B*	*C*	*D*	*E*	*F*
1. Pick up piece and place in jig	12	12	12	12	12	12
2. Swing cover strap and tighten lock screw	..	..	..	10	10	10
3. Tighten thumb screw	08	..	08	08	..	08
4. Tighten set screw	..	12	12	..	12	12
5. Loosen set screw	..	06	06	..	06	06
6. Loosen thumb screw	05	..	05	05	..	05
7. Swing cover strap back and loosen lock screw	..	..	..	08	08	08
8. Remove piece from jig	08	08	08	08	08	08
9. Blow out chips	12	12	12	12	12	12
Total	45	50	63	63	68	81

Note.—Add 0.32 min. when jig is strapped to table.
      Add 0.07 min. for each additional thumb screw.
      Add 0.08 min. for each additional set screw.

the time required to set the standard, and tends to bring greater accuracy and uniformity in time standards for a given class of work.

The next step in this direction is the preparation of formulas which will make it possible to calculate quickly time values for the machine elements. Thus, with standard-time data for the handling elements and calculated time values for the machine elements, it is possible to determine the time standard for a given operation without the necessity of making a stop-watch study at all. By using this procedure the time standard can readily be determined in advance of the actual production of the part. In this case a detailed drawing of the

TABLE XXV

ELEMENTAL TIME DATA FOR SENSITIVE DRILLS

Machine Manipulation Time

Classes:

A. Drilling, one drill and no bushing
B. Drilling, placing and removing bushing
C. Drilling, placing and removing drill
D. Drilling, placing and removing drill and bushing

Elements	Time, Hundredths of a Minute			
	A	B	C	D
1. Place bushing in jig...........................	..	06	..	06
2. Place drill in chuck...........................	..	..	04	04
3. Advance drill to work.........................	04	04	04	04
4. Raise drill from hole..........................	03	03	03	03
5. Remove bushing from jig.......................	..	05	..	05
6. Remove drill from chuck.......................	..	..	03	03
Total..	07	18	14	25

Note.—Add 0.15 min. when quick-change chuck is not used (cases B and C).
  Add 0.06 min. for advancing work to next spindle.
  Add 0.05 min. when reamer is oiled before entering hole.

part to be made and the operation sheet or the route sheet should be supplied to the time study department in advance.

Determining Time Standards for Variables.   On all kinds of machine tool work the time for manipulating the machine and for chucking and removing the piece is likely to remain constant for each element, provided the size and shape of the piece are within reasonably close limits.   The time for making the cut is the variable.   This machine time can often be calculated, particularly when positive power feeds are used.   For example, in milling-machine work with power feed, if the feed of the table in inches per revolution of the cutter is known, and if the speed of the cutter in revolutions per minute is known, it is a simple arithmetical problem to find the time required to mill a piece of a given length.   An allowance must be added to the length of the piece for the approach and for the overtravel of the cutter; however, these can also be easily calculated.   In a similar manner, if a shaft of a given length is chucked in a lathe, and if the speed and the feed are known, it is a simple matter to calculate the length of time required to make a cut across the piece. Therefore, on machine tool work the handling time (a constant) plus the machine time (a variable) plus allowances will equal the standard time for the performance of a given operation.

In the operation of soldering the side seam in making rectangular cans (see pages 311 to 316) the principal variable is the element "solder the full length of the seam." The time for this element varies directly as the length of the seam.

SETTING TIME STANDARDS FOR
MILLING SQUARE OR HEXAGON ON BOLTS, SCREWS, OR SHAFTS

With the aid of the following four tables it is possible to determine the time standard for setting up a milling machine and for milling a square or hexagon on the end of bolts, screws, or shafts. The data in Tables XXVI and XXVII were determined from stop-watch studies. A sufficient number of representative jobs were studied to give reliable data. Tables XXVIII and XXIX were compiled in order to facilitate the determination of the time standard for a given operation. Typical examples at the bottom of these two tables show how they are used.

There are two methods of milling squares and hexagons: (1) using a single mill which requires a separate cut for each side (use Table XXVIII), and (2) using a gang mill which cuts two sides at a time (use Table XXIX).

Computation of Data for Table XXVIII—Milling by Use of 6-Lip Mill. This milling operation is performed with a single milling cutter; hence four cuts are required to mill a square and six cuts to mill a hexagon. The dimension B (see sketches in Tables XXVIII and XXIX) is given as the turned diameter of the shaft rather than the width of the face to be cut, for the reason that detailed drawings (see Fig. 169) are dimensioned in that manner. Since the side of a square is equal to 0.7071 times the diameter of the circumscribed circle and since the side of a hexagon is equal to the radius of the circumscribed circle, it is easy to make the conversion.

When a single mill is used the cut is made across the face and the time for the cut varies as B and is independent of the dimension A, provided it falls within the scope of the data, that is, within $5/8$ inch to $1\frac{3}{4}$ inch. The total handling time (HT) plus the total cutting time (M) plus the allowances equals the total time for the operation.

TABLE XXVI

Time-Setting Data for Milling Machines

Machine Class 36

Setup Time

1. Base Setup Times

Time in Minutes

Type	Work Sizes		
	Small	Medium	Large
A. Strapped to table or angle plate (4 straps)	25	25	25
B. Held in vise..........................	25	25	25
C. Held in 2 vises........................	..	30	30
D. Vise with false jaws...................	35	35	35
E. Held in fixture........................	35	45	60
F. Held in dividing head chuck............	35	35	..
G. Held in dividing head and tail stock......	45	45	..

2. Additional Parts Used—Time to Be Added to Base Setup Time

Part	Part Sizes		
	Small	Medium	Large
H. Each additional strap..................	5	5	5
J. Angle plate...........................	10	15	15
K. Gang mills (1) fractional limits................ (2) decimal limits..................	10 15	10 15	10 15
L. False table...........................	10	15	20
M. Round table—hand feed...............	10	20	20
N. Round table—power feed..............	20	30	30
P. High-speed head......................	..	40	..
Q. Universal head.......................	..	60	..

TABLE XXVII

ELEMENTAL TIME DATA FOR MILLING SQUARE OR HEXAGON ON BOLTS, SCREWS, OR SHAFTS

Machine Class 36

Milling Table 1A

1. *Setup time*—Complete—See setup table
   Change size — End mill — 10 min.
   Gang mills — 20 min.
2. *Specifications*—
   A. Method of chucking—1—3-jaw chuck (small screws and bolts)
   2—Held on centers (shafts)
   3—Thread arbor in dividing head (small pieces with thread on or in end)
   B. Cutters—1—6-lip mill
   2—Gang mills (6-in. stagger tooth—side milling cutters)
   C. Length of flat — ⅝ in.–1¾ in.
   D. Size of sq. or hex. — ½ in.–1⅝ in.
   E. Number of cuts — 1 per side
   F. Material — SAE2315
   G. Indexing — Use rapid index plate wherever possible
3. *Operation Time.*—Machine manipulation and chucking time

Time in Minutes

Elements	Speed r.p.m.	Method of Chucking									
		1				2		3			
		Square		Hex.		Sq.	Hex.	Square		Hex	
		214	58	214	58	214	214	214	58	214	58
	Type of Mill	6-Lip Mill	Gang Mill	6-Lip Mill	Gang Mill	6-Lip Mill	6-Lip Mill	6-Lip Mill	Gang Mill	6-Lip Mill	Gang Mill
1. Stop machine..		0.04	0.04	0.04	0.04	0.04	0.04	0.04	0.04	0.04	0.04
2. Loosen dog in holder......		....	....	....	....	0.08	0.08	....	....	....	....
3. Loosen center..		....	....	....	....	0.08	0.08	....	....	....	....
4. Loosen work..		0.04	0.04	0.04	0.04	....	....	0.08	0.08	0.08	0.08
5. Remove work..		0.06	0.06	0.06	0.06	0.10	0.10	0.08	0.08	0.08	0.08
6. Remove dog...		....	....	....	....	0.08	0.08	....	....	....	....
7. Place dog.....		....	....	....	....	0.08	0.08	....	....	....	....
8. Clear chips....		....	....	....	....	0.05	0.05	0.08	0.08	0.08	0.08
9. Place piece....		0.08	0.08	0.08	0.08	0.08	0.08	0.12	0.12	0.12	0.12
10. Tighten.......		0.12	0.12	0.12	0.12	0.18	0.18	0.10	0.10	0.10	0.10
11. Start machine..		0.02	0.02	0.02	0.02	0.02	0.02	0.02	0.02	0.02	0.02
12. Advance to cut		0.04	0.06	0.04	0.06	0.04	0.04	0.04	0.06	0.04	0.06
13. Change depth.		*	*	*	*	*	*	*	*	*	*
14. Mill..........	2 ⅞† or 3 ⅝	M	M	M	M	M	M	M	M	M	M
15. Index‡.......		0.15	0.05	0.25	0.10	0.15	0.25	0.15	0.05	0.25	0.10
16. Return table...		0.05	0.07	0.05	0.07	0.05	0.05	0.05	0.07	0.05	0.07
TOTALS....		0.60	0.54	0.70	0.59	1.03	1.13	0.76	0.70	0.86	0.75

* Allow 0.08 when necessary.
† Feed in inches per minute—depending upon finish required.
‡ Above time is for rapid indexing. (Double indexing time when using precision crank.)

$$M = \text{Cutting time} = \frac{(L + OT) \times \text{No. cuts}}{\text{Feed}}$$

Base time = $H.T. + M$
Standard time = Base time + Allowances

The handling time is composed of machine-manipulation time and chucking and removing time as shown in Table XXVII. The cutting time can be calculated from the following formula:

$$M = \frac{(L + OT)\, N}{F}$$

Where: M = cutting time in minutes

L = length of cut in inches
    (a) $L = 0.707 \times B$ for square
    (b) $L = 0.5 \quad \times B$ for hexagon

OT = overtravel = $\frac{1}{2}$ diameter of mill in inches

N = number of cuts per piece
    (a) $N = 4$ for a square
    (b) $N = 6$ for a hexagon

F = table feed in inches per minute
    (a) for fine finish use $2\frac{7}{8}$ inches
    (b) for ordinary finish use $3\frac{5}{8}$ inches

Example: Assume that the shaft at the top of Table XXVIII has the following dimensions: $A = 1\frac{3}{4}$ inches; $B = 1$ inch; ordinary finish (feed = $3\frac{5}{8}$ inches per minute); mill square with $1\frac{3}{4}$-inch diameter, 6-lip mill; piece held in a 3-jaw chuck.

The handling time (HT) is obtained from Table XXVII, under method of chucking, 1, square, 6-lip mill, and is 0.60 minute.

The cutting time is calculated from the above formula.

$$M = \frac{(0.707 + 0.875)\, 4}{3.625} = \frac{6.328}{3.625} = 1.748$$

$L = 0.707 \times 1 = 0.707$
$OT = \frac{1}{2}$ of $1\frac{3}{4} = \frac{7}{8}$
$N = 4$
$F = 3.625$

$HT = 0.60$
$M = 1.748$

Total base time = 2.348
5 per cent allowance = 0.117

Total standard time = 2.465 use 2.5 minutes

Now with reference to Table XXVIII, since a single cutter is used and since A lies between the limits given, this table applies. Reading under symbol 8-D, the standard time equals 2.5 minutes which checks with that calculated above.

TABLE XXVIII

TIME-SETTING TABLE FOR MILLING SQUARE AND HEXAGON ON BOLTS, SCREWS, AND SHAFTS

Machine Class 36

Milling Table 1B

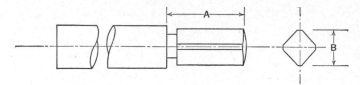

Case 1—Using a 6-Lip Mill (See Table 1C for Gang Mills)

Time per Piece in Minutes

Symbol	A (See Sketch Above)	B (See Sketch Above)	3-Jaw Chuck				On Centers				On Thread Arbor in Div. Head			
			Square		Hex.		Square		Hex.		Square		Hex.	
			Feed 2⅞	Feed 3⅝	Feed 2⅞	Feed 3⅝	Feed 2⅞	Feed 3⅝	Feed 2⅞	Feed 3⅝	Feed 2⅞	Feed 3⅝	Feed 2⅞	Feed 3⅝
			C	D	E	F	G	H	J	K	L	M	N	O
1		½	2.4	2.1	3.2	2.7	2.9	2.5	3.7	3.2	2.6	2.3	3.4	2.9
2		⁹⁄₁₆	2.5	2.1	3.3	2.8	3.0	2.6	3.7	3.2	2.7	2.3	3.5	2.9
3		⅝	2.6	2.1	3.3	2.8	3.0	2.6	3.8	3.3	2.8	2.4	3.5	3.0
4		¹¹⁄₁₆	2.6	2.2	3.5	2.9	3.1	2.7	3.9	3.4	2.8	2.4	3.6	3.1
5	⅝ in. to 1¾ in.	¾	2.7	2.3	3.5	3.0	3.2	2.8	4.0	3.4	2.9	2.5	3.7	3.1
6		¹³⁄₁₆	2.8	2.3	3.6	3.0	3.3	2.8	4.1	3.5	3.0	2.5	3.8	3.2
7		⅞	2.8	2.4	3.6	3.1	3.3	2.8	4.1	3.6	3.0	2.6	3.9	3.3
8		1	3.0	2.5	3.8	3.2	3.4	3.0	4.2	3.6	3.1	2.7	4.1	3.3
9		1⅛	3.1	2.6	4.0	3.3	3.5	3.0	4.4	3.7	3.3	2.8	4.2	3.4
10		1¼	3.2	2.7	4.1	3.4	3.7	3.2	4.5	3.9	3.4	2.9	4.3	3.6
11		1⅜	3.3	2.8	4.2	3.5	3.8	3.3	4.7	4.0	3.5	3.0	4.4	3.7
12		1½	3.5	2.9	4.4	3.6	4.0	3.4	4.8	4.1	3.7	3.1	4.5	3.8
13		1⅝	3.6	3.0	4.5	3.7	4.1	3.5	5.0	4.2	3.8	3.2	4.7	3.9

1. Values in this table vary as *B*, hence see that *A* falls within limits ⅝ in. to 1¾ in. before using data.
2. These time standards are based on:
   (a) Length of travel = *B* + overtravel
   (b) Handling time from Table 1A
   (c) Allowance of 5 per cent
3. Examples for reading above table:
   (a) Let *B* = ⅝ in., *A* = 1 in., Square head shaft, held on centers, 6-lip mill, 3⅝ in. feed. Since *A* lies between limits given this table applies. Read from table under 3-*H*, standard time = 2.6 min. per piece.
   (b) Let *B* = 1¼ in., *A* = 1½ in., Hexagon head bolt, held on thread arbor in div. head, 6-lip mill, 2⅞ in. feed. Since *A* lies between limits given this table applies. Read from table under 10-*N*, standard time = 4.3 min. per piece.

Computation of Data for Table XXIX—Milling by Use of Gang Mill. This milling operation is performed with a gang milling cutter; hence, two sides are cut at one time, two cuts being required for a square and three cuts for a hexagon. The direction of travel of the mill in making the cut is from the end toward the shoulder; hence the time for the cut varies as A and is independent of B provided it falls within the scope of the data, that is, provided the diameter of the shaft is between $\frac{1}{2}$ inch and $1\frac{5}{8}$ inches.

The total standard time for the operation is equal to the handling time (HT) plus the cutting time (M) plus the allowances. The handling time is taken directly from Table XXVII and the cutting time can be calculated from the following formula:

$$M = \frac{(L + OT)\,N}{F}$$

Where: M = cutting time in minutes

L = length of cut = A

OT = overtravel—since the direction of travel of the gang mill is from the end to the shoulder, no overtravel is allowed.

N = number of cuts per piece

(a) $N = 2$ for a square

(b) $N = 3$ for a hexagon

F = table feed in inches per minute

Example: The operation is that of milling hexagon on Tool Adjusting Screw, Part No. G12W-377A, as shown in Fig. 169. The following information is taken from the drawing (Fig. 169) and from the operation sheet (not shown): $A = 1\frac{1}{16}$ inch, $B = 0.578$ inch. 7-inch gang mill, ordinary finish, $3\frac{5}{8}$ inches per minute feed, piece held in 3-jaw chuck.

Handling time from Table XXVII = 0.59 minute.

Cutting time is calculated from the above formula.

$$M = \frac{(0.6875 + 0)\,3}{3.625} = 0.569 \text{ minute}$$

$L = 1\frac{1}{16} = 0.6875$
$OT = 0$
$N = 3$
$F = 3\frac{5}{8} = 3.625$

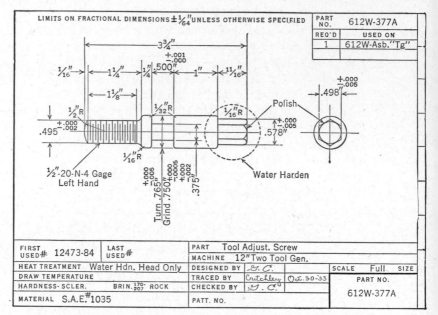

Fig. 169—Detail drawing of a tool adjusting screw, part G12W—377A.

Therefore the total time for the operation is:

$$HT = 0.59$$
$$M = 0.569$$

$$\text{Total base time} = 1.159$$
$$\text{5 per cent allowance} = 0.058$$

Total standard time = 1.217 use 1.25 minutes.

Now with reference to Table XXIX, since a gang mill is used and since B lies between the limits given, this table applies. Reading under symbol 2-F the standard time equals 1.25 minutes, which checks with that calculated above.

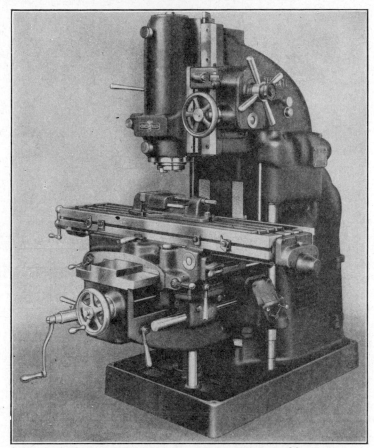

Fig. 170—Cincinnati vertical milling machine.

MACHINE DATA

Builder: Cincinnati Milling Machine Co.
Name of Machine: Cincinnati

Machine Class 30—Mach. No. 1817
Type of Machine: No. 3 Vertical

Specifications:

Table:
Working surface..........56" × 16½"
Size overall............60¼" × 16½"

Range:
Longitudinal.....................34"
Cross..........................14½"
Vertical knee....................14"
Head travel.....   8"
Quick traverse................Power

Spindle:
Size of taper........................14
No. of spindle speeds.................16
Range of spindle speeds.........15 to 414

Feed:
No. of feeds.........................16
Range of feeds......½" to 20" per min.

Table Feeds (in Inches per Minute)

½	1⅜	3⅝	9¾
⅝	1¾	4¾	12½
⅞	2¼	6⅛	16
1⅛	2⅞	7¾	20

Spindle Speeds in R.P.M.
Pulley Runs at 600 R.P.M.

15	37	86	214
19	47	118	269
23	58	134	335
29	72	166	414

TABLE XXIX

Time-Setting Table for Milling Square and Hexagon on Bolts, Screws, and Shafts

Machine Class 36

Milling Table 1c

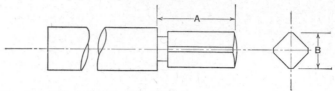

Case 2—Using Gang Mills (See 1*B* for 6-Lip Mill)

Time per Piece in Minutes

Symbol	A (See Sketch Above)	B (See Sketch Above)	3-Jaw Chuck				On Thread Arbor in Div. Head			
			Square		Hex.		Square		Hex.	
			Feed 2⅞	Feed 3⅝	Feed 2⅞	Feed 3⅝	Feed 2⅞	Feed 3⅝	Feed 2⅞	Feed 3⅝
			C	D	E	F	G	H	J	K
1	⅝		1.05	0.95	1.35	1.2	1.15	1.10	1.5	1.4
2	11⁄16		1.10	1.0	1.40	1.25	1.25	1.15	1.6	1.4
3	¾		1.15	1.05	1.5	1.25	1.35	1.20	1.7	1.5
4	13⁄16		1.20	1.05	1.6	1.30	1.35	1.25	1.7	1.5
5	⅞		1.20	1.10	1.6	1.35	1.40	1.25	1.8	1.6
6	15⁄16	½ in. to 1⅝ in.	1.25	1.15	1.7	1.45	1.45	1.30	1.8	1.7
7	1		1.35	1.20	1.8	1.50	1.50	1.35	1.9	1.7
8	1 1⁄16		1.35	1.20	1.9	1.5	1.6	1.35	2.0	1.8
9	1⅛		1.40	1.25	1.9	1.6	1.6	1.40	2.1	1.8
10	1 3⁄16		1.45	1.30	2.0	1.7	1.7	1.45	2.2	1.9
11	1¼		1.50	1.30	2.1	1.8	1.7	1.5	2.2	2.0
12	1⅜		1.60	1.40	2.2	1.9	1.8	1.6	2.4	2.1
13	1½		1.7	1.45	2.3	2.0	1.9	1.6	2.5	2.2
14	1⅝		1.8	1.6	2.5	2.1	2.0	1.7	2.6	2.3
15	1¾		1.9	1.6	2.6	2.2	2.1	1.8	2.7	2.4

1. Values in this table vary as *A*, hence see that *B* falls within limits ½ in. to 1⅝ in. before using data.
2. These time standards are based on:
    (*a*) Length of travel = *A*
    (*b*) Handling time from Table 1*A*
    (*c*) Allowance of 5 per cent
3. Examples for reading above table:
    (*a*) Let *A* = 1 in., *B* = 1 3⁄16 in., Square head bolt, held in chuck, gang mill, 3⅝ in. feed. Since *B* lies between limits given this table applies. Read from table under 7-*D* standard time = 1.20 min. per piece.
    (*b*) Let *A* = 11⁄16 in., *B* = 0.578 in., Hexagon head adjusting screw, held in chuck, gang mill, 3⅝ in. feed. Since *B* lies between limits given this table applies. Read from table under 2-*F*, standard time = 1.25 min. per piece.

CHAPTER 20

THE USE OF ELEMENTAL TIME DATA AND FORMULAS
TWO CASES: GEAR HOBBING AND SOLDERING CANS

TIME STANDARDS FOR GEAR HOBBING

The following example of the use of elemental time data and formulas for setting time standards of gear hobbing is included because it demonstrates how the principles already explained may be applied to rather complicated work. The data and procedure given here have been in constant use in a well-known machine-tool plant for a number of years and still serve their purpose satisfactorily.

Although the data apply to the cutting of both straight and helical spur gears, only those pertaining to cutting straight spur gears will be given here. These data are applicable to straight spur gears varying from 4 to 24 diametral pitch, of steel or cast iron and with round, square, or spline bore, either clean or copper plated. As the gears are used mostly on high-grade machine tools, the tooth surface and the running qualities of the gears must be maintained at a high standard. The speeds and feeds given in Tables XXXVII and XXXVIII were determined by experiment and were set to give this standard of quality. Number 12 Barber-Colman hobbers, such as that shown in Fig. 171, were used. The lot sizes of the gear blanks were small.

The following explanations concerning the several tables may make them more easily understood.

Table XXXII—Handling Time—Machine Manipulation. The time for machine manipulation will depend upon the way the gears are cut. Four different methods are shown. The time required to chuck and remove the gear is independent of the method of cutting and is shown in Table XXXIII.

Table XXXIII—Handling Time—Chucking and Removing. The data show that the time to chuck and remove the gears varies with the different types of bore, i.e., square, round, and spline, and also with the condition of the bore. When gears are casehardened it is frequently desirable to harden only the tooth surface so the blank is copper plated before cutting in order that only the surface where the copper plating has been removed will be affected. Owing to the copper plating on the bore, more time is required for chucking and removing as this table shows.

301

Fig. 171—Barber-Colman gear hobber.

MACHINE DATA

Machine class—No. 53B
Manufacturer—Barber-Colman
Used for—Spur gears, helical gears,
  sprockets, splining

Type of machine—hobber
Serial Nos.—1053, 1178, 1544, 1551, 1576

GENERAL SPECIFICATIONS

Capacity, diameter............... 12″
Capacity, width of face.......... 10″
Capacity, diametral pitch, cast iron   5
Capacity, diametral pitch, steel....   6
Diameter of hob spindle.......... 1¼″
Maximum diameter of hob........ 4″

Taper hole in spindle...........No. 12 B&S
Driving pulley...............14″ × 3¼″
Speed of driving pulley......300-400 r.p.m.
Number of changes of hob speed.......... 8
Hob speeds..............45 to 220 r.p.m
Range of feed.............. .015″ to .150′.

Floor space........................43″ × 76″
Net weight, approximately...............4600 lbs.

Table XXXVI—Overtravel Allowance. The overtravel required for rough hobbing is determined in the same manner as for milling. It is affected by the diameter of the hob and the depth of the cut.[1]

The ⅛-inch overtravel allowance for finishing hobbing is sufficient for clearance at the beginning and at the end of the cut.

[1] M. A. Lee and D. Vandevate, "Time Setting in a Machine Tool Plant," *Ind. Management,* Vol. 69, No. 3, p. 152, March, 1925.

TABLE XXX

Setup Time—Straight Spur Gears

Time in Minutes

Elements	Rough and Finish with Same Hob	Rough with Rough Hob. Finish with Finish Hob.
1. Ring clock, get drawing	2.00	2.00
2. Remove hob	0.60	0.60
3. Get hob and arbor from toolcrib	4.00	4.00
4. Place hob in machine	2.00	2.00
5. Set helix angle and check	1.00	1.00
6. Place and true-up arbor	6.00	6.00
7. Change index gearing	1.50	1.50
8. Check index gearing	2.65	2.65
9. Change speed gearing	0.75	0.75
10. Change feed gearing	1.50	1.50
11. Set for depth	0.75	0.75
12. Try for size (av. 3 trial cuts)	12.00	12.00
13. Ring clock	.....	2.00
14. Remove hob	.....	0.60
15. Place hob	.....	2.00
16. Set helix angle and check	.....	1.00
17. Change index gearing	.....	1.50
18. Change speed gearing	.....	0.75
19. Change feed gearing	.....	1.50
20. Set for depth	.....	0.75
21. Trial cuts (adjust index)	.....	5.00
TOTAL SETUP TIME	35.00	50.00

Cutting Time Formula:

$$M = \frac{N \times L}{F \times S \times H}$$

Where: M = cutting time in minutes
N = number of teeth
L = total length of cut (length of face plus overtravel)
F = feed in inches per revolution of work
S = speed of hob in r.p.m.
H = lead of hob
(a) single = 1
(b) double = 2

TABLE XXXI

Hob Change Time—Straight Spur Gears

Time in Minutes

1. Remove hob................................	.60
2. Place hob in machine..................	2.00
3. Set helix angle and check..............	1.00
4. Change index gearing.................	1.50
5. Check index gearing..................	2.65
6. Change speed gearing.................	.75
7. Change feed gearing..................	1.50
8. Make trial cuts......................	5.00
Total Hob Change Time..............	15.00

Hobbing is a continuous cutting action from the start to the finish of the travel of the hob across the entire gear face. One revolution of the work advances the hob a distance equal to the feed.

(1) $\dfrac{N \text{ (number of teeth)}}{H \text{ (lead of hob)}}$ = revolutions of hob per revolution of work

(2) $\dfrac{\dfrac{N}{H} \text{ (revolutions of hob per revolution of work)}}{S \text{ (speed of hob in r.p.m.)}}$ = time in minutes per revolution of work

(3) Since:

$\dfrac{L \text{ (the total length of face)}}{F \text{ (feed in inches per revolution of work)}}$ = number of revolutions of work required

(4) Then:

$$M = \dfrac{\dfrac{N}{H}}{S} \times \dfrac{L}{F} = \dfrac{N \times L}{F \times S \times H}$$

Example: In order to show how the data and formula are applied, the time required to hob a gear will be determined. It will be assumed that an order has been received for 20 Feed-Change Gears as shown in Fig. 172. The procedure is as follows:

1. The following necessary data are taken from the drawing of the gear (Fig. 172): Length of face = 1 inch, diametral pitch (*D.P.*) = 10, number of teeth (*N*) = 60, spline bore, S.A.E. 2315, hob S10R, plain spur gear.

TABLE XXXII

HANDLING TIME—STRAIGHT SPUR GEARS

Time in Minutes

A. Machine Manipulation

Procedure	Rough and Finish S. L. Hob		Rough with Rough Hob. Finish with Finish Hob.	Rough and Finish in One Cut.
	With Feed Change	No Feed Change		
1. Walk to machine..........	0.20	0.20	0.20	0.20
2. Run carriage back..........	0.15	0.15	0.15	0.15
3. Loosen arbor nut..........	0.09	0.09	0.09	0.09
4. Loosen and back steady rest.	0.08	0.08	0.08	0.08
5. Remove arbor nut..........	0.12	0.12	0.12	0.12
6. Remove gears..............	*	*	*	*
7. Chuck blanks..............	*	*	*	*
8. Set nut on arbor..........	0.20	0.20	0.20	0.20
9. Advance arbor steady rest..	0.12	0.12	0.12	0.12
10. Tighten nut on arbor.......	0.10	0.10	0.10	0.10
11. Loosen overarm nut........	0.06	0.06	....	....
12. Loosen 4 nuts on upright....	0.14	0.14	....	....
13. Set depth.................	0.15	0.15	....	....
14. Tighten 4 nuts on upright...	0.15	0.15	....	....
15. Tighten overarm nut.......	0.11	0.11	....	....
16. Change feed gearing........	1.50	....	....	....
17. Start machine.............	0.08	0.08	0.08	0.08
18. Feed in by hand...........	0.10	0.10	0.10	0.10
19. ROUGH CUT.............	M	M	M	M
20. Walk to machine..........	0.20	0.20	0.20	....
21. Run carriage back..........	0.15	0.15	0.15	....
22. Loosen arbor nut..........	....	....	0.09	....
23. Loosen and back steady rest.	....	....	0.08	....
24. Centerpunch gears.........	....	....	0.33	....
25. Remove arbor nut..........	....	....	0.12	....
26. Remove gears..............	....	....	*	....
27. Chuck gears and lineup.....	....	....	0.20	....
28. Set nut on arbor..........	....	....	0.20	....
29. Advance arbor steady rest...	....	....	0.12	....
30. Tighten nut on arbor.......	....	....	0.10	....
31. Loosen overarm nut........	0.06	0.06	....	....
32. Loosen 4 nuts on upright....	0.14	0.14	....	....
33. Set depth.................	0.15	0.15	....	....
34. Tighten 4 nuts on upright...	0.15	0.15	....	....
35. Tighten overarm nut.......	0.11	0.11	....	....
36. Change feed gearing........	1.50	....	....	....
37. Advance hob and set index..	....	....	1.00	....
38. Start machine.............	0.08	0.08	0.08	....
39. Feed in by hand...........	0.10	0.10	0.05	....
40. FINISH CUT.............	M	M	M	....
Hob change allowance........	0.30	0.30	0.30	0.30
Total handling time per chucking	6.29	3.29	4.26	1.54
" " " —roughing..			1.90	
" " " —finishing..			2.36	

* See Table XXXIII.

Note: When speed gearing must be changed between cuts add 1.50 minutes to total handling time.

2. Method of Cutting—from Table XXXIV. Use single lead hob on roughing and on finishing. Take a rough cut and a finish cut.
3. Setup Time—from Table XXX. Setup time = 35.00 minutes.
4. Number of Gears per Chucking—from Table XXXV.
   (A) Gears without hubs, 1-inch face or over, 3 per chucking.
5. Outside Diameter of Hob—from Table XXXIX. Hob S10R = 2.756 inches.

TABLE XXXIII

HANDLING TIME

B. Chucking and Removing

Time in Minutes

Bore	Chucking			Removing
	First Gear	Second Gear	Each Additional Gear	Any Number
1. Square bore—clean............	0.08	0.08	0.08	0.10
2. Square bore—copper-plated.....	0.25	0.20	0.15	0.25
3. Round bore—clean............	0.10	0.10	0.10	0.10
4. Round bore—copper-plated.....	0.25	0.20	0.15	0.25
5. Spline bore..................	0.10	0.08	0.08	0.20

TABLE XXXIV

METHOD OF CUTTING

Diametral Pitch	Material		Cast Iron
	Steel		
	Roughing	Finishing	Finishing
Over 16................	....	S.L.	All pitches one cut
16 and under...........	S.L.	S.L.	S.L.
except 4.......	D.L.	S.L.	S.L.

S.L = Single Lead Hob.   D.L. = Double Lead Hob.

TABLE XXXV

Number of Gears per Chucking

A. Gears without Hubs

Width of Face	Number per Chucking
1 in. or over.......	3
$1\frac{3}{16}$ in. to 1 in.	4
$\frac{5}{8}$ in. to $\frac{3}{4}$ in.	5
$\frac{1}{2}$ in. to $\frac{5}{8}$ in.	6
Under $\frac{1}{2}$ in.	7 or more

B. Gears with Hubs

1. When the hub projection is $\frac{1}{8}$ in. or less, add hub projection to width of face and use Table XXXV *A* above.
2. When the hub projection is greater than $\frac{1}{8}$ in., chuck not more than two blanks at one time.

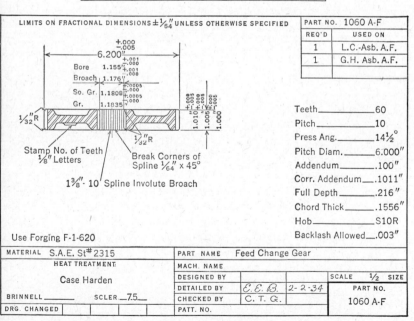

LIMITS ON FRACTIONAL DIMENSIONS $\pm\frac{1}{64}$" UNLESS OTHERWISE SPECIFIED

PART NO.	1060 A-F	
REQ'D	USED ON	
1	L.C.-Asb. A.F.	
1	G.H. Asb. A.F.	

6.200" +.000 −.005

Bore 1.155" +.001 −.000
Broach 1.176" +.001 −.000
So. Gr. 1.1808 +.0005 −.000
Gr. 1.1835 +.0005 −.000

$\frac{1}{32}$" R

$\frac{1}{32}$" R

Stamp No. of Teeth
$\frac{1}{8}$" Letters

Break Corners of Spline $\frac{1}{64}$" x 45°

$1\frac{3}{8}$". 10 Spline Involute Broach

Use Forging F-1-620

Teeth	60
Pitch	10
Press Ang.	$14\frac{1}{2}$°
Pitch Diam.	6.000"
Addendum	.100"
Corr. Addendum	.1011"
Full Depth	.216"
Chord Thick	.1556"
Hob	S10R
Backlash Allowed	.003"

MATERIAL	S.A.E. St# 2315		PART NAME	Feed Change Gear			
HEAT TREATMENT			MACH. NAME				
Case Harden			DESIGNED BY			SCALE	$\frac{1}{2}$ SIZE
			DETAILED BY	*E.E.B.*	2-2-34	PART NO.	
BRINNELL	SCLER 75		CHECKED BY	C.T.G.		1060 A-F	
DRG. CHANGED			PATT. NO.				

Fig. 172—Detail drawing of a change gear, part 1060A-F.

6. Speed of Hob—from Table XXXVII. For hob with $O.D.$ of 2.756 inches, S.A.E. 2315, speed = 138 r.p.m.
7. Feed—from Table XXXVIII. For $D.P.$ = 10, steel, ground hob, $S.L.$, rough and finish, feed = 0.050 inch per revolution.
8. Overtravel—from Table XXXVI.
    (A) Roughing, $D.P.$ = 10, $O.D.$ of Hob = 2¾ inches, overtravel = 0.74 inch.
    (B) Finishing = 0.125 inch.

TABLE XXXVI

OVERTRAVEL ALLOWANCE

A. Roughing

D.P.	Full Depth In Inches	Overtravel in Inches*							
		Outside Diameter of Hob in Inches							
		2	2¼	2½	2¾	3	3½	4	5
24	0.090	0.42	0.44	0.47	0.49	0.51	0.55		
20	0.108	0.45	0.48	0.51	0.54	0.56	0.61		
16	0.135	0.50	0.53	0.57	0.59	0.62	0.67		
14	0.154	0.53	0.57	0.60	0.63	0.66	0.72		
12	0.180	0.57	0.61	0.65	0.68	0.71	0.77	0.83	
10	0.216	0.62	0.66	0.70	0.74	0.78	0.85	0.90	1.02
8	0.270	......	0.73	0.78	0.82	0.86	0.93	1.00	1.13
7	0.301	......	......	0.82	0.86	0.90	0.98	1.06	1.19
6	0.360	......	......	......	0.93	0.97	1.06	1.15	1.29
5	0.432	......	......	......	......	1.05	1.15	1.24	1.40
4	0.540	......	......	......	......	1.15	1.26	1.37	1.55

* Derived from formula $O = \sqrt{h(2r-h)}$
  Where O = overtravel
      h = full depth of gear tooth
      r = radius of hob

B. Finishing—0.125 inch Overtravel Allowed

9. Calculation of Cutting Time—from formula on page 303.

$$M = \frac{N \times L}{F \times S \times H}$$

	Roughing	Finishing
$N =$	60	60
$L =$	(3 + .74)	(3 + 0.125)
$F =$	0.050	0.050
$S =$	138	138
$H =$	1	1

TABLE XXXVII

SPEED TABLE

Speed of Hob in Revolutions per Minute

Outside Diameter of Hob in Inches	Cast Iron		Rough and Finish S.A.E. 2315	Rough and Finish S.A.E. 1035	Rough and Finish S.A.E. 1020
	Rough (Double Lead) S.A.E. 2315	Rough (Single Lead) S.A.E. 2315	Rough Only S.A.E. 1035	Finish Only S.A.E. 2315 / Rough Only S.A.E. 1020	Finish Only S.A.E. 1035 / S.A.E. 1020
			Cutter Speed Feet Per Minute		
	90	100	110	125	140
2.00	161	189	189	189	189
2.20	161	189	189	189	189
2.40	138	161	189	189	189
2.50	138	161	161	189	189
2.60	138	138	161	189	189
2.75	120	138	138	161	189
2.90	120	138	138	161	189
3.00	110	120	138	161	189
3.10	110	120	138	161	189
3.25	110	120	138	138	161
3.40	110	110	120	138	161
3.50	110	110	120	138	161
3.75	82	110	110	120	161
4.00	82	82	110	120	138
4.25	82	82	82	110	138
4.50	76	82	82	110	120

Roughing:

$$M = \frac{60 \times (3 + 0.74)}{0.050 \times 138 \times 1} = 32.5$$

Finishing:

$$M = \frac{60 \times (3 + 0.125)}{0.050 \times 138 \times 1} = 27.2$$

Total cutting time = 32.5 + 27.2 = 59.7 minutes

10. Determination of Total Handling Time.

(A) Machine Manipulation—from Table XXXII column 2 (no feed change) = 3.29 minutes.

TABLE XXXVIII

Feed Table

Feed in Inches per Revolution of Work

Material	Steel				C.I.
Cut	Roughing	Roughing	Rough and Finish	Finishing	Rough and Finish
Lead of Hob	Single or Double	Single or Double	Single	Single	Single
Kind of Hob	Form	Ground	Ground	Ground	Ground
Dia. Pitch					
24	....	....	0.050	0.050	0.090
20	....	....	0.050	0.050	0.0875
16	....	....	0.050	0.050	0.0875
14	....	....	0.050	0.050	0.0834
12	....	....	0.050	0.050	0.0834
10	0.070	0.125	0.050	0.050	0.070
9	0.070	0.125	0.050	0.050	0.070
8	0.070	0.125	0.050	0.050	0.070
7	0.070	0.1125	0.045	0.045	0.0643
6	0.070	0.100	0.045	0.045	0.0643
5	0.0643	0.09375	0.041	0.041	0.0643
4	0.060	0.090	0.041	0.041	0.060

Feed changes between cuts are practicable only when the cuts are exceptionally long, and the change will make an appreciable net saving of time.

(*B*) Chucking and Removing—from Table XXXIII, spline, three blanks, chucking = 0.26 minute, removing = 0.20, total = 0.46 minute. Total handling time = 3.29 + .46 = 3.75 minutes.

11. Determination of Total Standard Time.

Total handling time for three gears	= 3.75
Total cutting time for three gears	= 59.7
Total base time for three gears	63.45
5 per cent allowance	3.17
Total standard time for three pieces	66.62

Total time for one piece = $\dfrac{66.62}{3}$ = 22.2 minutes.

TABLE XXXIX

Hob List

Hob No.	Hob O.D.	Hob No.	Hob O.D.	Hob No.	Hob O.D.	Hob No.	Hob O.D.
S24R	2.484	R277R	3.509	S8–10R	2.746	S5RD	3.210
S20R	2.502	S10R	2.756	S8–10L	3.006	S5R	3.989
S16–21R	3.529	S10RD	2.691	S7–R	2.934	S5L	3.989
S16R	2.407	S10–12R	2.738	4MR	3.028	R68R	3.367
S16RD	2.518	S9R	2.331	S6RD	3.594	R76L	4.063
S14R	2.500	R37R	2.315	S6R	3.381	S4RD	
S13R	2.933	R38L	2.393	S6L	3.251	S4R	4.501
S12R	2.749	S8RD		S6–8R	3.014	S4L	3.695
S12L	2.848	S8R	2.974	S6RD	3.210	S4R–20°	3.913
S11R	2.162	S8L	2.974	R555L	3.915		

TIME STANDARDS FOR SOLDERING SIDE SEAMS ON BODY OF CAN

Rectangular cans similar in shape to the one shown in Fig. 173 are made for export shipment of drawing and surgical instruments. Lot sizes are usually small and sixty different can sizes ranging in volume from a few cubic inches to one cubic foot are made. The total production of cans of any one size is not large enough to justify special can-making equipment.

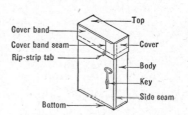

FIG. 173—Rectangular can for export shipment of instruments.

Operations in the Manufacture of Cans:

On Body:

1. Cut or slit body to length and width.
2. Make 4 breaks on the bar folder.
3. Solder the side seam.

On Cover:

1. Cut or slit cover band to length and width.
2. Punch hole in rip-strip tab.
3. Mark and make cut for loose end of the rip-strip and fold tab back 90 degrees.
4. Make first break on bar folder.

On Tops and Bottoms:
1. Cut to length and width.
2. Miter four corners.
3. Fold four sides.

Assembly:
1. Form cover band to body and solder band seam.
2. Solder the top to the cover, solder the bottom to the body, and then solder rip-strip key to the body.
3. Inspect, wash, and dry.

Since it is the primary purpose of this case to illustrate the application of principles, but one of the operations listed above will be considered in detail here. It is: "Solder the side seam of the body."

Determination of Standard Time for "Solder the Side Seam of the Body." It was found most satisfactory to use stop-watch studies for securing all of the data except those for the "soldering" element. Micromotion studies were used for that element.

Definition of Standard Elements for Soldering the Side Seam:

1. Position piece on rod and apply the flux to the seam.
   The time begins as the last finished can is released by the hand to a tote box.

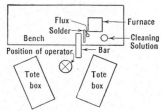

FIG. 174—Layout of work place for soldering rectangular cans.

The time ends as the hand completes the application of the flux and starts to move towards the soldering iron in the furnace.

2. Tack [2] the seam and then pick up the holder and position it on the can so as to hold the seam tightly together.
   The time begins as the hand starts toward the soldering iron from the preceding element.
   The time ends as the hand again starts toward the soldering iron in the furnace after positioning holder.

3. Solder the full length of the seam.
   The time begins as the hand starts toward the soldering iron in the furnace.
   The time ends as the hand releases the iron after disposing of it in the furnace.

4. Wipe the seam with a damp cloth and dispose.
   The time begins as the iron is released upon disposal in the furnace.
   The time ends as the hand releases the can into the tote box.

---

[2] "Tack" refers to placing a drop of solder on the seam to hold it in the correct position while it is being soldered. A long seam requires that more points be tacked than does a short seam.

Standard Time for Elements:

<table>
<tr><td></td><td align="center">*Elements*</td><td align="center">*Time Standard*
in Minutes per 100 *Cans*</td></tr>
</table>

1. Position piece on rod and apply the flux to seam 14.0
   This element is a constant for cans of all sizes.
2. Tack the seam and then pick up the holder and position it on the can to hold the seam tightly together.
   (*a*) Untacked (seams under 3 inches in length)   0
   (*b*) Two tacks per seam (seams 3.1 inches to 12 inches long) 16.0
   (*c*) Three tacks per seam (seams 12.1 inches to 24 inches long) 23.0

If the seam is under 3 inches in length this element is not required. If the seam is between 3.1 inches and 12 inches in length it must be tacked at two places and clamped with a special holder before soldering. If between 12.1 inches and 24 inches long the seam must be tacked at three points and clamped. Time standards were determined by stop-watch studies.

3. Solder the full length of the seam.

The operator grasps the soldering iron, dips it in the pot of cleaning solution, touches it against the bar of solder, and moves it to the seam and draws the tip of the iron along the seam, soldering it until the supply of solder on the iron is used up. The iron is then returned to the bar of solder for a new supply and the soldering operation is repeated. If the seam has been tacked, fewer contacts of the iron against the bar of solder will be needed.

(*a*) Grasp iron, dip in cleaning pot and dispose of iron to furnace = 0.08 minute, a constant per seam or series of seams. (From micromotion study.)

(*b*) Solder seam.

From a micromotion study of soldering seams of various lengths it was found that there was a straight line relationship between the time in minutes to solder a seam and the length of the seam in inches. This can be expressed as follows:

Time for soldering = $L \times 0.014$

(L = length of seam to be soldered in inches.)

(*c*) Touch iron to solder and move to seam = $N \times 0.04$ minute.
N = the number of dips necessary for seam. Table XL.

4. Wipe the seam with a damp cloth and dispose = 10.0 minutes per 100 cans—a constant for cans of all sizes.

TABLE XL

(N = Number of dips of iron against solder per seam)

Value of N	Seam Lengths in Inches	
	Untacked	Tacked
1	0– 6.0	0–10.0
2	6.1–12.0	10.1–20.0
3	12.1–18.0	20.1–30.1
4	18.1–24.0	
5	24.1–30.0	

(From stop-watch studies and micromotion studies)

Auxiliary Elements:

5. Handling of empty and full tote boxes. This time varies with the size of the can.

Handling time for the cans = $P \times 0.0009$ minute. ($P =$ the sum of the length, width, and depth of the can in inches.) From all-day stop-watch studies.

6. Filing, forging, and retinning soldering irons require 24 minutes per 525-minute day, or 4.6 per cent of the day. From all-day stop-watch studies.

The Sum of All Constant Elements:

Time Standard
in Minutes per
100 Cans

1. Position piece on rod and apply flux to the seam .... = 14.0
2. Tack seam and then pick up the holder and position it on the can
   (a) .... = 0.0
   (b) .... = 16.0
   (c) .... = 23.0
3. Wipe the seam with a damp cloth and dispose .... = 10.0

Formula for Determining Time Standard:

$$
\begin{bmatrix} \text{Standard Time} \\ \text{in Minutes per} \\ 100 \text{ Cans} \end{bmatrix} = 100 \left\{ \begin{bmatrix} \text{Time for} \\ \text{Constant} \\ \text{Elements} \end{bmatrix} + \begin{bmatrix} \text{Time for} \\ \text{Solder-} \\ \text{ing} \end{bmatrix} + \begin{bmatrix} \text{Time for} \\ \text{Handling} \\ \text{Can} \end{bmatrix} \right\} + \begin{bmatrix} \text{Time for} \\ \text{Maintain-} \\ \text{ing Iron} \end{bmatrix}
$$

$$
= 100 \ \{ D + [0.08 + (L \times 0.014) + (N \times 0.04)] + [P \times 0.0009] \}
$$
$$
+ 4.6 \{ D + [0.08 + (L \times 0.014) + (N \times 0.04)] + [P \times 0.0009] \}
$$
$$
= 104.6 \{ D + [0.08 + (L \times 0.014) + (N \times 0.04)] + [P \times 0.0009] \}
$$

TABLE XLI

(D = The sum of all constant elements)

Values of D in Min. per Can	Seam Lengths in Inches	No. of Tacks
0.24	under 3.0	0
0.40	3.0–12.0	2
0.47	12.1–24.0	3

Where:

L = the length of the seam to be soldered in inches
N = the number of dips necessary to complete the seam (from Table XL)
P = the sum of the length, width, and depth of the can in inches
D = the sum of all constants (from Table XLI)

Application of the Formula:

Can 439 has the following dimensions:

length   8⅝ inches
width   ¾ inch
depth   10⅛ inches

Values of above terms are:

L = 10.125
N = 2.0
P = 19.5
D = 0.40

Substituting these values in the formula, we have

Std. = $104.6\{0.40+0.08+(10.125\times0.014)+(2\times0.04)+19.5\times0.0009)\}$
= $104.6(0.40+0.08+0.142+0.08+0.0176)$
= 104.6×0.7196 = 75.27,   Use 75.3 minutes.

Although the method of setting up a formula for determining the time standard for soldering the side seam has been presented in some detail, it is not necessary to go through this rather long procedure for each new lot or for each new can size. This formula applies to the operation "solder side seam" for all rectangular cans of any size falling within the range of the studies. In fact, it is not even necessary to use the formula, for tables have been constructed from computations made with the formula and from these tables it is a very simple matter to determine the time standard for soldering operations on a can of any size.   These tables are as easy to use as the mileage chart on a road map.

Results.   Before standardizing the arrangement of the work place and the method of making the cans, all time standards were set by individual stop-watch studies.   Since but few can sizes had been studied most of this work was not on wage incentive.

After the completion of the standardization program and the computation of the tables for setting time standards, it was possible to determine quickly the time standard for the soldering operations on a can of any size.

Decrease in labor costs resulting from improved methods and from the application of time standards and wage incentives to soldering operations in can making brought about a saving of approximately $4000 per year.   A total of 510 hours were spent by the analyst in completing the motion and time study work on this project.

CHAPTER 21

DETERMINING TIME STANDARDS FOR DIE AND TOOL WORK

Tool-room work is one of the most difficult of all industrial operations to standardize and place on wage incentive. This is true because the making of tools and dies requires a high degree of accuracy and the work is non-repetitive since rarely is more than one tool of a given design required. Highly skilled die makers are required for this work and on some operations a considerable amount of hand filing, scraping, and fitting may be required along with the machine work. Although it may seem that no two tools are alike, yet all tools of a given class have similar parts, and each part requires similar operations for its manufacture. The variation in the time required for the same operation on similar parts is due to different characteristics of the particular part, such as its size and the kind of material. It is possible here, as it was in the several cases in preceding chapters, to separate each operation into those elements that remain constant and those elements that vary with the size, shape, or other characteristic of the part.

The material to be presented in this chapter is taken from an outstanding piece of work done by Floyd R. Spencer in standardizing the die and tool work in a large industrial plant. This included compiling elemental time data, and constructing charts and formulas for determining time standards. Using these standards, a wage incentive system was installed which materially reduced the cost of this work. The tool makers had confidence in this method of setting time standards and believed it to be far superior to the rather crude method of "estimating" time on such work, as practiced in most tool rooms. The incentive plan based on these time standards permits the tool makers to earn substantially more wages than formerly.

•The time required to determine the standard time by means of charts, curves, and formulas is one-fourth to one-half that required for estimating as formerly done. For example, it takes 3 to 5 minutes to set the time standards for all operations required in making the plain blanking die shown in Figs. 175 and 176, whereas it would take 10 to 15 minutes to "estimate" the time by the old procedure. One

317

person now determines time standards for a department employing 125 tool makers, whereas in most shops one estimator is needed for every 30 tool makers employed.

Types of Dies. The various types of dies for which standard data are now available are:

1. Plain Blanking
2. Compound Blank and Perforate
3. Single and Multiple Perforator
4. Shearing
5. Blank and Draw
6. Forming
7. Miscellaneous

Plain Blanking Dies. The plain blanking die (such as the one shown in Fig. 175) will be used as an illustration because of its simplicity and general use. An explanation will be given of the method used in classifying all blanking work, the way the elemental time data, charts, and formulas were established, and finally a specific case will be given to show how the standard time is established for making a particular die.

The tool room for which these data apply normally employs 125 tool makers and serves a manufacturing plant employing 4000 to 5000 workers. The products manufactured are widely diversified in kind and are fairly small in size.

The first step in establishing a method for setting time standards on making blanking dies was to classify all blanks that would normally be manufactured by this type of die. A survey of all such work led to the following general classification:

1. Round blanks
2. Square or rectangular blanks
3. All blanks of other shapes

Under the general classifications of pieces with round outlines and those with square or rectangular outlines a further classification must be made in regard to projections or indentations. It is generally advisable to use inserts for projections or indentations on the piece in question. These inserts would be used in the pad and punch (see Figs. 175 and 176) for projections and in the die block for indentations. The inserts are used because of the low repair cost in breakage of these projections. A complete classification of blanks is given in Table XLII.

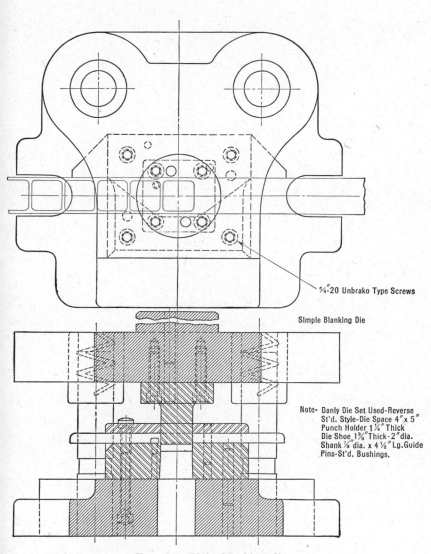

¼"-20 Unbrako Type Screws

SImple Blanking Die

Note- Danly Die Set Used-Reverse
St'd. Style-Die Space 4"x 5"
Punch Holder 1¼" Thick
Die Shoe 1⅜"Thick-2"dia.
Shank ⅞"dia. x 4½"Lg.Guide
Pins-St'd. Bushings.

FIG. 175—Plain blanking die.

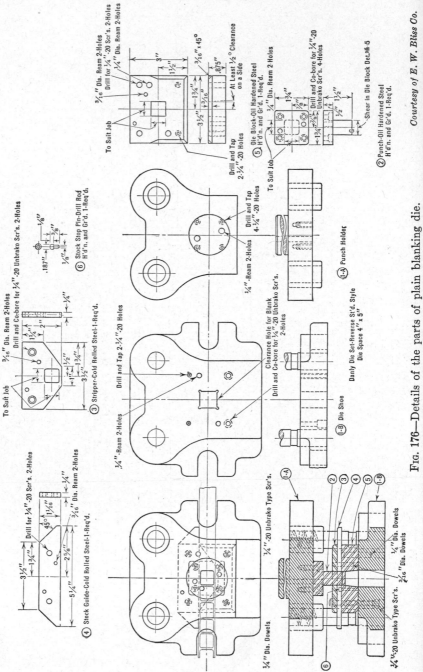

FIG. 176—Details of the parts of plain blanking die.

Courtesy of E. W. Bliss Co.

Courtesy of E. W. Bliss Co.

FIG. 177—Inclined punch press, No. 21 Bliss.

This photograph shows an operator blanking, forming, and piercing bicycle bell bases at the rate of 1300 per hour. The material is cold rolled steel, 0.035 inch stock.

TABLE XLII

CLASSIFICATION OF WORK DONE ON PLAIN BLANKING DIES

Classification	No. 1	No. 2	No. 3
Shape of Blank	Round blanks	Square or rectangular blanks	All blanks of other shapes
	Round..........	Plain outline.....	(a) Blanks whose outline is made up of smooth curves and straight lines or a combination of the first two classifications.
	Round with indentations........	With indentations	(b) Blanks whose outline is very irregular, having no similarity with blanks of round or straight-sided outline.
	Round with projections.........	With projections..	
Size of blank	½-in. diam. to 4 in. diam.	$\tfrac{3}{8} \times 1\tfrac{1}{2}$ in. to $5\tfrac{1}{2} \times 7$ in.	Same range as in classifications No. 1 and 2

It is customary to purchase the die sets from manufacturers specializing in making these parts. The die set consists of two parts as Figs. 175 and 176 show, namely the punch holder, part 1A, and the die shoe, part IB. The classification of die sets is given in Table XLIII.

TABLE XLIII

PURCHASED DIE SETS CLASSIFIED BY SIZE RANGE

Size in Inches

Symbol	B1	B2	B3	B4	B5	B6	B7	B8
Maximum size round blank	$1\frac{3}{8}$	$1\frac{7}{8}$	$2\frac{3}{8}$	$3\frac{1}{8}$	$3\frac{7}{8}$	$4\frac{1}{4}$	5	6
Maximum size rectangular blank.......	$\frac{3}{8}\times1\frac{1}{2}$	$\frac{1}{2}\times2$	$1\frac{1}{8}\times2\frac{3}{8}$	$2\frac{1}{4}\times3\frac{1}{4}$	3×4	$4\frac{1}{4}\times4\frac{1}{4}$	$4\frac{1}{2}\times7$	$5\frac{1}{2}\times7$

Parts of a Blanking Die. The principle of a plain blanking die is very simple. The strip of sheet metal stock to be blanked is fed in the die from right to left as shown in Fig. 175. The punch, which is the shape of the blank to be made, is moved downward by the action of the press (see Fig. 177) and punches a piece from the stock, the blank being forced through the die block by the punch. The stripper removes the stock from the punch as it returns to its normal position.

Figure 175 shows an assembly drawing of a plain blanking die and Fig. 176 shows the component parts of this die. A list of all the parts of this die is given here:

1A Punch Holder ⎫
1B Die Shoe ⎬ Die Set (purchased)
                   ⎭
2 Punch
3 Stripper
4 Stock Guide
5 Die Block
6 Stock Stop Pin (a standard part)

Operations on Punch Holder—Part 1A. Although the die sets, composed of punch holder and die shoe, were purchased from an outside source, the following operations were performed on these parts:

Operation 1 Set up mill, mill stem to height
Operation 2 Lay out, drill and tap for screw holes, drill and ream for dowels

The next step was to determine the variables or the basic factors that governed the time required for each operation and the percentage of the extent of total time that each factor controlled.

Percentage

Operation 1   Size and weight of punch holder   100
Operation 2   Number of screw and dowel holes   85
              Size and weight of punch holder   15

In the tool room actual studies were made of the operations required to machine the punch holder. Data were taken for many different sizes and weights and finally after being checked and tested for accuracy these data were compiled in tabular form for convenient use as shown in Tables XLIV and XLV.

Operations on Die Block—Part 5. The die block is perhaps the most important part of the tool and it must be made accurately in order to produce blanks to meet production requirements. In determining time standards for making the die block the following procedure was used:

1. A list was made of all variables or governing factors that would in any way affect the time required to make the die block. These were:

    a. Length of outline of blank
    b. Number of inside angles
    c. Number of sides (0.250 inch in length or over)
    d. Number of radii
    e. Curves on blank whose center is outside of blank
    f. Specifications of stock to be blanked

2. A list was made of the operations which the tool maker must perform to make the die block, and the factors which have a bearing on the time required were noted. (See Table XLVI.)

3. Time standards were determined for each operation over the entire range of the governing factors. This was a much more difficult task than determining time standards for making the punch holder because so many more variables entered into making the die block. Approximately 100 die blocks of every conceivable shape were studied and a considerable period of time was required for securing and classifying these data, and for establishing correct relationships.

Curves for Setting Time Standard for Operation 4. Of the seven operations required to make the die block, perhaps the most interesting one for illustrative purposes is operation 4, "Work out shape through block." The five variables or factors which govern the time

TABLE XLIV

Governing Factor—Size of Die Set Required to Blank Part

Time in Hours

Operation No.	Percentage of Time Controlled by Factor	Symbol of Purchased Die Set Sizes							
		B1	B2	B3	B4	B5	B6	B7	B8
1	100	0.70	0.75	0.78	0.80	0.88	0.96	1.08	1.22
2	15	0.10	0.15	0.21	0.27	0.32	0.39	0.44	0.50

TABLE XLV

Governing Factor—Number of Screws and Dowels

Time in Hours

Operation No.	Percentage of Time Controlled by Factor	3 Screws 2 Dowels	4 Screws 2 Dowels	6 Screws 2 Dowels	8 Screws 3 Dowels	12 Screws 4 Dowels	14 Screws 6 Dowels	18 Screws 8 Dowels	20 Screws 10 Dowels
2	85	0.50	0.65	0.85	1.10	1.39	1.70	2.10	2.30

TABLE XLVI

OPERATIONS AND GOVERNING FACTORS FOR DIE BLOCK—PART 5

Operation No.	Operation	Governing Factor
1	Cutoff......................	(a) Grade of material
		(b) Size of piece
2	Machine to size—Grind all over	(a) Grade of material
		(b) Size of piece
3	Layout shape on block surface	(a) Length of outline
		(b) Number of inside angles
		(c) Number of sides
		(d) Number of radii
		(e) Number of curves with centers outside blank
4	Work out shape through block	(a) Same factors as above— Operation 3
5	Drill and tap screw holes, drill and ream dowel holes.........	(a) Number of screw and dowel holes
		(b) Size of holes
6	Harden.....................	(a) Grade of material
7	Grind......................	(a) Grade of material
		(b) Size of piece

required for performing this operation are listed in Table XLVI. The curves in Fig. 178 show the relationship between the variables and the time required. These data are also given in Table XLVII.

Example: To determine the time required to perform operation 4, "Work out shape through die block," for the blank shown in Fig. 179 the procedure would be as follows:

			Curve (Fig. No.)	Standard Time In Hours
(a) Outline in inches [1]	....	10.75	178a	9.00
(b) Inside angles	....	4	178b	2.50
(c) Number of sides	....	12	178c	5.00
(d) Number of radii	....	6	178d	1.75
(e) Number of radii with centers outside	....	0	—	—
Total standard time in hours for operation		4		18.25

[1] The outline of irregular dies is determined by means of a map measure—a simple instrument reading distance directly in inches.

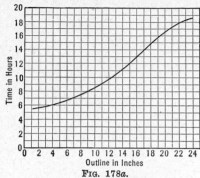

FIG. 178a.
PLAIN BLANKING DIE.
Part 5.—Die Block.
Op. 4.—Work out shape through block.
Factor (a).—Length of outline of blank.

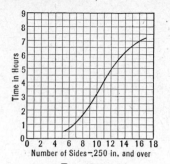

Number of Sides—.250 in. and over
FIG. 178c.
PLAIN BLANKING DIE.
Part 5.—Die Block.
Op. 4.—Work out shape through block.
Factor (c).—Number of sides.—
0.250 in. or over.

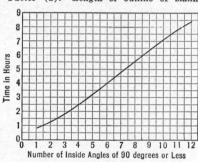

Number of Inside Angles of 90 degrees or Less
FIG. 178b.
PLAIN BLANKING DIE.
Part 5.—Die Block.
Op. 4.—Work out shape through block.
Factor (b).—Number of inside angles of
90 degrees or less.

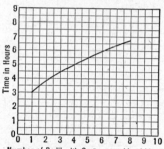

Number of Radii with Centers outside of blank
FIG. 178e.
PLAIN BLANKING DIE.
Part 5.—Die Block.
Op. 4.—Work out shape through block
Factor (e).—Number of curves
with centers outside of blank.

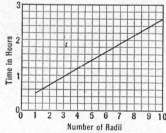

Number of Radii
FIG. 178d.
PLAIN BLANKING DIE.
Part 5.—Die Block.
Op. 4.—Work out shape through block
Factor (d).—Number of radii.

FIG. 178—Curves for setting time standards for operation 4 on die block—plain blanking die.

TABLE XLVII

STANDARD TIME FOR PERFORMING OPERATION 4

WORK OUT SHAPE THROUGH DIE BLOCK

Time in Hours

(a) Outline in inches......	1	3	6	10	12	14	18	20	24
Time...............	5.5	5.9	6.9	8.5	9.6	11.3	15.0	16.7	18.7
(b) Inside angles, 90° or less.	1	2	3	4	5	6	8	10	12
Time...............	0.8	1.2	1.75	2.6	3.3	4.1	5.6	7.1	8.4
(c) Number of sides (length 0.250 inch and over).	5	6	7	8	9	10	12	14	16
Time...............	0.5	0.7	1.1	1.7	2.3	3.3	4.9	6.2	6.9
(d) Number of radii.......	1	2	3	4	5	6	8	10	
Time...............	0.5	0.7	0.9	1.2	1.4	1.7	2.1	2.6	
(e) Number of radii, centers outside............	1	2	3	4	5	6	7	8	
Time...............	3.0	3.8	4.5	5.0	5.5	5.9	6.3	6.7	

The standard curves shown in Fig. 178 cover all possible combinations of contour and size affecting operation 4. Space does not permit the inclusion of the curves and data for the other operations on the die block. The same procedure was followed not only for the remaining operations on the die block but also for all operations on the other parts of the blanking die.

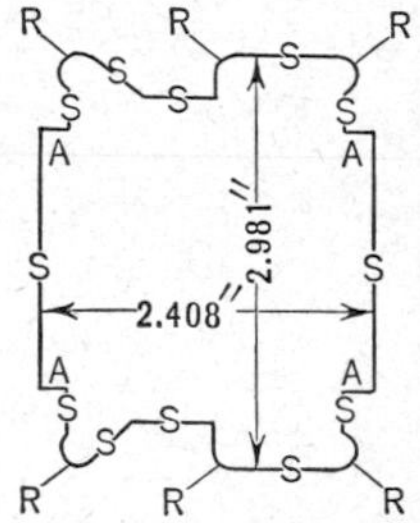

In a similar manner elemental data, charts, curves, and formulas were developed for the seven classes of dies listed on page 318.

Quality Classification. It is necessary to show how the quality of the tool enters into the determination of the time standard for making the die.

FIG. 179—Shape of blank. A. Inside angles; R. Radii; S. Sides.

The quality requirements for a die depend upon the following factors:

1. Appearance of the product
2. Total production requirements of the product
3. Use of the product
4. Working action of the parts produced
5. Cost factors of the products

A study of the above factors resulted in the establishment of the following quality classification:

Class C—Reading from curves and charts—direct
Class B—Reading from curves and charts multiplied by 112 per cent
Class A—Reading from curves and charts multiplied by 130 per cent

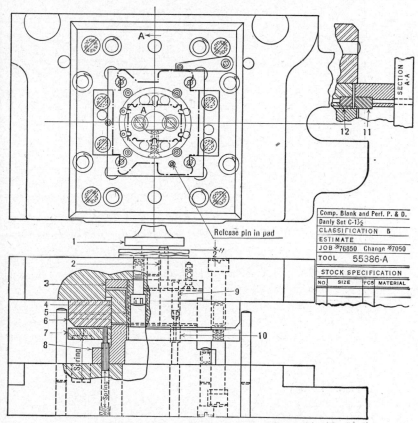

FIG. 180—Compound blank and perforate die.

The decision as to the classification of the various punches and dies is made before they are designed and the classification is noted on the drawings when they are made.

TABLE XLVIII

Chart No.	Part of Punch and Die	Base of Chart (abscissa)
20–21–22	Pad — blank punch — stripper — punch plate	Outline in inches—Number of sides with angles 90° or less
5–7–13	Die shoe—punch holder—assembly work—hardening and miscellaneous	Size of die set
8	Perforators A. Round B. Square and rectangular C. Odd-shaped	A. Diameter of perforator B. Outline of perforator C. Outline of rough stock—Number of angles Outline of perforator—Length of slots
10	Placing round center holes through pad and punch—not center	Diameter of perforator
11	Placing square, square with indentations and projections, and odd-shaped holes through pad — punch—die shoe	Outline of perforator—Number of angles—Number of curves—Number of projections—Length of slot 0.125 wide and under
12	Bushings	Diameter of perforator—Number required
13	Minor curves	Number of curves requiring additional filing
13A	Inside radii	Number of radii requiring additional filing
14	Projections and indentations in blanking or perforating punch (with or without inserts)	Number of projections or indentations
14A	Projections and indentations (continued)	Length of outline for stock removed

The Wage-Incentive Application. Since punch-press parts usually require a series of operations for their manufacture, the several dies required to make a part completely are designed at one time. It is customary to design each tool in assembly, showing the construction of the tool, listing the material required, and indicating any special features but not showing the individual parts in detail. Time standards are then established by the method already described. The order for the series of tools is then given to a group leader in the tool room

TABLE XLIX

CALCULATION OF STANDARD TIME FOR BLANK AND PERFORATE PUNCH AND DIE

Compound Die Shown in Fig. 180

Chart Number	Information Required	Information Applicable to Die in Figure 180	Reading from Curves—Standard Time in Hours
20 and 21	Outline of blank	10¾	34
22	Number of sides	18	17¾
	Outside angles 90° or less	6	4¾
5–7–13	Size of die set	C1½	27¼
	General outline	Square	
	Total number of perforations	5	1¼
8A	Number of perforators	4	2¼
	Diameter of perforators	0.068	
	Type—Perforator	Type B	
8B	Outline of perforator	5¼	5¾
	Number of perforators	1	
8C	Outline of stock from which blank is made		
	90° angles or less		
	Width up to 0.125 in.		
	Outline of perforator		
10	Number of perforators	4	6
	Diameter of perforators	0.068	
11A	Outline of perforator	5¼	9¼
	Number of projections on perforator punch	10	11
11B	Number of 90° angles or less		
	If form of slot 0.125 wide or less— Length		
12	Number of bushings	4	2½
	Size of inside diameter	0.068	
13	Number of minor curves		
13A	Number of radii	6	8½
14	Number of projections or indentations	10	50½
14A	Length of outline for stock removed		

Standard Time   180.75 hrs.

Quality Classification $C = 180.75$
" " $B = 180.75 \times 112 = 202.44$. Use 205 hours.

to whom is assigned as many assistants as can do the job efficiently. These tool makers complete the entire series of tools for a given part as a group and share in the savings through a bonus which is based upon the difference between the time actually used and the time standard set for the job. At the completion of this series of tools the group dissolves and new groups are formed for other tools.

Compound Blank and Perforate Dies. Compound blank and perforate dies are more complicated than plain blanking dies in that the compound dies have more parts. The method, however, for standardizing and establishing standard data for making these dies is exactly like that already described for the plain blanking die.

Space does not permit the presentation of similar material for compound dies but Table XLVIII gives a list of the parts and the summary in Table XLIX gives the standard time required to make complete the compound die shown in Fig. 180.

For additional information in this field see: C. N. Harwood, "Time Standards for the Drop Forge Die Shop," *Heat Treating and Forging*, Vol. 23, No. 11, pp. 549-555, November, 1937; also December, 1937, pp. 604-609; January, 1938, pp. 19-25; and February, 1938, pp. 65-70.

CHAPTER 22

DETERMINING TIME STANDARDS FOR ASSEMBLY OPERATIONS

CLASSIFICATION AND DEFINITION OF MOTIONS
DETERMINATION OF TIME VALUES

Elemental time values determined from stop-watch time studies are widely used for rate setting, and the process of establishing such values is relatively simple, as has been described in the preceding chapters.

There is a trend toward the use of standard time values for therbligs or combinations of therbligs, and under certain conditions such time values may be more useful than the time values for longer elements obtained from stop-watch time studies.

The plan described below for classifying and using therblig time values was worked out at the Bridgeport Plant of the General Electric Company and has been successfully used for several years by that company. Although they use these data for estimating labor costs on new products, for determining and balancing the amount of work to be given to each operator on an assembly line, and for other purposes, it is apparent that this technique is a valuable one for setting time standards.

Greatest success is obtained with this synthetic method of setting time values when a thorough analysis of a given kind of work is made, a suitable classification setup, and standard time values established for carefully defined therbligs or combinations of therbligs.

In arriving at the classification of motions and the time values for each group the company (1) made extensive studies by means of motion pictures, (2) investigated operating conditions on the manufacturing floor, and (3) compared departmental time studies with motion-picture studies.

DERIVATION OF ASSEMBLY TIME STANDARDS

Assembly Elements. In an assembly operation a variety of parts are supplied to an operator who assembles them in definite positions.

The operator must *"Get"* each part and *"Place"* it in proper position in relation to the rest of the assembly. When parts are fastened together, hand tools or machines may be *"Used."* Lastly, after completing an assembly cycle the device or assembly must be *"Placed Aside"* or *"Disposed."* All assembly operations are composed of a sequence of these elements. For practical purposes of analysis, it is unnecessary to reduce these four divisions to still smaller elements if the variables which affect them are recognized and properly evaluated.

"Grasp" a Primary Variable. Throughout any assembly operation, time is consumed in obtaining, maintaining, or releasing the control of parts, tools, or machines. In the assembly operations studied, this control was largely manual.

It was determined that the type of grasp used in controlling the part being assembled was perhaps the most important variable affecting get or place times. Although special features of design or relative difficulty of assembly may affect it, the type of grasp used is largely a function of the size of the part. Hence, for practical purposes, the size of parts may be used as one base for evaluating the variation of get or place times.

Size of Part and Type of Grasp. The size of parts is a satisfactory base for evaluating variations of get and place times when size is defined according to the type of grasp employed. It must be remembered, however, that one grasp may be used to *get* a given part and another used to *place* it efficiently.

Analysis of many individual operations indicates that grasp may be classed readily into four divisions or types. These indicate the size of the parts which *normally* employ each type of grasp.

Four Types of Grasp. These four types of grasp are:

a. Three fingers and thumb (*3F*)

This grasp is used on any object large enough to permit placing three fingers and thumb around it (in at least two dimensions) without crowding and not large enough to require extension of the fingers to control it. This grasp, on parts of this size, is the easiest to obtain and in most cases provides maximum control. (See Fig. 181.)

b. Extend hand (*H*)

This grasp is used on any object where size requires extension of the hand, and weight, finish, or control requirements do not necessitate use of two hands. Control is good and readily obtained.

c. Two fingers and thumb (*2F*)

This grasp is used where it is impossible to obtain a three-finger grasp on an object because of its small size.

CONDITION OF GRASP Facility with which grasp is performed	(Medium) 3 F Three fingers and thumb	E
CONDITION A Very best grasp facility possible. The object is pre-positioned for grasp, or the grasp is not hindered by other objects in contact with the object grasped.	0.005 Get screwdriver, 8 inches to right of work place on assembly table.	Get power work place.
CONDITION B Good grasp facility. But parts may be in quantities requiring some selection of a single part. No untangling or difficult separation is required.	0.008 Get small gear-blank, one of several in pile 8 inches to right of work place.	Get aluminu... of operator
CONDITION C The design of parts or kind of finish prevents ready grasping. Parts may tangle, nest together, or be packed with separators, or require special handling.	0.011 Get terminal box subassembly from supply 8 inches to left of work place. Wires may tangle.	Get toaster and behind protect finis

Fig. 181—Standard

Table illustrating the four different types of grasp (by size of object... minutes are also shown. Trans...

Corrections for Data in Fig. 181

1. When more than one grasp is required in one get, multiply base ti... base time (0.011) by 1.30 = 0.014 minute, standard value.
2. For gets made simultaneously by both hands, multiply base time (0.011) by 1.30 = 0.014 minute, standard value.
3. To correct base time for transport empty distances in excess of 8 ... empty distances over 20 inches usually involve the slower back and hip m...

CONDITION OF GRASP Facility with which grasp is performed	(Medium) 3 F Three fingers and thumb	E
CONDITION A Very best grasp facility possible. The object is pre-positioned for grasp, or the grasp is not hindered by other objects in contact with the object grasped.	0.006 Get screwdriver, 8 inches to right of work place on assembly table.	Get power work place.
CONDITION B Good grasp facility. But parts may be in quantities requiring some selection of a single part. No untangling or difficult separation is required.	0.006 Get small gear-blank, one of several in pile 8 inches to right of work place.	Get aluminu of operator.
CONDITION C The design of parts or kind of finish prevents ready grasping. Parts may tangle, nest together, or be packed with separators, or require special handling.	0.011 Get terminal box subassembly from supply 8 inches to left of work place. Wires may tangle.	Get toaster and behind protect finis

FIG. 181—STANDAI

Table illustrating the four different types of grasp (by size of object minutes are also shown. Trans

Corrections for Data in Fig. 181

1. When more than one grasp is required in one get, multiply base ti base time (0.011) by 1.50 = 0.017 minute, standard value.

2. For gets made simultaneously by both hands, multiply base time (0.011) by 1.30 = 0.014 minute, standard value.

3. To correct base time for transport empty distances in excess of 8 empty distances over 20 inches usually involve the slower back and hip m

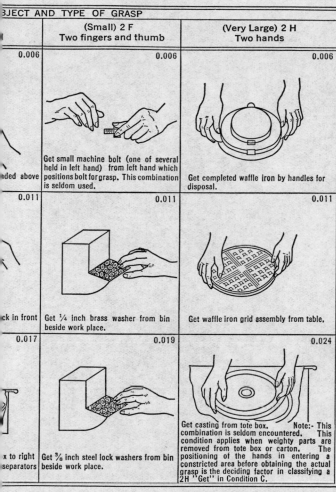

	(Small) 2 F Two fingers and thumb	(Very Large) 2 H Two hands
0.006	0.006	0.006
ded above	Get small machine bolt (one of several held in left hand) from left hand which positions bolt for grasp. This combination is seldom used.	Get completed waffle iron by handles for disposal.
0.011	0.011	0.011
ck in front	Get ¼ inch brass washer from bin beside work place.	Get waffle iron grid assembly from table.
0.017	0.019	0.024
x to right separators	Get ⅜ inch steel lock washers from bin beside work place.	Get casting from tote box. Note:- This combination is seldom encountered. This condition applies when weighty parts are removed from tote box or carton. The positioning of the hands in entering a constricted area before obtaining the actual grasp is the deciding factor in classifying a 2H "Get" in Condition C.

UES FOR "GET."

d the three different conditions of grasp. Standard time values in distances not over 8 inches.

r grasp. For example, get two bolts (from bin) in one hand: multiply

example, get two cup washers, one in each hand: multiply base time

ss than 20 inches, add 0.0004 minute per inch of excess. As transport d 0.0006 minute per inch in excess of 20 inches.

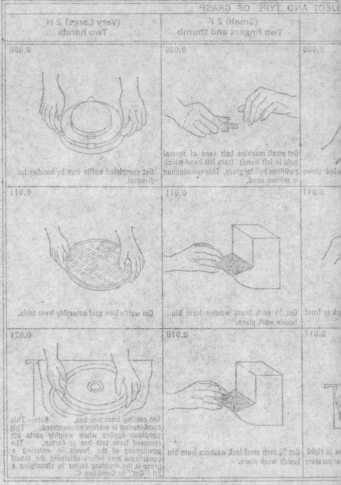

d. Two hands (2*H*)

This grasp is used where size, weight, design, or finish requires the use of two hands in moving the object, or where positioning is so difficult as to require a guiding hand.

Limitations of Get. In establishing standards for get times it seemed reasonable to include in get only two movements—transport empty and grasp (or select and grasp). Time for grasp is affected not only by the size of part grasped, as has already been discussed, but it is affected also by the variations imposed by the physical setup of the work place or the peculiar design of parts. These variations are more or less arbitrarily classified and are explained more completely below. Transport empty time is, in most cases, directly variable with distance. It has been treated as such with the exception of the larger distances which bring into play back and hip movements.

Conditions of Get. Each of the four types of grasp explained above varies with the operation conditions present. These variations are grouped into three classes, depending upon the facility with which grasp may be performed under those conditions. (See Fig. 181.)

Condition A—Very best grasp facility possible. The object is pre-positioned for grasp or the grasp is not hindered by other objects in contact with the object grasped.

Condition B—Good grasp facility is provided, but parts may be in quantities requiring some selection of a *single* part. No untangling or difficult separation is required.

Condition C—The design of parts or kind of finish prevents ready grasping. Parts may tangle, nest together, or be packed with separators or require special handling.

Figure 181 gives illustrations for each of the four different types of grasp (size of object) for each of the three different conditions of grasp. The standard time values in minutes are also shown. These values are correct when the transport empty distance is not over eight inches.

Limitations of Place. The establishing of place times presented a more difficult problem since place is taken to include transport loaded, position (pre-position), and release load. Based on the amount of positioning or pre-positioning required, four classes have been determined from the study. These and several additional variations are explained below.

Conditions of Place. The variations in placing conditions have been grouped into four classes, depending largely upon the amount of positioning required. (See Fig. 182.)

Condition A—Positioning is normally little more than releasing the object or moving it slightly on the work place.

Condition B—Positioning of parts on or into definite locations with ample tolerances, simple open nests or fixtures, or assemblies with one point of location.

Condition C—Positioning of parts on or into difficult or complicated locations, assemblies, or fixtures requiring the positioning of parts with respect to two definite points, or location in two directions.

Condition D—Positioning is much the same as Condition C but in addition may involve close tolerances, greater care of finishes, three or more points or directions of location, or final application of force to assemble.

TABLE L
Standard Times for Basic Distances

Get Times in Minutes

Subdivision Number	Time	
1.	0.006	Obtain control of any object where a simple, single-part grasp is possible. (Part of any size, Condition A, and 3F parts, Condition B.)
2.	0.011	Obtain control of any object where simple grasp is not possible but parts have no tendency to tangle or nest. (Condition B with parts of any size other than 3F, 3F objects with Condition C.)
3.	0.017	Get large objects H requiring extended hand grasp with Condition C.
4.	0.019	Get small 2F objects in Condition C.
5.	0.024	Get large or weighty 2H objects with Condition C.

Place Times in Minutes

Subdivision Number	Time	
1.	0.006	Place objects in Condition A position, any size other than 2H, place 3F objects in Condition B position.
2.	0.011	Place 2H objects in Condition A position and 2F or H objects in Condition B position. Place 3F objects in Condition C position.
3.	0.019	Place 2H objects in Condition B position, or 2F or H parts in Condition C position, or 3F objects in Condition D position.
4.	0.024	Place small parts into very difficult locations, 2F parts in Condition D position.
5.	0.030	Place large parts into or on difficult assemblies, 2H objects in Condition C position.
6.	0.042	Place large parts into or on very difficult assemblies, 2H objects in Condition D position.

"Dispose" Is a "Place." As "Condition D dispose operations" are in reality a placing aside of a part, tool or fixture, they have been evaluated on exactly the same base as place operations. An analysis of a large number of dispose times indicates that, if properly classified under grasp and operation conditions, the time values established for place will apply.

Method of Developing Time Values. The motion-picture films of various assembly operations were analyzed, breaking down the operation cycles into gets, places, uses, and disposes, and the film time for each element was recorded. Subsequent analysis of the data was made, correcting for observed operator effort. The result of this analysis was the establishment of relatively consistent time values for the various combinations of size and for get or place conditions. The time values do not represent the minimum values encountered for any particular combination, but are those selected as most representative of normal conditions and are corrected to represent normal operator effort.

CORRECTIONS FOR TRANSPORT DISTANCES

As shown above there are only seven basic time values for get and place operations, although these values may be adjusted when necessary for particular operation variations. It was also pointed out that corrections for normal transport empty and transport loaded distances could be made for each time value and thus eliminate repetition of this calculation for the user.

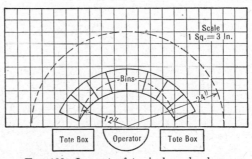

FIG. 183—Layout of typical work place.

Where factory operations do not dictate otherwise the assembly work place should be set up closely resembling the sketch shown in Fig. 183. Parts are to be supplied to the operator in *well-designed* bins, trays, hoppers, or other containers located in the areas indicated. In progressive assembly operations subassemblies will be delivered to the operator within the work area outlined (24 inches from the edge of fixture or bench nearest the operator). This setup provides the operator with an approved motion study work place and is the basis on which corrected standard time values have been established.

With the work place arranged as shown above, all but a very few of the operator's transport empty or transport loaded motions will be confined to distances less than 24 inches. As the majority of assembly parts are in the small or medium class, average transport empty or transport loaded distances will be much less than 24 inches. Consequently transport empty and transport loaded corrections are calculated slightly in excess of the anticipated average and distances to 24 inches are allowed.

GET TIMES CORRECTED FOR TRANSPORT EMPTY

CLASS 1

	Std. Time for Basic Distance [1]	Correction	Maximum Transport Empty	Standard to Be Used
Subdivision 1	0.006 min.	0.001 min.	12 in.	0.007 min.

A. Very best grasp facility possible, due to design or pre-positioning of object for grasp; no interference or hindrance with grasp by other objects. Size of object need not be considered. (3F, H, 2F, and 2H.)

B. Get medium-sized parts (3F) even when in quantities, provided no separation or untangling is required.

For Class 1 gets, transport empty distance is usually short although 12 inches is allowed. This simple get is employed very infrequently for obtaining parts *to be brought* to the assembly; consequently 12 inches maximum is ample. Ten and one-half inches is used as the distance in calculating the correction. $(10\frac{1}{2} - 8) \times 0.0004 = 2\frac{1}{2} \times 0.0004 = 0.001$ min.

Examples: a. Get completed assembly for disposal.
          b. Get bolts from bin.

CLASS 2

Subdivision 2	0.011 min.	0.002 min.	24 in.	0.013 min.

A. Grasp is easily made but parts may be in quantities requiring some selection of a single part. Parts may be small (2F), large (H), or very large (2H).

B. The design or finish of parts prevents ready grasping, parts may tangle, nest together, or be packed in separators. Parts must be of medium size (3F).

[1] From Table L on page 336.

In this class of get parts will normally be located at distances of 6 inches to 16 inches from the assembly. A transport empty distance of 12 inches should be ample, but allowance is made for 13 inches, giving a correction of 0.002 minute and allowing transport empty up to 24 inches.

Examples: a. Get standard screws, washers, nuts, or pins from properly designed trays.
b. Get terminal box with terminal leads assembled.

CLASS 3

Subdivision 3   *0.017 min.*   *0.004 min.*   *24 in.*   *0.021 min.*

Get large parts (H) or object requiring extended hand grasp. Parts may tangle, nest together, etc.

A part of this class almost invariably will be supplied at a greater than average distance from the assembly; hence, a correction of 0.004 minute, permitting combining with ($2F$, Subdivision 4) parts, which are almost invariably supplied within 12 inches.

Example: Get toaster basket from tote box.

Subdivision 4   *0.019 min.*   *0.002 min.*   *24 in.*   *0.021 min.*

Get small parts ($2F$) whose design or finish prevents ready grasp or which tend to tangle or nest.

As explained above, small parts are almost invariably supplied within 6 inches to 16 inches from the assembly; hence, a correction for transport empty of 0.002 minute, allowing for 24 inches maximum transport empty.

Example: a. Get coiled spring from tray, 12 inches transport empty.

CLASS 4

Subdivision 5   *0.024 min.*   *0.002 min.*   *24 in.*   *0.026 min.*

Get very large parts requiring two hand control ($2H$), the design or finish of which prevents ready grasping. Parts may tangle, nest together, etc. Very large parts, owing to space requirements, are normally supplied at distances greater than 24 inches. Also, there is usually but one very large part per assembly. For these reasons a correction was applied to bring the corrected standard time value into agreement with that of place, Class 4. This procedure is justified since an extra correction for transport empty over 24 inches is usually applied and the error of this one element is proportionately small in a complete assembly cycle.

Example: a. Get electric fan motor.

PLACE TIMES CORRECTED FOR TRANSPORT LOADED

CLASS 1

	Std. Time for Basic Distance [2]	Correction	Maximum Transport Loaded	Standard to Be Used
Subdivision 1	0.006 min.	0.001 min.	12 in.	0.007 min.

A. Place small (2F), medium (3F), or large (H) objects where positioning is normally little more than releasing the object or moving it slightly on the work place.

B. Place medium-sized (3F) objects where positioning consists of some definite location, simple open nests or fixtures. Loose tolerances.

As in Class 1 gets, a transport distance of only 12 inches is allowed. This is justified, as by far the greater majority of such places fall well within this distance.

Examples: a. Reverse or turn over subassembly on work place.
  b. Place waffle iron handle in nest in assembly fixture.

CLASS 2

Subdivision 2	0.011 min.	0.002 min.	24 in.	0.013 min.

A. Place very large parts (2H) where positioning is normally little more than releasing the object or moving it slightly on the work place.

B. Place small (2F) or large (H) parts which require some definite positioning in simple open nests or fixtures or on assemblies with one point of location. Loose tolerances.

C. Place medium-sized parts (3F) in difficult or complicated locations or fixtures, requiring positioning of parts with respect to two points or locations in two directions.

Parts being placed in this class will be obtained from all locations of the work place. Transport loaded correction is based on the majority of parts being located within 12 inches and sufficient allowance made to include parts supplied at a maximum distance of 24 inches.

Examples: a. (1) Turn over waffle iron assembly.
  (2) Place sandwich grill subassembly on work place.
  b. Place washer on screw.
  c. Place socket wrench on nut.

[2] From Table L on page 336.

CLASS 3

Subdivision 3   *0.019 min.*   *0.002 min.*   *24 in.*   *0.021 min.*

A. Place very large parts (2*H*) where positioning consists of some definite location, simple open nests or fixtures or assemblies with one point of location.

B. Place small (2*F*) or large (*H*) parts where positioning is in difficult or complicated positions, assemblies or fixtures require the positioning of parts with respect to two points of location.

C. Place medium-sized parts (3*F*) in B type locations but with close tolerances, or on assemblies with three or more points of location.

The basis for transport loaded correction is the same as for Class 2.

Examples: a. Place 12-inch or 16-inch fan motor in fixture.
   b. (1) Place screw in tapped hole, *start* thread only.
       (2) Place power driver on stud and nut.
   c. Place small fan rotor shaft in end bearing.

CLASS 4

Subdivision 4   *0.024 min.*   *0.002 min.*   *24 in.*   *0.026 min.*

Place small parts (2*F*) into very difficult assemblies requiring three or more points of location, close tolerances, or special precaution for finish. Place very small parts in inaccessible location. The basis for transport loaded correction is the same as for Class 2.

Examples: a. Place cup washer over screw and lead.
   b. Place screw through hole in waffle iron cover into tapped hole. Location is restricted by handle bracket.

CLASS 5

Subdivision 5   *0.030 min.*   *0.006 min.*   *24 in.*   *0.036 min.*

Place very large parts (2*H*) into difficult or complicated locations, assemblies or fixtures, requiring the positioning of parts with respect to two definite points, or location in two directions.

Since very large parts are usually supplied at distances about 24 inches from the work place, a transport loaded correction of 0.006 minute is applied. The operator is given full allowance for a transport loaded distance of 24 inches, and where transport loaded is greater than 24 inches an extra correction is applied.

Example: Place waffle-iron unit on grid.

CLASS 6

Subdivision 6   *0.042 min.*   *0.006 min.*   *24 in.*   *0.048 min.*

Place very large parts ($2H$) into very difficult or complicated locations or fixtures, requiring location of three or more points or in three or more directions. Transport loaded correction is calculated as in Class 5.

Examples: a. Place toaster body in power screwdriver fixture, lining up two holes.

Get and Place Times Corrected for Transport Distances over 24 Inches. Occasionally get or place operations require transport distances greater than 24 inches and a correction must be applied for this condition. Transport distances in excess of 24 inches are fairly well limited to a maximum of 36 inches or a maximum correction of 0.0072 minute (12 in. $\times$ 0.006 min. per in.). (See Note 3 below Fig. 181.)

The average transport distance in this range will be somewhat less than 36 inches; so a liberal correction of 0.006 minute is allowed. This value is added to each transport empty and transport loaded which exceeds 24 inches.

On some infrequent assemblies it is necessary to effect a transport empty or transport loaded greater than 36 inches. When this is necessary the operator must "walk and carry." For distances up to 7 feet operators usually shuffle sideways. Analysis has shown that a value of 0.007 minute per foot (each foot over 36 inches up to a total of 7 feet) is a reasonably accurate value to apply.

This same correction will apply in those instances where an operator moves from one fixture to another in a progressive assembly cycle.

Development of Standard Times for Simultaneous Gets and Places. In the preceding pages four get times and six place times were developed for direct use with transport distances up to 24 inches except for simple gets and places which were allowed only 12 inches. These times were developed for the getting or placing of a single part *only*. Whenever possible, motion economy requires the getting and placing of two parts, one in each hand simultaneously.

Standard times including transport empty and transport loaded have been developed for "get or place two parts simultaneously" for the same conditions outlined above for single parts. The method used in this development is shown for Time Class 1 and 2, gets and places.

Class 1.

Basic time for Class 1 Get (Table L)...................... = 0.006 min.
Transport empty correction for 12 inches maximum instead of
8 inches.[3] $(12 - 8) \times 0.0004 = 4 \times 0.0004$............ = 0.0016 min.
Corrected time value for 12 inches = $(0.006 + 0.0016)$...... = 0.0076 min.
Simultaneous get factor (see Note on Fig. 181)............ = 1.3
Standard time for simultaneous get $0.0076 \times 1.3 = 0.0099$ use = 0.010 min.

Basic time for Class 1 Place (Table L)...................... = 0.006 min.
Transport empty correction for 12 inches maximum instead of
8 inches. $(12 - 8) \times 0.0004 = 4 \times 0.0004$............ = 0.0016 min.
Corrected time value for 12 inches = $(0.006 + 0.0016)$...... = 0.0076 min.
Simultaneous place factor (see Note on Fig. 182)........... = 1.4
Standard time for simultaneous place $0.0076 \times 1.4 = 0.01065$
use... = 0.011 min.

Class 2.

Basic time for Class 2 Get (Table L)...................... = 0.011 min.
Transport empty correction for 13 inches instead of 8 inches
(24 inches maximum) $(13 - 8) \times 0.0004 = 5 \times 0.0004$... = 0.002 min.
Corrected time value for 13 inches = $(0.011 + 0.002)$....... = 0.013 min.
Simultaneous get factor (see Note on Fig. 181)............ = 1.3
Standard time for simultaneous get $0.013 \times 1.3 = 0.0169$ use = 0.017 min.

Basic time for Class 2 Place (Table L)...................... = 0.011 min.
Transport empty correction for 13 inches instead of 8 inches
(24 inches maximum) $(13 - 8) \times 0.0004 = 5 \times 0.0004$... = 0.002 min.
Corrected time value for 13 inches = $(0.011 + 0.002)$....... = 0.013 min.
Simultaneous place factor [4] (see Note on Fig. 182)......... = 1.5
Standard time for simultaneous place $0.013 \times 1.5 = 0.0195$
use... = 0.020 min.

Summary. The foregoing has presented a means of classifying the great majority of the assembly operations found in the Appliance Section. It establishes a means of defining operations in a manner which largely eliminates variations in judgment on the part of those using the data.

When familiarity with the basic operation conditions has been attained, the proper classification of any operation is easily and quickly

[3] As "Simultaneous Gets" include the large class of simple gets, the average transport empty distance is properly at the maximum of the class, 12 inches.
[4] It was decided to allow the larger simultaneous factor for all classes except Class 1 in order to provide for simultaneous placing of both like and unlike parts.

recognized. It will be noted that the two figures (Figs. 181 and 182) contain only *seven* different time values for the total twenty-seven separate combinations of conditions. For practical purposes these time values may be increased directly by the average amount of transport empty or transport loaded correction required by the standard work place. Such time values are shown in Figs. 184 and 185.

It should be noted that the time values given in this chapter apply to carefully defined groups of motions. Moreover, the classifications shown are mainly used for assembly operations of electrical appliances.

Although the material presented in this chapter is largely limited in its application to assembly operations in the plant of the company that developed it, the method has wide application as demonstrated by the fact that an increasing number of companies are using it.

CONDITION OF PLACE Amount of positioning required	(Medium) 3 F Three fingers and thumb
CONDITION A Positioning is normally little more than releasing the object on the work place.	0.006 Place small gear blank in other hand.
CONDITION B Positioning of parts on or into definite locations with ample tolerances, simple open nests or fixtures, or assemblies with one point of location.	0.008 Dispose of screwdriver into funnel type holder 5 inches to right of work place.
CONDITION C Positioning of parts on or into difficult or complicated locations. Assemblies or fixtures requiring the positioning of parts with respect to two definite points, or location in two directions.	0.011 Position in two directions. Place screwdriver wrench over standard nut.
CONDITION D Positioning is much the same as Condition D but in addition may involve close tolerances, greater care of finishes, three or more points, or directions of location, or application of force to assemble.	0.018 Position in three directions. Place screwdriver on screw in assembly.

FIG. 182—STAND...

Table illustrating the four different types of grasp (by size of obj... minutes are also shown. Tra...

Corrections for Data in Fig. 182

1. When both hands place identical parts simultaneously, multiply ...
2. When both hands place unlike parts simultaneously, multiply bas...
3. When large parts are obtained by one hand and placed with two ... second hand.
4. Two or more parts first assembled in the hands and subsequent ... pieces and the two-handed (2H) place.
5. To correct base time for transport loaded distances in excess of ... loaded distances over 20 inches involve back and hip movement, add 0.0...
6. When one hand gets a part and the other hand places another p...

CONDITION OF PLACE Amount of positioning required	(Medium) 3 F Three fingers and thumb	
CONDITION A Positioning is normally little more than releasing the object on the work place.	0.006 Place small gear blank in other hand.	Place t subseq
CONDITION B Positioning of parts on or into definite locations with ample tolerances, simple open nests or fixtures, or assemblies with one point of location.	0.006 Dispose of screwdriver into funnel-type holder 8 inches to right of work place.	Dispose
CONDITION C Positioning of parts on or into difficult or complicated locations. Assemblies or fixtures requiring the positioning of parts with respect to two definite points, or location in two directions.	0.011 Position in two directions Place screwdriver wrench over standard nut.	Place of se
CONDITION D Positioning is much the same as Condition C but in addition may involve close tolerances, greater care of finishes, three or more points, or directions of location, or application of force to assemble.	0.019 Position in three directions Place screwdriver on screw in assembly.	Th

FIG. 182—STANDA

Table illustrating the four different types of grasp (by size of obje
minutes are also shown. Tra

Corrections for Data in Fig. 182

1. When both hands place identical parts simultaneously, multiply l
2. When both hands place unlike parts simultaneously, multiply bas
3. When large parts are obtained by one hand and placed with two second hand.
4. Two or more parts first assembled in the hands and subsequentl places and the two-handed (2H) place.
5. To correct base time for transport loaded distances in excess of loaded distances over 20 inches involve back and hip movement, add 0.0
6. When one hand gets a part and the other hand places another pa

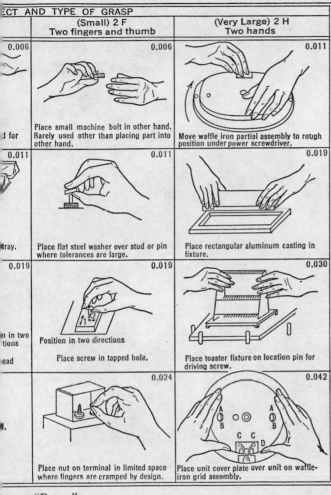

ECT AND TYPE OF GRASP		
	(Small) 2 F Two fingers and thumb	(Very Large) 2 H Two hands
0.006	0.006	0.011
d for	Place small machine bolt in other hand. Rarely used other than placing part into other hand.	Move waffle iron partial assembly to rough position under power screwdriver.
0.011	0.011	0.019
tray.	Place flat steel washer over stud or pin where tolerances are large.	Place rectangular aluminum casting in fixture.
0.019	0.019	0.030
n in two tions	Position in two directions	Place toaster fixture on location pin for driving screw.
ead	Place screw in tapped hole.	
	0.024	0.042
l.	Place nut on terminal in limited space where fingers are cramped by design.	Place unit cover plate over unit on waffle-iron grid assembly.

S FOR "PLACE."

l the four different conditions of place. Standard time values in listances not over 8 inches.

time for two-handed (2H) place and add 0.005 for grasping with the

jor assembly or fixture require the sum of the times for simultaneous

s than 20 inches, add 0.0004 minute per inch in excess.   As transport nch in excess of 20 inches.
y, use the element having the greater time value.

CONDITION OF GRASP Readily with which grasp is performed	(Medium) 3 F Three fingers and thumb	SIZE OF (Large) H Extended hand
CONDITION A Very best grasp easily possible. The object is in pre-positioned for grasp, or the grasp is not obstructed by other objects in contact with the object grasped.	Time Class No. **1** One Hand 8—0.006 One Hand 12—0.007 Two Hands Sim. 12—0.010  Get screwdriver, 6 inches to right of work piece on assembly table.	Time Class No. **1** One Ha— One Ha— Two Hands Si— Get power screwdriver suspended abo
CONDITION B Good grasp facility. But parts may be in quantities requiring some selection of a single part. Re-orienting or difficult separation is required.	Time Class No. **1** One Hand 8—0.008 One Hand 12—0.007 Two Hands Sim. 12—0.010 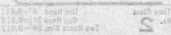 Get small gear-blank, one of several in pile 8 inches to right of work place.	Time Class No. **2** One Ha— One Ha— Two Hands Si— Get aluminum casting from stack to fe
CONDITION C The design of parts, or kind of finish prevents ready grasping. Parts may tangle, nest together, or be packed with separators, or require special handling.	Time Class No. **2** One Hand 8—0.011 One Hand 24—0.013 Two Hands Sim. 24—0.017 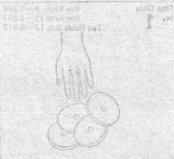 Get terminal box subassembly from supply, 8 inches to left of work place. Wires may tangle.	Time Class No. **3** One Ha— One Ha— Two Hands Si—  Get toaster basket from tote box to rig operator. Tissue separators may be l

Fig. 154—Standard Time Values for Ge

CONDITION OF GRASP		SIZE OF
Facility with which grasp is performed	(Medium) 3 F Three fingers and thumb	(Large) H Extended hand
CONDITION A Very best grasp facility possible. The object is pre-positioned for grasp, or the grasp is not hindered by other objects in contact with the object grasped.	Time Class No. **1** One Hand 8″=0.006 One Hand 12″=0.007 Two Hands Sim. 12″=0.010	Time Class No. **1** One Ha One Ha Two Hands Si
	Get screwdriver, 8 inches to right of work place on assembly table.	Get power screwdriver suspended abo
CONDITION B Good grasp facility. But parts may be in quantities requiring some selection of a single part. No untangling or difficult separation is required.	Time Class No. **1** One Hand 8″=0.006 One Hand 12″=0.007 Two Hands Sim. 12″=0.010	Time Class No. **2** One Har One Har Two Hands Sir
	Get small gear-blank, one of several in pile 8 inches to right of work place.	Get aluminum casting from stack in fr
CONDITION C The design of parts or kind of finish prevents ready grasping. Parts may tangle, nest together, or be packed with separators, or require special handling.	Time Class No. **2** One Hand 8″=0.011 One Hand 24″=0.013 Two Hands Sim. 24″=0.017	Time Class No. **3** One Ha One Ha Two Hands Si
	Get terminal box subassembly from supply 8 inches to left of work place. Wires may tangle.	Get toaster basket from tote box to rig operator. Tissue separators protect fi

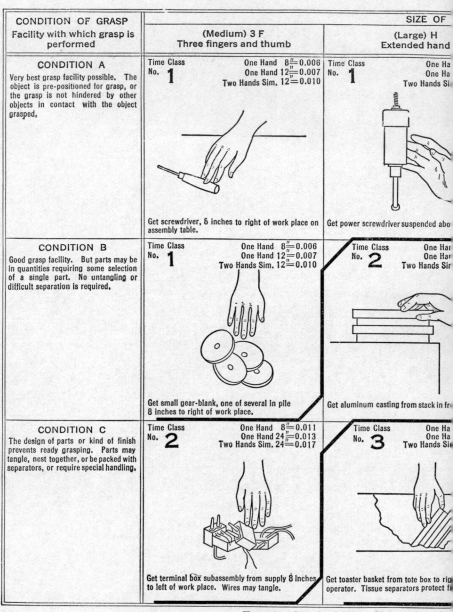

Fig. 184—Standard Time Values for "Ge

			GET TIME Class No.	STD. TIME Corrected for Transport Distance

⊃ TYPE OF GRASP

(Small) 2 F — Two fingers and thumb	(Very Large) 2 H — Two hands		GET TIME Class No.	STD. TIME Corrected for Transport Distance
Time Class No. 1 — One Hand 8″=0.006, One Hand 12″=0.007, Two Hands Sim. 12″=0.010	**Time Class No. 1** — Two Hands 8″=0.006, Two Hands 12″=0.007		1	0.007
Get small machine bolt (one of several held in left hand) from left hand which positions bolt for grasp. Seldom used.	Get completed waffle iron by handles for disposal.			
Time Class No. 2 — One Hand 8″=0.011, One Hand 24″=0.013, Two Hands Sim. 24″=0.017	**Time Class No. 2** — Two Hands 8″=0.011, Two Hands 24″=0.013		2	0.013
Get ¼ inch brass washer from bin beside work place.	Get waffle-iron grid assembly from table.			
Time Class No. 3 — One Hand 8″=0.019, One Hand 24″=0.021, Two Hands Sim. 24″=0.028			3	0.021
	Time Class No. 4 — Two Hands 8″=0.024, Two Hands 24″=0.026		4	0.026
Get ⅜ inch steel lock washer from bin beside work place.	Get casting from tote box. Note: This combination is seldom encountered. This condition applies when weighty parts are removed from tote box or carton. The positioning of the hands in entering a constricted area before obtaining the actual grasp is the deciding factor in classifying a 2H "Get" in Condition C.			

...ted for transport distances. Time in minutes.

Fig. 155—Standard Time Values for "Place."

CONDITION OF PLACE Amount of positioning required	SIZE OF (Medium) 3 F Three fingers and thumb	(Large) H Extended han

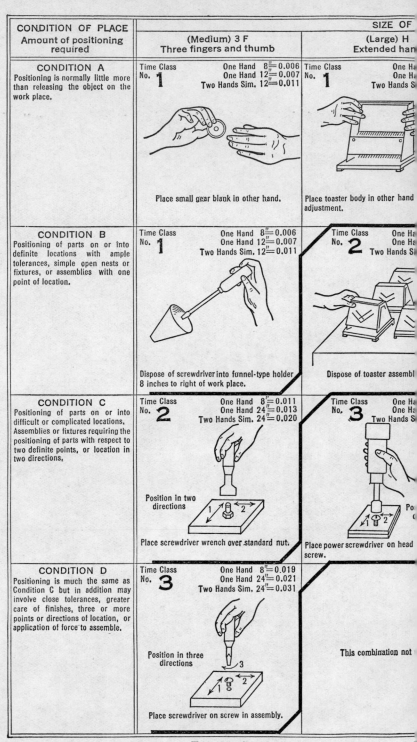

CONDITION A
Positioning is normally little more than releasing the object on the work place.

Time Class No. **1**   One Hand $8''=0.006$ One Hand $12''=0.007$ Two Hands Sim. $12''=0.011$

Place small gear blank in other hand.

Time Class No. **1**   One Ha...   One Ha...   Two Hands S...

Place toaster body in other hand adjustment.

CONDITION B
Positioning of parts on or into definite locations with ample tolerances, simple open nests or fixtures, or assemblies with one point of location.

Time Class No. **1**   One Hand $8''=0.006$ One Hand $12''=0.007$ Two Hands Sim. $12''=0.011$

Dispose of screwdriver into funnel-type holder 8 inches to right of work place.

Time Class No. **2**   One Ha...   One Ha...   Two Hands S...

Dispose of toaster assembl...

CONDITION C
Positioning of parts on or into difficult or complicated locations. Assemblies or fixtures requiring the positioning of parts with respect to two definite points, or location in two directions.

Time Class No. **2**   One Hand $8''=0.011$ One Hand $24''=0.013$ Two Hands Sim. $24''=0.020$

Position in two directions

Place screwdriver wrench over standard nut.

Time Class No. **3**   One Ha...   One Ha...   Two Hands S...

Po...

Place power screwdriver on head screw.

CONDITION D
Positioning is much the same as Condition C but in addition may involve close tolerances, greater care of finishes, three or more points or directions of location, or application of force to assemble.

Time Class No. **3**   One Hand $8''=0.019$ One Hand $24''=0.021$ Two Hands Sim. $24''=0.031$

Position in three directions

Place screwdriver on screw in assembly.

This combination not ...

FIG. 185—Standard Time Values for "Place."

(Small) 2 F Two fingers and thumb	(Very Large) 2 H Two hands	PLACE TIME Class No.	STD. TIME Corrected for Transport Distances
Time Class No. **1** One Hand 8"=0.006 One Hand 12"=0.007 Two Hands Sim. 12"=0.011		1	0.007
	Time Class No. **2** Two Hands 8"=0.011 Two Hands 12"=0.013		
Place small machine bolt in other hand. Rarely used other than for placing part into other hand.	Move waffle iron partial assembly to rough position under power screwdriver.	2	0.013
Time Class No. **2** One Hand 8"=0.011 One Hand 24"=0.013 Two Hands Sim. 24"=0.020	Time Class No. **3** Two Hands 8"=0.019 Two Hands 24"=0.021		
Place flat steel washer over stud or pin where tolerances are large.	Place rectangular aluminum casting in fixture.	3	0.021
Time Class No. **3** One Hand 8"=0.019 One Hand 24"=0.021 Two Hands Sim. 24"=0.031		4	0.026
	Time Class No. **5** Two Hands 8"=0.030 Two Hands 24"=0.036		
Position in two directions Place screw in tapped hole.	Place toaster fixture on locating pin for driving screw.	5	0.036
Time Class No. **4** One Hand 8"=0.024 One Hand 24"=0.026 Two Hands Sim. 24"=0.039	Time Class No. **6** Two Hands 8"=0.042 Two Hands 24"=0.048		
Place nut on terminal in limited space where fingers are cramped by design.	Place unit cover plate over unit on waffle-iron grid assembly.	6	0.048

d for transport distances. Time in minutes.

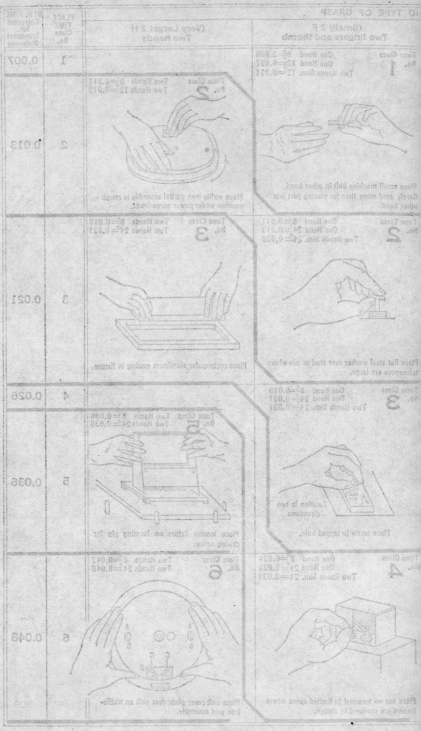

CHAPTER 23

DETERMINING TIME STANDARDS FOR ASSEMBLY OPERATIONS

AN APPLICATION

Convenient Use of Standard Times. A "Standard Times Computation Sheet" has been constructed, based upon the standard times established in the preceding chapter. This computation sheet, reproduced in Figs. 186 and 187, combines established time values into an easily used table. An experienced analyst will find this table to be more easily and quickly used on assembly operations than a stop watch. As it is based on an analytical method with proved therblig time values, it produces results which are largely free from variations due to the human element. It assists the user in analyzing the operations, permitting undivided attention to be applied to analysis as the operation progresses.

The back or "Breakdown" side of the computation sheet (Figs. 187 and 190) consists of six major sections as numbered in the small circles.

These six sections are:

(1) *Operation:* Description of the operation analyzed, including designation of the product involved.
(2) *Elements of the Operation:* The chronological description of the assembly cycle. In this section the user records the successive elements of assembly for each part or tool which the operator gets, places, or uses.
(3) *Standard Times:* Sections 3, 4, and 5 comprise a tabulation of the stand-
(4)   ard therblig time values established for: (3) Get or place parts
(5)   within normal distances; (4) Correction for operations exceeding normal distances; (5) Use times of common assembly tools and machines. The time values are given in column 5(b) and are recorded in column 5(a).
(6) *Total Time in Minutes:* This space is provided for recording total assembly time or, where desirable, the time for each group of elements.

345

STANDARD TIMES COMPUTATION SHEET

DEPT.:		DEPT. NO.:		ANALYST:

DRAWING NUMBER :   DATE: FOREMAN:

$$\text{Time to Move Tote Boxes} = \frac{.40 \times \text{No. Bxs.}}{\text{No. Pcs./Bx.}} = \frac{.40 \times}{} = \quad \text{Min.}$$

Fatigue Allowance $= \%$ } $=$ $\%$
Replenish Sm. Parts $= \%$

$\left[\begin{array}{l}\text{Total Time} \\ \text{in Minutes}\end{array}\right] + \begin{array}{l}\text{Move Tote Bx.} \\ \text{Time/Pc.}\end{array} \left.\right] + \left[\begin{array}{l}\% \\ \text{Allowance}\end{array}\right.$ or $\left.\right] = \begin{array}{l}\text{STANDARD TIME} \\ \text{IN MINUTES}\end{array}$

WORK PLACE Scale: 1 unit$=3''$ EQUIPMENT (Check on Work place):

Bins

Fixture

Tote Box   Operator   Tote Box

COMMENTS:

GENERAL ASSEMBLY STANDARD TIMES		SIZE OF OBJECT:	M. (3F)	L. (H)	S. (2F)	V.L. (2H)	TIME CLASS
	OPERATION CONDITIONS		TIME IN MINUTES				
Get Condition A	Very best grasp facility possible. The object is pre-positioned for grasp, or the grasp is not hindered by other objects in contact with the object grasped. Size of object need not be considered.		.007	.007	.007	.007	C 1
Get Condition B	Grasp is easily made but parts may be in quantities requiring some selection of a single part. No untangling or difficult separation is required.		.007	.013	.013	.013	C 2
Get Condition C	The design of parts or kind of finish prevents ready grasping. Parts may tangle, nest together, or be packed with separators, or require special handling.		.013	.021	.021	.026	C 3 / C 4
Place Condition A	Place objects where positioning is normally little more than releasing the object or moving it slightly on the work place.		.007	.007	.007	.013	C 1 / C 2
Place Condition B	Place objects where positioning consists of some definite location, simple open nests, or fixtures with ample tolerances, or assemblies with one point of location.		.007	.013	.013	.021	C 3
Place Condition C	Place objects where positioning is in difficult or complicated locations. Assemblies or fixtures requiring the positioning of parts with respect to two definite points, or location in two directions.		.013	.021	.021	.036	C 4 / C 5
Place Condition D	Positioning is much the same as Condition C but in addition may involve close tolerances, greater care of finishes, three or more points or directions of location, or application of force to assemble.		.021	.026	.026	.048	C 6

FIG. 186—Standard Times Computation Sheet—Front or "Summary Side."
Size 8½ × 11 inches.

PROCESS TIMES

PROCESS	SMALL LIGHT	MEDIUM	HEAVY LARGE
Power Driver	.020		
Tub. Riveter-Air Press	.010		
Sm. Punch Press or Welder	.011		
Operate Kick Press	.024		
Hd. Sc. Driver/Thread	.018		
Inspect/Point	.003		

PROCESS	LIGHT SMALL	MEDIUM	HEAVY LARGE
Drive Sc.-Friction Dr.	.020	—	.036
Oper. Hand Press	.010	—	.025
Pitching	.015	.020	.030
Cementing	.020	.030	.040
Spinning	.020	.030	.050
Soldering (No. 'Place', included)	.030	.030	.050

STANDARD TIMES — CLASS

	C 1 12" MAXIMUM			C 2 24" MAXIMUM			C 3 24" MAXIMUM			C 4 24"		C 5 24"	C 6 24"	T.E.&T.L.OVER 24" UP TO 36"	WALKING PER FOOT	PROCESS	TOTAL TIME IN MINUTES
	G&P	G2	P2	G&P	G2	P2	G&P	G2	P2	G&P	P2	P	P				
	.007	.010	.011	.013	.017	.020	.021	.028	.031	.026	.039	.036	.048	.012	.007		

OPERATION:

ELEMENTS OF THE OPERATION

G or P = "Get" or "Place" parts individually
G2 or P2 = "Get" or "Place" two parts (one with each hand) simultaneously
Walking = Transport Empty & Transport Loaded over 36 in. up to 7 ft.

Fig. 187—Standard Times Computation Sheet—Back or "Breakdown Side."

It will be noted that Section 3 consists of six columns headed C1 through C6. These columns represent the six classes of get G or place P times developed for individual parts.

Column C1 includes three subcolumns: on the left is a column headed G and P, 0.007. This column is used for any get or place element involving one individual part and included in the definitions of Class 1 get or place (see Figs. 184 and 185). The center column headed $G2$, 0.010, is used for any get element involving parts and conditions defined in Class 1, where two parts are obtained simultaneously. Similarly, the right-hand column headed $P2$, 0.011, is used for simultaneous placing of two parts, one in each hand, where Class 1 conditions apply.

Standard Times, Definition of Class Times. Familiarity with the six classes used in the computation sheet may be obtained more readily by a study of the charts shown in Figs. 184 and 185. They represent the time values of the two charts, Figs. 181 and 182, corrected for normal operation transport distances.

It will be noted that the first four classes of place have the same time value as the four classes of get. It must be remembered, however, that combined get and place classes do not represent the same combinations of grasp and operation conditions.

Use of the Computation Sheet. The Standard Times Computation Sheet may be used for estimating assembly costs on pre-production designs or for establishing time standards on assembly operations where procedure and methods are already in effect.

Example: Assemble parts of waffle iron. The following example taken from the assembly line of the No. 119 Y 197 waffle iron is used to explain the procedure:

1. *Operation*
   The operation consists of: Assemble unit and cover to lower waffle iron grid casting.
2. *Equipment*
   The equipment provided for this operation is:
   (1) One Millers Falls power nut-driver
   (2) Conveyorized bench
   (3) Chair
   (4) Two tote boxes and floor stands
   (5) Two cardboard boxes (4" × 5" × 3" deep)
3. *Parts*
   There are five parts (see Fig. 188) used in this assembly cycle:
   (1) Lower grid casting in tote box to operator's left.

(2) Unit, porcelain ring and element subassembly, on conveyor belt in center of bench.

(3) Cover, in tote box to operator's right.

(4) Stud, $\frac{1}{4}''$-20, 1" long in cardboard box.

(5) Nut, $\frac{1}{4}''$-20, in cardboard box.

4. *Fixture*

No fixture is used.

5. *Description of Cycle*

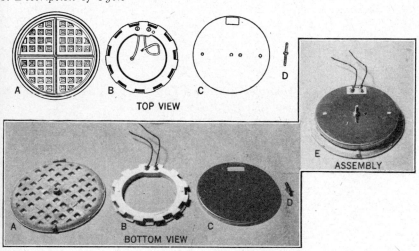

Fig. 188—Parts for waffle-iron lower grid assembly. *A*. Lower grid casting; *B*. Unit-porcelain ring and element subassembly; *C*. Steel cover; *D*. Stud and nut; *E*. Assembly of parts *A*, *B*, *C*, and *D*.

(1) The operator reaches into the tote box on the left and selects one grid casting.

(2) She lifts the casting, examining the edges, and face, and lays it on the bench, face down with the hinge lug toward her.

(3) She reaches with left hand to a pile of units on the conveyor, picks up the top unit, and with both hands—

(4) Places it on the grid casting with the wire leads above the hinge lug.

(5) While the left hand straightens and raises these leads the right hand holds the unit.

(6) The right hand then reaches into the tote box at right and obtains one cover plate which is then—

(7) Placed over the leads onto the grid and unit.

(8) The right hand then reaches into the box containing the studs, obtains one and—

(9) Inserts it through the cover into a tapped hole in the casting.

(10) Then the right hand reaches to the second box and obtains the nut and—

(11) Starts it on the stud. During these last operations (8 through 11) the left hand has held the assembly. After starting the nut the right hand—

(12) Obtains the power driver (meanwhile the left hand has pushed the assembly to a rough position below the power driver), then—

(13) The right hand places the power driver on the stud and nut and—

(14) Operates the power driver. As the right hand—

(15) Releases the power driver the left hand lifts the assembly from the bench. The right hand then—

(16) Grasps the assembly and—

(17) Places it on a stack of completed assemblies to the right of the work place and returns to the work place empty.

Procedure

1. *Record all Pertinent Data for the Job*

   a. On the front or "Summary Side" of the Computation Sheet (Fig. 189) write, in the spaces indicated: The department, department number, analyst's name, drawing number of the assembly, date, and the name of the foreman in charge.

   b. Also, list under "Equipment," and note position of each item on the sketch, those pieces of equipment and all parts provided for the operation.

   c. On the back of the sheet write a brief title or description of the operation in the section headed operation (section 1 of Fig. 190).

2. *Analyze the Assembly Cycle*

   a. Reduce the operation to a succession of smaller elements based on a combination of "Get and Place" or "Get, Place, Use, and Dispose" for each part and tool in the cycle.

   b. List these elements on the back of the sheet in section 2 (Fig. 190) under "Elements of the Operation."

   c. Analyze each of these elements successively. Evaluate any inherent qualities or peculiarities of design or setup for each element and determine the proper classification of each in relation to the class definitions.

   d. Check the proper class (sections 3 and 5) opposite each assembly element.

   e. Check in section 4 those elements involving transport distances greater than the allowed maximum for the class.

   f. Analyze complete assembly and note possible need for any inspection before, during, or after assembly. Indicate probable frequency of such inspection if required.

   g. Analyze the setup for allowances for replenishing both major and small parts. Make the proper notations required.

3. *Calculate the Assembly Operation Time*
   a. Add the check marks in each column of sections 3, 4, and 5 (Fig. 190).
   b. Multiply the standard time for each by the number of check marks in that column.
   c. Total the results and enter in column 6.

4. *Standard Time Calculation*
   a. The total time for the assembly cycle, foot of column 6 (Fig. 190), is entered on the summary page (Fig. 189), following "Total Time," in this case 0.434 minute.
   b. The allowance for replenishing parts is calculated in two parts.
      (1) Two tote boxes, 20 parts in each, supply the two large parts. Proper values are inserted in the formula, $\dfrac{(0.40 \text{ min.} \times \text{no. boxes})}{(\text{No. pcs. per box})} = \text{time}$ per cycle, on the summary page (Fig. 189). The time per cycle is calculated and posted. $\left(\dfrac{0.40 \times 2}{20} = 0.040 \text{ min.}\right)$
      (2) Replenishing small parts, nut and stud, is handled on a percentage basis. Two per cent is added to the operator's fatigue and personal allowance for this item.
   c. To the Total Time (a) above is added the time per cycle for moving tote boxes. The sum of these two values is entered in the center of the fourth line. (0.434 + 0.040 = 0.474 minute.)
   d. The total percentage allowance given the operator for fatigue and personal time and for other reasons is then recorded to the right on the third line.
      This percentage in this instance is 8 per cent fatigue and personal + 2 per cent for parts replenishing, or a total of 10 per cent.
   e. This percentage (d) is added to the total time (c) and the sum in minutes is entered on the fourth line at the right, preceding "Standard Time." 0.474 + (0.10 × 0.474) = 0.474 + 0.047 = 0.521 minute.

DETAILS OF ANALYSIS

Analysis of the Cycle. In the "Description of Cycle" the operation has been outlined in step form. Breaking this outline down into Elements of the Operation in form appropriate for recording on the back of the Computation Sheet (Fig. 190), we have:

1. Get (1) and Place (2) grid on table (see page 349).
2. Get (3) and Place (4) unit on grid.
3. Get and Place (5) wire leads. Adjustment only. (This is a simple position-adjusting operation.)
4. Get (6), and Place (7) cover.
5. Get (8), Place and Start (9) stud.
6. Get (10), Place and Start (11) nut.

STANDARD TIMES COMPUTATION SHEET

| DEPT.: Appliance | DEPT. NO.: 53 | ANALYST: L.A. Smith |

DRAWING NUMBER: 119Y197

DATE: 1-5-40   FOREMAN: R.T. Moore

Time to Move $=\dfrac{.40 \times \text{No. Bxs.}}{\text{No. Pcs./Bx.}} = \dfrac{.40 \times 2}{20} = .040$ Min.

Tote Boxes

Fatigue Allowance $= 8\%$

Replenish Sm. Parts $= 2\%$ $\} = 10\%$

$\left[\begin{array}{c}\text{Total Time}\\\text{in Minutes}\end{array}\right] .434 + \left[\begin{array}{c}\text{Move Tote Bx.}\\\text{Time/Pc.}\end{array}\right] = .474 + \left[\begin{array}{c}10\%\\\text{Allowance}\end{array} \text{ or } .047\right] = .521$ STANDARD TIME IN MINUTES

WORK PLACE   Scale: 1 unit = 3"

EQUIPMENT (Check on Work place):

1. Power Driver
2. Tote Box-Grids
3. Tote Box-Covers
4. Porcelain Units, Stacked
5. Studs
6. Nuts
7. Completed Assemblies

1   4   Bins 5   6   7   Fixture   Tote Box 2   Operator   Tote Box 3

COMMENTS:

Studs and Nuts are Supplied in Cardboard Boxes,
3 in. Deep x 4 in. x 5 in.

Foreman finds it necessary for operator to inspect
all grid castings for tapped holes, grinding marks,
and cleanliness.

GENERAL ASSEMBLY STANDARD TIMES	SIZE OF OBJECT:	M. (3F)	L. (H)	S. (2F)	V.L. (2H)	TIME CLASS
OPERATION CONDITIONS		TIME IN MINUTES				
Get Condition A	Very best grasp facility possible. The object is pre-positioned for grasp, or the grasp is not hindered by other objects in contact with the object grasped. Size of object need not be considered.	.007	.007	.007	.007	C 1
Get Condition B	Grasp is easily made but parts may be in quantities requiring some selection of a single part. No untangling or difficult separation is required.	.007	.013	.013	.013	C 2
Get Condition C	The design of parts or kind of finish prevents ready grasping. Parts may tangle, nest together, or be packed with separators, or require special handling.	.013	.021	.021		C 3
					.026	C 4
Place Condition A	Place objects where positioning is normally little more than releasing the object or moving it slightly on the work place.	.007	.007	.007		C 1
					.013	C 2
Place Condition B	Place objects where positioning consists of some definite location, simple open nests, or fixtures with ample tolerances, or assemblies with one point of location.	.007	.013	.013	.021	C 3
Place Condition C	Place objects where positioning is in difficult or complicated locations. Assemblies or fixtures requiring the positioning of parts with respect to two definite points, or location in two directions.	.013	.021	.021		C 4
					.036	C 5
Place Condition D	Positioning is much the same as Condition C but in addition may involve close tolerances, greater care of finishes, three or more points or directions of location, or application of force to assemble.	.021	.026	.026	.048	C 6

FIG. 189—Standard Times Computation Sheet for waffle-iron assembly—Front.

OPERATION: Assemble unit & cover to lower grid casting 119Y197 waffle iron.

STANDARD TIMES

ELEMENTS OF THE OPERATION	C 1 12" MAXIMUM G&P .007	C 1 G2 .010	C 1 P2 .011	C 2 24" MAXIMUM G&P .013	C 2 G2 .017	C 2 P2 .020	C 3 24" MAXIMUM G&P .021	C 3 G2 .028	C 3 P2 .031	C 4 24" G&P .026	C 4 P2 .039	C 5 24" P .036	C 6 24" P .048	T.E. AT L. OVER 24" UP TO 36" .012	WALKING PER FOOT .007	PROCESS Power Driver	TOTAL TIME IN MINUTES
1. Get & Place Grid on Table							GP						P				.054
2. Get & Place Unit on Grid				G								P		✓			.049
3. Get & Place Wire Leads (Adjustment Only)	GP																.014
4. Get & Place Cover							G						P	✓			.081
5. Get, Place, & Start Stud	SS						GP										.056
6. Get, Place, & Start Nut	SN						GP										.056
7. Get, Place, Use, & Dispose Power Driver	D G						P							✓		✓	.058
8. Get & Dispose Assembly	G						D										.040
9. Inspect Grid Castings (100% Inspection)																	.026
																	.434

Notes: (element 7) Part of element 1 above. (element 9) Examine for tapped hole, and grinding marks on edge, and clean lines.

G or P = "Get" or "Place" parts individually
G2 or P2 = "Get" or "Place" two parts (one with each hand) simultaneously
Walking = Transport Empty & Transport Loaded over 36 in. up to 7 ft.

PROCESS TIMES

PROCESS	LIGHT SMALL	MEDIUM	HEAVY LARGE	
Power Driver	.020	—	.036	.020
Drive Sc.-Friction Dr.	.020	—	.010	.010
Tub. Riveter-Air Press	.010	—	.025	.011
Sm. Punch Press or Welder	.015	.020	.030	.024
Operate Kick Press	.020	.030	.040	.018
Hd. Sc. Driver/Thread	.020	.030	.050	.003
Inspect/Point	.030	.030	—	
Soldering (No "Place" included)	.030	.030	.050	

Fig. 190—Standard Times Computation Sheet for waffle-iron assembly—Back.

7. Get (12), Place (13), Use (14), and Dispose (15) of power driver.
8. Get (16) and Dispose (17) of assembly.
9. Inspect Grid Castings [included in (2)]. An inspection element is kept separate from the cycle elements as unusual conditions may alter its importance from time to time. In this particular instance the inspection is 100 per cent.

Analysis of Elements of the Operation. Section 1 (Operation) and Section 2 (Elements of Operation) of the "Breakdown" side of the Computation Sheet (Fig. 190) have now been filled in. The method of evaluating each Element is presented below. In this example, the letters G, P, D, and S are used for the sake of clarity instead of check marks. These indicate the nature of the check, Get, Place, Dispose, and Start, respectively.

1. *Get and Place Grid Casting on Work Place*

    Get   The grid casting is supplied in a tote box to the operator's left. The distance from the work place is 30 inches. The grid is a *large* part leaning against others. This is a Class 3 Get as the parts are not supplied with easy grasp provided.
    Check G and P, Class 3, 0.021 minute.

    Place   The grid is placed on the work place bottom side up with the hinge lug toward the operator. This is a Class 3 Place as the grids are not supplied in a manner to permit this position automatically, hence, although the part does not go into a fixture, Class 3 is preferred to Class 2.
    Check G and P, Class 3, 0.021 minute.
    Since the grid casting is supplied at 30 inches an additional transport empty and transport loaded allowance is required.
    Check transport empty and transport loaded over 24 inches up to 36 inches, 0.012 minute.

2. *Get and Place Unit on Grid*

    Get   The porcelain units are supplied by the previous operator who stacks them, five or six per pile, about 20 inches from the work place. There is no difficulty encountered in grasping the unit. This is a Class 2 Get as the parts are in quantities, but there is no tangling or difficult separation involved.
    Check G and P, Class 2, 0.013 minute.

    Place   The brick is placed on the grid casting lining up two recesses in the brick with two bosses on the grid. The bricks are always supplied right side up.
    This is a Class 5 Place as the part is guided by two hands into a position involving two points of location.
    Check P, Class 5, 0.036 minute.

3. Get and Place Wire Leads

This is merely an adjustment of the leads, already assembled to the brick, to facilitate the next assembly operation.

Get   The left hand grasps the two leads, which are pointing toward the operator and afford easy grasp. A simple Class 1 Get. Check *G* and *P*, Class 1, 0.007 minute.

Place   The left hand raises the leads to a vertical position and straightens them as they slide through the fingers. A simple Class 1 Place. Check *G* and *P* Class 1, 0.007 minute.

4. Get and Place Cover

Get   The covers are supplied in a tote box to the operator's right at a distance from the work place of about 30 inches. The cover is a large part leaning against, or piled upon, others. This is a Class 3 Get as the parts are not supplied with easy grasp provided in Class 2. Check *G* and *P*, Class 3, 0.021 minute.

Place   The cover is placed over the vertical leads from the unit (one point of location) and with two hands is placed on the assembly, lining up two holes in the cover with two bosses on the brick (second and third point of location). Large parts placed with two hands, location on 3 points of assembly require Place Class 6. Check *P*, Class 6, 0.048 minute.

Since the cover is supplied at 30 inches an additional transport empty and transport loaded is required.

Check transport empty and transport loaded over 24 inches up to 36 inches, 0.012 minute.

5. Get, Place, and Start Stud

Get   Screws, nuts, and other non-tangling hardware items normally are provided with Class 2 Get. In this case well-designed trays have not been provided for the stud. Grasp is hindered by the size and shape of the containers and Class 3 Get is used. Check *G* and *P*, Class 3, 0.021 minute.

Place   The stud is inserted through a large hole in the cover into a tapped hole in the grid. The stud and tapped hole are designed to facilitate assembly and would normally be Class 2, but the difficulty of placing through the hole in the cover justifies use of Class 3. Check *G* and *P*, Class 3, 0.021 minute.

Start   Place includes insertion of the stud but rigidity requires an additional turning of the stud. Allow a simple Get and Place Class 1 for turning the stud an additional one or two threads. Check *twice G* and *P* Class 1, 0.007 minute.

6. *Get, Place, and Start Nut*

Get   The nut is also supplied in an improper container. This is also a Class 3 Get for the same reasons as 5 above.
Check *G* and *P*, Class 3, 0.021 minute.

Place   The nut requires as much location as the stud, but in addition must be kept perpendicular to the stud in starting. This element is usually Class 3. .
Check *G* and *P*, Class 3, 0.021 minute.

Start   Check *twice G* and *P*, Class 1, for same reason as 5 above.

7. *Get, Place, Use, and Dispose of Power Driver*

Get   The power driver is suspended over the work place providing nearly perfect grasp facility. This is properly a Class 1 Get. However, the left hand is positioning the assembly during the Get so the Get is properly a Class 1 simultaneous Get.
Check *G* 2, Class 1, 0.010 minute.

Place   Placing the power driver on the stud and nut requires locating the driver in two directions. (Class 3 definition.)
Check *G* and *P*, Class 3, 0.021 minute.

Use   Driving the stud and nut with the power driver has been determined on an average basis and a separate column incorporated for this element.
Check Process times, Power Driver, 0.020 minute.

Dispose As the power driver is spring suspended, disposing of it is a simple motion to approximate position and a release. This is Class 1 Place.
Check *G* and *P*, Class 1, 0.007 minute.

8. *Get and Dispose of Assembly*

Get   The left hand has been holding the assembly during the use of the power driver. While the right hand disposes of the driver the left raises the assembly, positioning it for grasp. This is necessary as the progressive assembly moves from left to right and the completed assembly is stacked at the right. Since the assembly is pre-positioned for grasp, the Get is Class 1.
Check *G* and *P*, Class 1, 0.007 minute.

Dispose The assembly is placed on a stack of previously completed assemblies. This requires precise positioning, definite location. Use, Place, Class 3.
Check *G* and *P*, Class 3, 0.021 minute.
The dispose distance is over 24 inches so check transport empty and transport loaded over 24 inches up to 36 inches, 0.012 minute.

9. *Inspect Grid Castings, 100 Per Cent*

In each cycle it is necessary to give the grid casting a quick inspection. This element is an addition to the place element (1). It has been evaluated on therblig time values.

1. Examine casting for tapped hole:
    a. focus eyes on hole .... 0.002 minute
    b. examine hole .... 0.003 minute
2. Examine edge for grinding marks and face for cleanliness:
    a. turn casting over .... 0.003 minute
    b. focus eyes three times (3 × 0.002) .... 0.006 minute
    c. examine three points (3 × 0.003) .... 0.009 minute
    d. turn casting over .... 0.003 minute

    Total .... 0.026 minute

Classification of Parts Assembled in a Department. After the basic classification has been worked out and put in use it is customary to compile a list of the parts assembled in a given department, listing them by (kind of grasp) size of part.

The following is an abbreviated list of the parts for the Appliance Manufacturing Department.

1. *Small*

Parts held by two fingers and thumb. Any parts whose small size will not accommodate three fingers and thumb, fingers not crowding.

Examples: Screws   Bearings (mixer)
          Nuts   Brushes (carbon)
          Washers   Fuse links
          Studs   Fuses (small cartridge or percolator)
          Pins

2. *Medium*

Parts held by three fingers and thumb. Any parts which can accommodate three fingers and thumb without crowding or extending of the hand. These parts are the easiest to control.

Examples: Percolator units   Mixer and small fan
          Standard sockets   motors
          Waffle iron side   Radio tubes
            handles   Standard outlets
                   Standard glass fuses

3. *Large*

Parts held by the extended hand. Any parts which require the extending of the hand to hold them.

Examples: Toaster baskets
          Percolator lids
          Percolator body
          Percolator bases

Large fuse cut-outs
Sandwich grill support
Waffle grill support

4. *Very large*

Parts held by two hands. Any parts whose size, weight, design, or finish makes a two-handed control necessary.

Examples: 12″ and 16″ fan motor
          Waffle iron base
          Bundle of unwrapped
             cords

Waffle iron
Mixer motor (less handle)
Roaster body
Fan guards (large)

CHAPTER 24

TRAINING THE OPERATOR

It is not the purpose here to discuss the broad field of employee training but rather to present some specific methods that have been found useful in training operators to do a particular job. Such training is usually given by the supervisory force although the motion and time study analyst or a special instructor may handle this work.

Although we often have pictured for us large groups of workers performing identical routine operations over long periods, actually this is not the typical situation even in large plants. Not only does the worker normally perform many different operations in the course of a month but with constant changes in methods, with improvements in materials, and with the rapid introduction of new models, there is a never-ending succession of new jobs which the operator must learn. It seems that the worker today, more than ever before, must be able to do a variety of work, which tends to increase the amount of training required in industry.

Training Methods on Simple Operations. The best method imaginable for doing a given task is of little value unless the operator can and will do the work in the prescribed manner. Where one or a very few persons are employed on a given job and where the work is relatively simple, the ordinary instruction sheet forms an excellent guide for training the operator. Also, on semi-skilled work where the worker is familiar with the operation of the machine but needs instructions for the performance of particular operations, the simple instruction sheet is satisfactory. For example, the one shown in Fig. 191 not only gives a written description of the elements required for turning the gear blank but the drawing at the top of the sheet shows the exact location of the tools and of the parts to be machined. The time value for each element is also included as well as the total standard time for the operation.

Where the work is entirely manual, instructions prepared on the order of the operation chart shown in Fig. 16 on page 41 are of value in that they indicate exactly what hand motions are required and show the layout of the work place as well.

INSTRUCTION SHEET

Customer Amer. Tool Co.

Part Name Spur gear   Case D

Part No. 1073 A–F

Operation Name Drill, rough one side and ¾ of outside diameter

Operation No. 5 TR.

Dept. 11   Machine class, 5S   Machine name, Jones & Lamson

Made by S. R. K.   Approved by S. M.   Date 7–9–35 Mat'l SAE2315

Tool layout

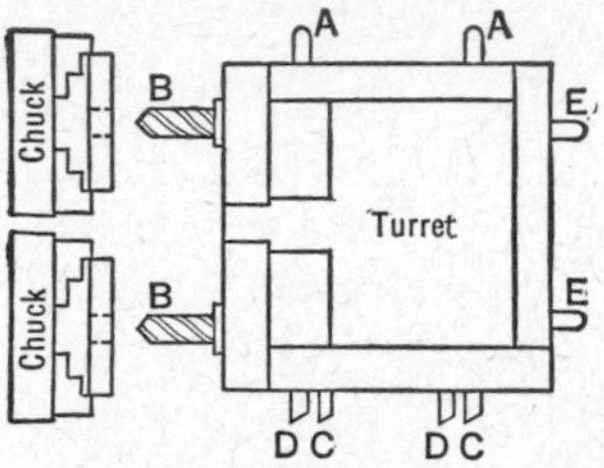

Set-up Time:
New set-up   60.00
Change of size 30.00

No.	Procedure	Tools—jigs, etc.	Speed Setting	Ft./ min.	Feed Setting	In./ rev.	Base time
1	Pick up and chuck 2 pieces						0.12
2	Start machine and true up (if necessary)						0.10
3	Change speed						0.03
4	Adv. turret and throw in feed						0.06
5	ROUGH OUTSIDE DIAMETER (¾)	A. ¾×1¼ in. tools	70	71	0.014		2.32
6	Back turret and index						0.07
7	Advance turret, set headstock, throw in feed and change speed						0.12
8	DRILL	B. 1 3⁄16 in. drills	60	71	0.014		0.58
9	Back turret and index						0.07
10	Advance turret and lock						0.08
11	Advance headstock, change speed and throw in feed						0.08
12	ROUGH FACE 1 SIDE	C. ¾×1¼ in. tools	70	71	0.014		1.65
13	ROUGH FACE HUB	D. ¾×1¼ in. tools	30	71	0.014		
14	Unlock, back and index turret						0.07
15	Advance turret and set head stock						0.09
16	CHAMFER INSIDE FLANGE	E. ¾×1¼ in. Form tools	70	Hand			0.10
17	Advance head stock						0.06
18	CHAMFER HUB	E. ¾×1¼ in. Form tools	30	Hand			0.10
19	Back turret and index						0.07
20	Set head stock						0.12
21	Stop machine						0.03
22	Loosen and remove 2 pieces						0.10
	Total handling time for two pieces						1.47
	Total machine time for two pieces						4.55
	Total base time for two pieces						6.02
	Total base time for one piece						3.01
	Allowances 10 per cent						0.30
	Standard time in minutes per piece						3.31

FIG. 191—Instruction sheet for turret lathe operation, size 8½ × 11 inches.

Another case is taken from a chocolate factory. When a new box or a new assortment of chocolates is to be packed the pattern is determined and then the operators are required to pack by this pattern. The customary procedure was to send a sample package to the supervisor, along with the order for packing. Very often the first order was a rush one and a number of operators were put on packing at once. In order for the operators to begin work the supervisor had to pack a sample box for each of them, often having the girls standing around waiting while this was being done. The use of an instruction sheet similar to that shown in Fig. 192 prepared in advance, and reproduced by hectograph, has not only saved the waiting time on the part of the operators but has also enabled them to bring their packing speed up to standard in a very short time.

The use of still pictures in connection with written instructions as shown in Fig. 193 has proved very effective in supplementing the efforts of the instructor in training operators at an eastern rubber company.[1] It seems that much of the skill required in doing some kinds of manual work centers around the exact way certain therbligs are performed, particularly grasp, hold, position, and pre-position. It appears that the transport and use therbligs require less attention and are more easily taught. In other words, it is more useful to show the operator how to take hold of the object previous to moving it, and how to position it before releasing it, than it is to show actually the transportation or movement of the object. Therefore, a satisfactory explanation of how to do the work can frequently be presented without reproducing the "motions" involved, which would require motion pictures. Since a series of key pictures is required for each instruction sheet, the problem of quickly making these pictures is a rather important one. It was solved by A. Williams, Jr., by mounting a camera, exposure meter, and framing device on one unit as shown in Fig. 194. This setup insures proper "framing" of the subject and correct location of the camera for distance. Whenever needed, two reflectors with photoflood lamps may be clamped to the sides of the board which carries the camera.

Another example of the usefulness of still pictures is given in Fig. 82 on page 166 showing how the operator grasps the bone and how she positions it at the beginning of the creasing motion in folding paper.

Training Methods on Complex Operations. There are some operations that are complex in nature and may require considerable skill on

---

[1] A. Williams, "Teach It With Pictures," *Factory Management and Maintenance,* Vol. 94, No. 12, pp. 50-51, December, 1936.

½ Lb. BLUE RIBBON BOX (Flange) List No. 4623–12

Cups	Unit No.	Name	Cups	Unit No.	Name
Round	203	Raspberry Cup	Round	376	Caramelized Brazil
"	204	Apricot Cup	"	392	Croquante Whirl
"	221	Strawberry Creme	"	393	Vanilla Caramel
"	275	Coffee Creme	"	394	Marzipan Sandwich
"	371	Orange Marzipan	"	396	Tosca Pate

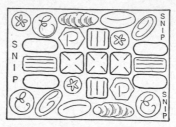

Heavy lines
= Foil Covered
Units

Make weight with Accommodation Units, one less than weight of last Chocolate.
If Light Add: 1 Croquante Whirl, 1 Apricot Cup.
If Heavy Take Out: 1 Apricot Cup.

	No.		Patt. No.	Paper No.
Linings (Center) (Emb. E.				
Foil)...........	1	13, ⅜ × 6, ⅞	Shaped	8795
" (Ends)...........	2	4, ⅞ × 2, ¹⁵⁄₁₆	3226	8796
Top-Pad.................	1	6, ¹³⁄₁₆ × 4, ¹³⁄₁₆	....	4990
" Stock No. 04990—				
To be cleared first				
Cups (Round)...........	25	....	.....	3569
Wrap..................	1	14, ¹³⁄₁₆ × 11, ⅛	2716	142
Wrap fastened on bottom				
with Gloy, ends folded				
and fastened on bottom				
with Gloy.				
Printed Identification Key.	1	8, ¾ × 6, ⅞	....	5070

Snip—Brown.
Filled on Printed Identification.
Tear-off Price Seal (Stk. No. 2878) on wrap, top-left.

Foil (Stock No. 8666) Blue and Silver E. Design—to be used when Stk.
No. 08666 is cleared.

FOILS

Stock No. 08666—Blue Printing on Silver.

Symbol No. F. 136.
Outer No. R. 976—Packed ¼ dozen.
Outer tied String—Single.

Width of Reel 3″ for Tosca Pate, Marzipan Sandwich and Strawberry Creme.

First packing to be sent to Inspection Office.
Issued to Inspection Office from New Lines Office.

New Lines Office,
January 14, 1937.

FIG. 192—Instruction sheet for packing chocolates, size 8½ × 11 inches.

the part of the operator for their satisfactory performance. A much longer training period is ordinarily required for this type of work than for simpler operations.

Where a sizable group of employees is engaged on such work there is an opportunity for a more elaborate training program. Some companies find it profitable under such conditions to establish a vestibule training school or a separate training department apart from the regular production departments, although the tendency is away from this procedure.

With over 100 operators on the semi-automatic lathe operation described on page 19 the company established a special school for training new operators for this work. Whereas it formerly took six months to train these operators it now requires but six to eight weeks.

To cite another case [2] of group training on complex operations, L. P. Persing of the Fort Wayne works of the General Electric Company supervised the training of 200 new operators hired for a rush job of assembling large numbers of extremely delicate parts required in the manufacture of electric meters.

The entire assembly process was broken down into small assemblies and these were studied in order to determine the best way of making these subassemblies. Where special trays, fixtures, and combination tools were required these were built and the correct layout of the work place was arranged. One operator was trained by the instructor and, after she became proficient in the new method, motion pictures were made of the operation so they might be used in the training of the other operators.

It was found practicable to train 18 operators at one time. The training of this group was carried out in the following way. Eighteen duplicate sets of trays and tools were installed in exactly the same way on tables in the motion study laboratory (see Fig. 28 on page 73. The operators were all seated at these tables facing the motion-picture screen at the front of the room. A general explanation of the operation was made and instructions were given in the care that should be exercised in handling the parts so that the finish would not be marred or intricate and delicate parts damaged during the assembly operation. The motion pictures of the operation were then projected several times on the screen, both forward and backward and at reduced speed so that the new operators could see the correct way of doing the work. With the projector running very slowly the instructor

    [2] L. P. Persing, "Motion Study—The Teacher," *Factory and Ind. Management*, Vol. 83, No. 9, pp. 337-340, September, 1932.

OPERATION: Lacing
TYPES: L.T.T.—S.U.
DETAIL: 1 Spindle
MACHINE: Ensign
CODE: No. 52

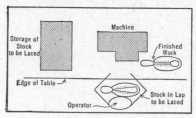

Sketch of Layout

Get next upper like this, first finger of left hand between eyelet edges.

Lift upper from stack with left hand, inserting second, third, and fourth fingers in top of shoe. Insert first finger of left hand between eyelet edges.

Line up eyelet edges by moving hands in opposite directions and closing eyelet edges together.

Get top end of eyelet edges between thumb and first finger of right hand. Move first finger of left hand out from between eyelet edges and grasp edges like this.

Position fifth eyelet over spindle.

Pull upper down onto spindle.

Press down pedal to start machine and move fingers to this position.

Hold upper while being laced. As spindle is automatically removed, upper is moved up and slightly to right while machine ties knot and cuts thread. Laced upper is finished in this position.

Move finished upper to a position over stack of finished uppers.

Place finished upper on stack.

Repeat Cycle.

FIG. 193—Instruction sheet for lacing tennis shoes.

pointed out the correct way of grasping, carrying, positioning the parts, and of performing each of the other motions of the cycle. Two instructors were used; one operated the projector and explained the motions, and the other, an experienced operator, gave individual instruction and inspected the work for the group.

By employing the ordinary method of using an experienced operator to train one or two new operators on the production floor the experienced operator produced but 40 to 50 per cent of her normal output. Also this method of training required an exceedingly long

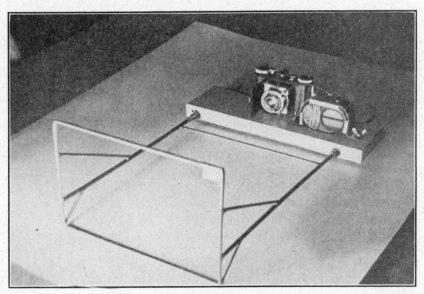

Fig. 194—Camera setup for taking still pictures used with instruction sheet on page 364.

training period. Using the new method two instructors trained eighteen new operators in a separate room where there was no interference with the regular manufacturing operations. At the end of one week of training the eighteen operators were transferred to the production floor properly trained for their task. This was but one-third the time required for training new operators by the old method.

Mr. Persing gives the following reasons why they prefer to train the operators in a separate room: [3]

[3] *Ibid.*, p. 339.

1. We could get 100 per cent attention. There was not the confusion and noise of other activities to distract the operator's attention such as you have on the average manufacturing floor.
2. The operator does not get as nervous when trained in a separate room. There are not a lot of other workers watching the instructor teach the new cycle of motions, which in general are a great deal different from those they have seen before, and the layout of the trays is a curiosity.
3. When any problem came up that was of interest to all the operators, you could get their attention at once and explain how to overcome or correct the fault.
4. As the operators on this particular operation were to be taught the cycle of motions by watching the experienced operator assemble the register on the moving-picture screen, it was necessary that the room be in semi-darkness.

Training School for New Employees. Metropolitan-Vickers in Manchester, England, gives instruction in the basic principles of motion economy to all new girls at the time they are employed. Miss A. G. Shaw, who has charge of this work, explains the training program as follows: "There is little mass production in the factory as nearly all the work is made to order and few operators are on the same job all the time. Thus it is impossible to train operators on any specific job. A job analysis of all women's work in the factory revealed features common to various groups. It was possible, with this in mind, to organize a training school that would teach the operators the correct work methods within such groups and give them general ideas of motion economy.

"During the first week in the training school, the girls are taught to use both hands and to handle a screwdriver and hammer correctly. Concurrently, they are given lectures explaining the reasons why certain things are done in certain ways, supplemented by a series of talks on general factory procedure. It is felt that, unless they understand why an operation is performed in a certain way, they will not be able to transfer the benefits of their training when confronted with a different set of circumstances in the shops. At the end of the first week they are tested on these points, and, if they pass at Standard A, they move to another group of more difficult jobs, either assembly, coil taping, inspection, or machine work. They are subsequently tested each week on this special work and when they reach a specified standard, and only then, they are transferred to the various departments in the factory. Girls who fail in the first test repeat the preliminary course again and, if they pass at the end of the second week at Standard A, they follow on as previously outlined—this allows for those who are slow learners. If they pass at Standard B, they go on to simpler work, and if they fail they are discharged as unsuitable.[4] All work done in the training school is productive, having to meet inspection standards before passing to the departmental stores, thus none of the work is wasted, and trainees feel they are contributing to the work of the factory. They are paid the standard hourly rate for their age and towards the end of their training period work to piece rates. The fulfilment of this scheme means that ultimately all women in the factory will be using motion study methods." [5]

The Colonial Radio Corporation is now successfully operating a school for training new assembly operators. All girls at the time of employment are given two to three days' training in a separate room under the supervision of a competent instructor.

The classroom contains assembly benches with jigs, fixtures, hand tools, and the necessary parts and bins to handle such typical factory operations as screwdriver work, assembly and bench work with pliers, and soldering operations. Groups of 8 to 12, and never more than 15, are trained at a time. The girls are paid their regular base wage during the training period. At the beginning of the training period a simple explanation of the purpose of the course is given to the group. Extracts from this explanation are given below:

"As you are probably aware, the purpose of this class is to teach a better way of performing some of our more common assembly operations which involve such familiar parts as nuts, screws, lockwashers, wires, condensers, resistors, etc.

"All of us realize the fact that certain ways of doing a thing are better than others. It has been established that there is a best way of performing any given act, and we have also made the discovery, which most of you have probably known all along, that the best way is almost invariably, also, the easiest way. Haven't you found this to be the case in your experience?

"Just as you in your home attempt to find the best way of performing your household duties, so, in industry, we attempt to find the best way of doing the things required of us.

"It has been established that at least 25% of the motions used by the average employee in the average factory operations are wasted

---

[4] The program is arranged to permit a girl to complete the training work in the school in as short a period as two weeks if she is able to pass the tests.

[5] A. C. Shaw, "Motion Study and Its Applications," *The Woman Engineer*, Vol. 4, No. 4, p. 59, London, September-October, 1935.

motions. These wasted motions are needless motions which contribute only one thing as far as the operator or the operation is concerned, and that is fatigue.

"Naturally you may ask—'What is the purpose of finding the best and easiest way of performing operations in the plant?' This can be stated briefly as follows:

"It is the desire on the part of Colonial to build a better radio set at a lower cost without, however, requiring the expenditure of any more physical effort on the part of those of us directly engaged in building them.

"All of you realize the amount of work we have in our plant depends on the number of radio sets the Sales Organization of the Colonial Radio Company can sell. When you and I, and millions of other consumers, decide to buy a radio set, or any other merchandise, we always attempt to get the best product we can for the money we want to spend, and, if the best radio set we can buy for a given sum of money happens to be a Colonial radio, we will buy it. In other words, the welfare of the Colonial Radio Corporation and, coincidentally in a large measure, all of us, depends on the ability of Colonial to build at least as good a set as any other manufacturer at the same or at a lower price."

After the above explanation has been made and any questions by members of the class have been discussed, the group is given a simple assembly operation to perform. An explanation is given of what the finished job must be like and then each person is allowed to do the task in any way that she wishes. Each girl is given a timer and pencil and paper to record the time for making ten assemblies.

She continues to do this task for an hour or so, recording the time for each set of ten assemblies.

Then an assembly fixture and improved bins are given to the operator. The proper arrangement of the work place is made and the girl is carefully instructed in the proper method of doing the work. An explanation is also given as to the principles of motion economy employed and why the new method is easier and faster than the old one.

After the girl understands how to do the task in the proper way, she again works for an hour or so timing herself for groups of ten pieces and recording the time as before.

The fact that the improved method saves time is obvious to her since she has set her own pace and read and recorded her own time. She is well aware that motion study is not a "speed up" but that it enables her to do more work with less fatigue.

After the new girl has worked on a simple assembly operation, she is given other jobs that are typical of those she will see in the factory and perhaps some of which she will work on after the training period is over.

Although the main purpose of school is to train new operators in the principles of motion economy, Colonial has found that the school also serves another very important function in that it shows the employees in a most convincing manner that improving methods of doing work is for their benefit as well as for the company and that actually the best way from a motion study angle is invariably the least fatiguing way and the most satisfactory way in every respect for the operator.

Incidentally, it requires approximately 50 per cent less time for a girl who has been through the training school to attain standard performance than for new girls going directly onto the production floor without the training.

During the past two years more than 700 girls have been trained in the manner described above.

PROBLEMS

Chapter 1

1. Define motion and time study according to (a) Taylor, (b) Gilbreth, and (c) Farmer.[1]

2. Explain fully the meaning of the phrase "most economical way of doing work."

3. What does the field of industrial engineering include? Show how motion and time study fits into this picture.

Chapter 2

4. Give a sketch of the life of Frederick W. Taylor.

5. Summarize Taylor's investigations of: (a) handling pig iron; (b) cutting metals; (c) shoveling.

6. Give a sketch of the life of Frank B. Gilbreth.

7. Summarize Gilbreth's investigations of: (a) bricklaying; (b) work at the New England Butt Co.; [2] (c) work for the handicapped.[3]

8. Give the chief criticisms of motion and time study and evaluate each.

Chapter 3

9. What factors affect the extent to which motion and time study may be profitably used?

10. Indicate the extent of a motion and time study investigation for a department in a plant with which you are familiar.

11. Explain the "law of diminishing returns," in relation to the desirable elaborateness of a motion and time study program in a plant.

Chapter 4

12. Construct a process chart for the following:

   (a) Writing a letter and mailing it.

   (b) Making a cheese sandwich.

   (c) Making a small gear from a gray iron casting.

   (d) Dressing, having breakfast, and leaving the house in the morning.

[1] Eric Farmer, "Time and Motion Study," *Ind. Fatigue Research Bd.*, Report 14, H. M. Stationery Office, London, 1921. Also see C. S. Myers, "Industrial Psychology in Great Britain," Jonathan Cape, London, 1926; M. S. Viteles, "Industrial Psychology," W. W. Norton & Co., New York, 1932; J. G. Jenkins, "Psychology in Business and Industry," John Wiley & Sons, New York, 1935.

[2] John G. Aldrich, "The Present State of the Art of Industrial Management," Discussion *Trans. A.S.M.E.*, Vol. 34, pp. 1182-87, 1912.

[3] F. B. and L. M. Gilbreth, "Motion Study for the Handicapped," George Routledge & Sons, London, 1920.

13. Work out improvements in Problem 12 *a, b, c,* and *d* and construct a process chart of the new way.

14. Make a right- and left-hand operation chart of the following:
    (*a*) Filling a fountain pen.
    (*b*) Driving a nail in the end of a board.
    (*c*) Drilling a hole in the end of a square bar of steel.
    (*d*) Assembling mounting spring for refrigerator.
    See Fig. 195 on page 373.

CHAPTER 5

15. What would be the ultimate effect on the personnel of an organization of a training program in principles of motion economy for every new employee?

16. Why has micromotion study been used at such an accelerated rate during the past five years?

CHAPTER 6

17. Illustrate each of the 18 therbligs by means of an operation with which you are familiar.

CHAPTER 7

18. Examine three different makes of motion-picture cameras and projectors and evaluate the important features of each for use in micromotion study work.

19. Explain the relationship between "speed" and "f. setting" of a camera.

20. Give the characteristics of ordinary panchromatic and supersensitive panchromatic motion-picture film when used in (*a*) daylight and in (*b*) artificial light (photoflood lamps).

21. Describe the use of an exposure meter.

CHAPTER 8

22. Make a motion picture of:
    (*a*) Drilling ¼-inch hole in the end of a small steel shaft.
    (*b*) Picking up a fountain pen and writing.
    (*c*) Inserting a letter in an envelope and sealing it.
    (*d*) Stapling two 3-inch by 5-inch cards together.

CHAPTER 9

23. Make an analysis sheet of the followng operations. List the therbligs for both hands, omitting the time values.
    (*a*) Assembling the parts of a fountain pen cap.
    (*b*) Filling a fountain pen.
    (*c*) Assembling an automatic pencil.

24. Analyze the film of the operations in Problem 22 and record data on an analysis sheet similar to that shown in Fig. 37 on page 92.

25. Make a simo chart of the operations listed in Problem 22. Use a form similar to that shown in Fig. 38 on page 93.

CHAPTER 10

26. Investigate several different methods of inserting folded letters and cards into envelopes. Is any one method superior to the rest? In what way?

27. Ten brass bolts ³⁄₁₆ inch in diameter project 1 inch above a plastic molded plate in which the head has been imbedded. The bolts are 1 inch apart. Is it better to grasp several nuts at one time and hold them in the palm of the hand while assembling them onto the bolts, or is it better to grasp each nut separately? Explain.

CHAPTER 11

28. What are the main criticisms of the common definition of fatigue? [1]

29. Study the reports of (a) The *Industrial Health Research Board* [2] and (b) the *National Institute of Industrial Psychology* [3] in Great Britain and present a summary of the nature of the work of these two organizations.

30. Give a résumé of the findings of the investigations on fatigue made at the Hawthorne Works of the Western Electric Company.

CHAPTERS 12, 13, and 14

Determine the most economical method of performing the operations described below. Prepare an instruction sheet (omitting the time for each element) of the proposed method showing the motions of the two hands. Include a layout of the work place.

31. The Sampson Paper Company folds 3,000,000 sheets of paper per year. The output consists of fourteen sizes of folded sheets, ranging from 3 inches by 5 inches to 10 inches by 12 inches. The paper is cut and sent to the folding department in bundles of approximately 500 sheets. The operator folds the sheets across the narrow width making a 3-inch by 10-inch flat sheet into a 3-inch by 5-inch folded sheet. After being folded, the sheets are "jogged" into a neat pile and a string is tied around the bundle of 100 sheets. The bundles are placed on the back of the work table.

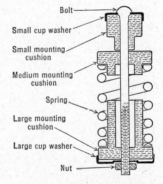

FIG. 195—Mounting spring for refrigerator.

32. An electrical appliance manufacturer has received an order for 50,000 connection plugs for attaching the cord to an electric iron. The plugs are to be shipped in equal installments of 2000 per day. Determine the most economical method of making the final assembly of this unit.

33. The Miller Refrigerator Company has received an order for 100,000 mounting springs similar to the one shown in Fig. 195. Determine the most economical method of assembling the parts.

[1] E. Mayo, "The Human Problems of an Industrial Civilization," Macmillan Co., New York, 1933.

[2] Reports published by H. M. Stationery Office, London.

[3] Official monthly publication *The Human Factor*, Aldwych House, London, W.C. 2.

34. A cabinet manufacturer uses several round-headed wood screw and washer assemblies (see Fig. 196) in the final assembly of one of his products. Orders on hand show that 100,000 of these assemblies will be needed each month for the next six months. On this basis (a total of 600,000 screw and washer assemblies) determine the most economical method for making the assemblies.

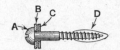

FIG. 196—Wood screw and washer assembly. *A.* Wood screw ³⁄₁₆ × 2¼ inches; *B.* Steel washer ½ inch outside diameter, ⁷⁄₃₂ inch diameter of hole, ¹⁄₁₆ inch thick; *C.* Fiber washer; *D.* The point of the screw is coated with beeswax for a distance of 1 inch.

CHAPTER 15

35. Prepare a written standard practice for Problems 31 to 34 inclusive.

36. The London plant of an American manufacturing company is about to begin manufacturing metal container covers and bottoms similar to those shown on page 42. The manager of the London plant has asked for a description of the method used by the parent plant. (*a*) Outline the essential information that should be included in a motion picture of a simple "blank and draw" operation required for making such a can. (*b*) Prepare the supplementary written data that should accompany the film.

CHAPTER 16

37. Give the arguments that are often presented in favor of time wage rather than an incentive wage for paying factory workers.

38. Interview twenty-five of your acquaintances who are now working in a factory or office. Analyze their comments on the subject of motion and time study.

39. You are the foreman of the assembly department of a plant manufacturing electrical supplies. A program of motion and time study has been in successful operation in your department for two years. John Willis, one of your best employees, asks you if the results of this work will not mean fewer jobs and less work for the employees in the plant. How will you answer?

CHAPTERS 17 and 18

Make a stop-watch study of the following operations. Use the "average" method of selecting the time and include proper allowances. Make an instruction sheet for the operation.

40. Assembling parts of some small article such as a plug for attaching an electric iron.

41. Drilling a hole in a small piece held in a jig.

42. Turning a piece in a lathe.

43. Milling a piece strapped to the table.

CHAPTER 19

44. Determine the standard time for drilling the part shown on sketch at the bottom of the observation sheet on page 263 if the piece is 1.750 inches in diameter and the actual drilling time is 0.94 minute. Use time-setting tables for the sensitive drill.

45. Determine the time required to mill the hexagon, using a gang mill, on part G12W-377A (Fig. 169 on page 298) if the dimension *A* (length of the hexagon) is 1.125 inches and all other dimensions are as shown.

CHAPTER 20

46. Calculate the standard time for cutting teeth on feed change gear part 1060-AF (see Fig. 172 on page 307). Length of face 1.250 inches, diametrical pitch 10, number of teeth 60, spline bore, S.A.E. 2315, hob S10R, plain spur gear. Size of order 50 gears.

47. Determine the standard time required for the operation "solder the side seam" of rectangular can with the following dimensions: length 8.125 inches, width 1 inch, depth 8.5 inches.

CHAPTER 21

48. Determine the standard time required to perform operation 4. "Work out shape through die block" for the blank for the part shown in Fig. 175 on page 319. The blank is 2,000 square with round corners of ¼-inch radius. Quality required is Class B.

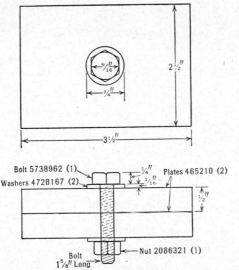

FIG. 197—Plate assembly.

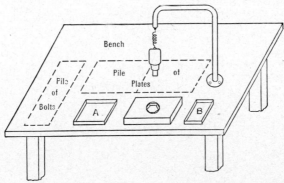

FIG. 198—Arrangement of the work place for the plate assembly.

49. (*a*) Determine the standard time required to "assemble two plates, two washers, bolt and nut," as shown in Fig. 197. The arrangement of the work place is shown in Fig. 198, and the sequence of motions for the right hand and the left hand is given below.

SEQUENCE OF MOTIONS

Operation.—Assembly of 2 plates, 2 washers, bolt and nut

Left Hand	Right Hand
Get nut from tray A	Get washer from tray B
T. E. + G.	T. E. + G.
Place nut in fixture (nest)	U. D.
T. L. + P. + R. L.	
	Place washer in fixture (nest) over nut
	T. L. + P. + R. L.
Get plate from pile	Get plate from pile
T. E. + G.	T. E. + G.
Place plate in fixture	U. D.
T. L. + P. + R. L.	
	Place plate in fixture
	T. L. + P. + R. L.
Get bolt from pile	Get washer from Tray B
T. E. + G.	T. E. + G.
U. D.	Place washer on plate over hole
	T. L. + P. + R. L.
Place bolt in hole	Get power driver
T. L. + P. + R. L.	T. E. + G.
U. D.	Place driver on bolt head
	T. L. + P. + R. L.
	Use time—drive bolt
Get completed assembly	Dispose of driver
T. E. + G.	T. L. + P. + R. L.
Place aside on bench	
T. L. + P. + R. L.	

(*b*) If the plates were placed in one pile rather than two, what difference would it make in the assembly time?

(*c*) How much faster would it be if a dual fixture were used?

(*d*) Would it be advantageous to mount the driver under the bench and drive the nut from below? How might such a setup be arranged?

(*e*) In the present layout the washer is placed over the hole on the plate. Would it be quicker and easier to assemble the washer to the bolt first? Design a fixture which would make such an arrangement possible. Determine the standard time.

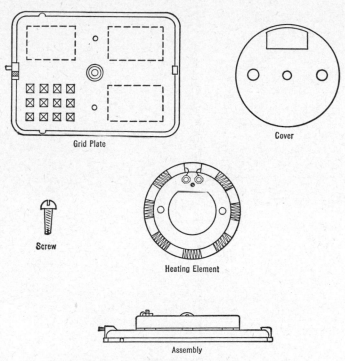

Fig. 199—Parts for heating element assembly.

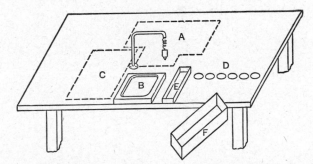

Fig. 200—Arrangement of the work place for the assembly of heating elements.

50. (a) Determine the standard time required to "assemble heating element to grid," as shown in Fig. 199. The arrangement of the work place is shown in Fig. 200, and the sequence of motions for the right hand and the left hand is given on the next page.

Sequence of Motions

Operation.—Assemble heating element to grid

Left Hand	Right Hand
Get aluminum grid from pile A on bench T. E. + G. Place in fixture B	Get aluminum grid from pile A on bench T. E. + G. Get heating element from pile D on bench (from next bench) T. E. + G.
Get cover from pile C on bench	Place heating element in position on aluminum grid
T. E. + G. Place cover over heating element T. L. + P. + R. L. Get power driver T. E. + G. Place driver on screw T. L. + P. + R. L.	T. L. + P. + R. L. Get screw from tray E T. E. + G. Place screw in hole T. L. + P. + R. L. (Guide screw)
Place driver aside T. L. + P. + R. L. U. D.	Use time—drive screw Get assembled part T. E. + G. Place assembled part (in pairs) aside in tote box F T. L. + P. + R. L.

(b) If tray E containing the screws were placed on the left-hand side of the work place alongside covers at C, what difference would it make in the total assembly time? Make up chart showing motion sequence with this rearrangement of parts.

Chapter 24

51. Discuss the advantages and the disadvantages of training the operator at the machine vs. training in a separate training school.

52. Indicate the training that would be given to a new employee beginning work on operations described in Problems 31 and 33.

BIBLIOGRAPHY

Books

ALFORD, L. P., Editor, "Cost and Production Handbook," Ronald Press Co., New York, 1934, 1544 pages.

AMAR, JULES, "The Human Motor," George Routledge & Sons, London, 1920, 470 pages.

AMAR, JULES, "The Physiology of Industrial Organization and the Reemployment of the Disabled," Macmillan Co., New York, 1919, 371 pages.

ANDERSON, V. V., "Psychiatry in Industry," Harper & Bros., New York, 1929, 364 pages.

BAINBRIDGE, F. A., "The Physiology of Muscular Exercise," 3rd Ed., rewritten by A. V. BOCK and D. B. DILL, Longmans, Green & Co., New York, 1931, 272 pages.

BARNES, RALPH M., "Industrial Engineering and Management," McGraw-Hill Book Co., New York, 1931, 366 pages.

BARNES, RALPH M., "An Investigation of Some Hand Motions Used in Factory Work," Univ. Iowa Studies in Engg., Bul. 6, February, 1936, 63 pages.

BARTLETT, F. C., "The Problem of Noise," Cambridge Univ. Press, 1934, 87 pages.

BENEDICT, F. G., and E. P. CATHCART, "Muscular Work, a Metabolic Study with Special Reference to the Efficiency of the Human Body as a Machine," Carnegie Institution of Washington, Pub. 187, 1913, 176 pages.

BERG, R. M., "Bibliography of Management Literature," to January, 1931, American Society of Mechanical Engineers, New York, 1931, 142 pages.

BROWN, A. BARRETT, "The Machine and the Worker," Nicholson & Watson, London, 1934, 215 pages.

BURTT, H. E., "Psychology and Industrial Efficiency," D. Appleton & Co., New York, 1929, 395 pages.

CARROLL, PHIL, "Timestudy for Cost Control," McGraw-Hill Book Co., New York, 1938, 305 pages.

CATHCART, E. P., "The Human Factor in Industry," Oxford Univ. Press, London, 1928, 105 pages.

COPLEY, F. B., "Frederick W. Taylor, Father of Scientific Management," Vols. 1 and 2, Harper & Bros., New York, 1923.

COX, J. W., "Manual Skill," Cambridge Univ. Press, London, 1934, 247 pages.

CROWDEN, G. P., "Muscular Work, Fatigue and Recovery," Isaac Pitman & Sons, Ltd., London, 1932, 74 pages.

DANA, R. T., and A. P. ACKERMAN, "The Human Machine in Industry," Codex Book Co., Inc., New York, 1927, 307 pages.

DONALD, W. J., Editor, "Handbook of Business Administration," McGraw-Hill Book Co., New York, 1931, 1753 pages.

DREVER, JAMES, "The Psychology of Industry," E. P. Dutton & Co., New York, 1921, 148 pages.

379

FLORENCE, P. S., "Economics of Fatigue and Unrest and the Efficiency of Labor in English and American Industry," Henry Holt & Co., New York, 1924, 426 pages.

FLORENCE, P. S., "Use of Factory Statistics in the Investigation of Industrial Fatigue," Columbia Univ. Press, New York, 1918, 153 pages.

GALE, A. L., and R. C. HOLSLAG, "Making Better Movies," Amateur Cinema League, Inc., New York, 1935, 241 pages.

GILBRETH, F. B., "Bricklaying System," Myron C. Clark Publishing Co., Chicago, 1909, 321 pages.

GILBRETH, F. B., "Motion Study," D. Van Nostrand Co., New York, 1911, 116 pages.

GILBRETH, F. B. and L. M., "Applied Motion Study," Sturgis & Walton Co., New York, 1917, 220 pages.

GILBRETH, F. B. and L. M., "Fatigue Study," 2nd Ed., Macmillan Co., New York, 1919, 175 pages.

GILBRETH, F. B. and L. M., "Motion Study for the Handicapped," George Routledge & Sons, Ltd., London, 1920, 165 pages.

GILBRETH, L. M., "The Psychology of Management," Sturgis & Walton Co., New York, 1914, 344 pages.

GOLDMARK, JOSEPHINE C., "Fatigue and Efficiency," Charities Publication Committee, Russell Sage Foundation, New York, 1912, 591 pages.

HAGGARD, H. W., and L. A. GREENBERG, "Diet and Physical Efficiency," Yale Univ. Press, New Haven, Conn., 1935, 180 pages.

HILL, A. V., "Living Machinery," Harcourt, Brace & Co., New York, 1927, 306 pages.

HILL, A. V., "Muscular Activity," Williams & Wilkins, Baltimore, Md., 1926, 115 pages.

HILL, A. V., "Muscular Movement in Man; The Factors Governing Speed and Recovery from Fatigue," McGraw-Hill Book Co., New York, 1927, 104 pages.

HOLMES, W. G., "Applied Time and Motion Study," The Ronald Press Co., New York, 1938, 335 pages.

HOXIE, R. F., "Scientific Management and Labor," D. Appleton & Co., New York, 1915, 302 pages.

JENKINS, J. G., "Psychology in Business and Industry," John Wiley & Sons, New York, 1935, 388 pages.

KUMMER, HANS, "Zeitstudien bei Einzelfertigung" (Time Studies in Piece Work), Julius Springer, Berlin, 1926, 113 pages.

LAHY, J. M., "Le système Taylor et la physiologie du travail professionnel" (The Taylor System and Physiology of Professional Work), Gauthier-Villors & Co., Paris, 1921, 216 pages.

LAIRD, D. A., "How to Use Psychology in Business," McGraw-Hill Book Co., New York, 1936, 378 pages.

LEE, F. S., "The Human Machine and Industrial Efficiency," Longmans, Green & Co., New York, 1919, 119 pages.

LICHTNER, W. O., "Time Study and Job Analysis," Ronald Press Co., New York, 1921, 397 pages.

LOWRY, S. M., H. B. MAYNARD, and G. J. STEGEMERTEN, "Time and Motion Study," McGraw-Hill Book Co., New York, 2nd Ed., 1932, 471 pages.

LUCKIESH, M., "Seeing and Human Welfare," Williams & Wilkins Co., Baltimore, Md., 1934, 193 pages.

LUDWIG, F., "Der Mensch im Fabrikbetrieb" (The Man in Factory Work), Julius Springer, Berlin, 1930, 204 pages.

LYTLE, C. W., "Wage Incentive Methods," Ronald Press, New York, 1929, 457 pages.

MATHEWSON, STANLEY B., "Restriction of Output among Unorganized Workers," The Viking Press, New York, 1931, 212 pages.

MAYNARD, H. B., "Methods Engineering Installation," Modern Machine Shop, Vol. 9, p. 62, July, 1936.

MAYNARD, H. B., and G. J. STEGEMERTEN, "Operation Analysis," McGraw-Hill Book Co., New York, 1939, 298 pages.

MAYO, ELTON, "The Human Problems of an Industrial Civilization," Macmillan Co., New York, 1933, 194 pages.

McLACHLAN, N. W., "Noise," Oxford Univ. Press, London, 1935, 148 pages.

MERRICK, DWIGHT V., "Time Studies as a Basis for Rate Setting," Engineering Magazine Co., New York, 1920, 366 pages.

MILES, G. H., "The Problem of Incentives in Industry," Sir Isaac Pitman & Sons, Ltd., London, 1932, 58 pages.

MILES, G. H., "The Will to Work," George Routledge & Sons, London, 1929, 80 pages.

MOEDE, W., "Arbeitstechnik" (Work Technique), Ferdinand Enke Verlag, Stuttgart, 1935, 267 pages.

MOEDE, W., "Lehrbuch der Psychotechnik" (Textbook of Industrial Psychology), Julius Springer, Berlin, 1930, 443 pages.

MOGENSEN, A. H., "Common Sense Applied to Motion and Time Study," McGraw-Hill Book Co., New York, 1932, 228 pages.

MOORE, B. V., and G. W. HARTMANN, "Readings in Industrial Psychology," D. Appleton & Co., New York, 1931, 560 pages.

MOSSO, A., "Fatigue," G. P. Putnam's Sons, New York, 1904, 334 pages.

MÜNSTERBERG, H., "Psychology and Industrial Efficiency," Houghton Mifflin Co., New York, 1913, 321 pages.

MUSICO, B., "Lectures on Industrial Psychology," George Routledge & Sons, London, 1920, 300 pages.

MYERS, C. S., "Industrial Psychology in Great Britain," Jonathan Cape, Ltd., London, 1926, 164 pages.

MYERS, C. S., Editor, "Industrial Psychology," Thornton Butterworth, Ltd., London, H. Holt & Co., New York, 1930, 252 pages.

MYERS, C. S., "Mind and Work," G. P. Putnam's Sons, New York and London, 1921, 175 pages.

NYMAN, R. C., and E. D. SMITH, "Union-Management Cooperation in the 'Stretch Out'," Yale Univ. Press, 1934, 210 pages.

PEAR, T. H., "Fitness for Work," Univ. of London Press, Ltd., London, 1928, 187 pages.

PEAR, T. H., "Skill in Work and Play," E. P. Dutton & Co., New York, 1924, 107 pages.

POFFENBERGER, A. T., "Applied Psychology," D. Appleton & Co., New York, 1927, 586 pages.

REFA, Zweites Refa-Buch (Second Book by the German National Committee on Time Study), Beuth-Verlag GMBH, Berlin, 1933, 122 pages.

REUTER, FRITZ, "Handbuch der Rationalisierung" (Handbook of Rationalization), Industieverlag Spaeth & Linde, Berlin, 1932, 1327 pages.

SCHELL, E. H., and F. F. GILMORE, "Manual for Executives and Foremen," McGraw-Hill Book Co., New York, 1939, 185 pages.
SHANNON, W. J., "Movie Making Made Easy," Moorfield Shannon, Nutley, N. J., 1934, 219 pages.
SOCIETY OF INDUSTRIAL ENGINEERS, "Bibliography of Time Study Engineering," H. W. Wilson Co., New York, 1933, 63 pages.
TAYLOR, F. W., "The Principles of Scientific Management," Harper & Bros., New York, 1911, 144 pages.
TAYLOR, F. W., "Shop Management," Harper & Bros., New York, 1919, 207 pages. Reprinted from Trans. A.S.M.E., pp. 1337-1480, Vol. 24, 1903.
THOMPSON, C. B., Editor, "Scientific Management," Harvard Univ. Press, Cambridge, 1914, 878 pages.
VERNON, H. M., "Industrial Fatigue and Efficiency," G. Routledge & Sons, Ltd., London, 1921, 264 pages.
VERNON, H. M., "The Shorter Working Week," G. Routledge & Sons, Ltd., London, 1934, 201 pages.
VERNON, M. D., "The Experimental Study of Reading," Cambridge Univ. Press, 1931, 190 pages.
VITELES, M. S., "Industrial Psychology," W. W. Norton & Co., Inc., New York, 1932, 652 pages.
VITELES, M. S., "The Science of Work," W. W. Norton & Co., New York, 1934, 442 pages.
WATSON, W. F., "Machines and Men," Allen & Unwin, Ltd., London, 1935, 226 pages.
WATSON, W. F., "The Worker and Wage Incentives," Hogarth Press, London, 1934, 46 pages.
WATTS, F., "An Introduction to the Psychological Problems of Industry," Allen & Unwin, Ltd., London, 1921, 240 pages.
WECHELER, DAVID, "The Range of Human Capacities," Williams & Wilkins Co., Baltimore, Md., 1935, 159 pages.
WELCH, H. J., and G. H. MILES, "Industrial Psychology in Practice," Sir Isaac Pitman & Sons, Ltd., London, 1932, 249 pages.
WELCH, H. J., and C. S. MYERS, "Ten Years of Industrial Psychology—An Account of the First Decade of the National Institute of Industrial Psychology," Sir Isaac Pitman & Sons, Ltd., London, 1932, 146 pages.
WHITEHEAD, T. N., "The Industrial Worker," Harvard University Press, Cambridge, 1938, Two volumes.

PERIODICALS AND SPECIAL REPORTS

Advanced Management, quarterly publication of the Society for the Advancement of Management, New York.
Factory Management and Maintenance, monthly publication, McGraw-Hill Publishing Co., Inc., New York.
J. of Ind. Hygiene, monthly publication, Harvard Press, Cambridge, Mass.
Occupational Psychology, quarterly publication of the National Institute of Industrial Psychology, Aldwych House, London, W.C. 2.
Personnel J., monthly publication, Personnel Research Federation, New York.
Reports of the Industrial Health Research Board (formerly the Industrial Fatigue Research Board), H. M. Stationery Office, Kingsway, London, W.C. 2.

INDEX

A

Abnormal time values, 268
Accumulative timing, 265
Accuracy, importance of, 286
Allowances, 278
  table for, 279
American Hard Rubber Company, 116
American Institute Laundry, 192
Analysis of hand motions, 87
Anderson, A. G., 280
Arm rest, 211
Arrangement of equipment, 176
Assemble (therblig), check list for, 129
  definition of, 64
  example of, 128
  symbol for, 63
Assembly operations, time standards
  for, 333
Average method of selecting time, 268

B

Ballistic movements, 169
Barber-Colman gear hobber, 302
Barrett, R. H., 4
Barrow work, 136
Bars, positioning, 121
Bench, packing, 181
Bench grinder case, 253
Bench vice, foot-operated, 216
Bibliography, 379
Bins, study of, 187
  types of, 185
Blakelock, R. M., 56
Blank and perforate, time standard for,
  332
Blanking dies, plain, 318
Blocks in slots, positioning, 122
Board, observation, 257

Bolt and washer assembly, analysis
  sheet of, 92
  description of, 147
  operation charts of, 40, 41
  pictures of, 90, 91
  process charts of, 25
  simo charts of, 93, 95
Book, packing, 179
Booth, projection, 77
Breaking operation into its elements,
  261
Bricklaying, improved method of, 13
Bridgeport Plant of General Electric,
  333
Brush, push, 51
Bushings, inserting pins in, 119

C

Cadillac, 181, 217
Cameras, 67
Candy dipping, 168
Can-making, method of, 311
Carnegie Foundation for the Advance-
  ment of Teaching, 232
Carrying loads, 137
Carton, packing book in, 179
Cathcart, E. P., 142
Chair of proper height, 213
Change direction, time for, 165
Charts, man-and-machine process, 26
  operation, 40, 41
  possibility, 102
  process, 22, 25
  simo, 93
Checker's table, 184
Checking overall time, 286
Cheddar cheese, packing, 102
Chronocyclegraph, 15

383

Cincinnati vertical milling machine, 299
Classification, of hand motions, 161
  of types of dies, 318
  of work done on plain blanking dies, 322
Clean-up work, 48
Coal mining, investigation of, 168
Collecting data for formulas, 288
Colonial Radio Company, 236, 367
Color, use of, 107
Compensation, 250, 330
Computation sheet, 346
Computations of time standards, 281
Conditions, of get, 335
  of place, 335
Containers, types of, 185
Continuous timing, 262
Cooperation resulting from motion study, 59
Core-making, description of, 284
  study of, 281
Cost Reduction Report, 242
Countersinking operation, 190
Cox, C. H., 181
Crossbars, design of, 240
Curved motions, 164
Curves for setting time standards on die and tool work, 327
Cycle timing, 265
Cyclegraph, 15
Cylinders, grasping, 114

D

Data, for formulas, 301, 317
  standard, 288
Delay, allowances for, 280
Design, of parts, 158
  of tools and equipment, 216, 222
Desk, typist's, 178
Die and tool work, time standards for, 317
Die block, operations on, 324
Dill, D. B., 142
Dipping candy, 168
Dishwashing department, 34
Dispose, 337

Division of operation into elements, 261
Door-knob assembly, 220
Douglas-Haldane apparatus, 136
Dovrak, A., 231
Drill press, foot-operated, 219
  for burring, 190
  standard data for, 289
Drop deliveries, use of, 189

E

Effort, rating of, 269, 273
Elemental time data, 288
Elements, breaking job into, 261
  foreign, 266
Elevator scales, 31
Envelopes, placing inserts in, 111
Equipment, micromotion study, cameras, 67
  microchronometer, 72
  motion picture film, 74
  photoflood lamps, 72
  projectors, 76
  stop-watch time study, board, 257
  slide rule, 259
  stop watches, 255
Errors in time values, 286
Expression, formula, 303, 314
Extractor, operation of, 45
Eye movements, 150, 156, 202
Eyestrain, relief of, 201

F

Factor, leveling, 272
Farmer, Eric, 10
Fatigue, 134
  effect on rhythm, 172
File for standard data, 286
Film, indexing and storing, 75
  kinds of, 74
Film analysis, 86
Fine assembly work, 201
Fingers, capacities of, 231
Fixation movements, 169
Fixations, two and three, 156

Fixed stations for tools and materials, 174
Fixtures for painting metal containers, 42
Flagler, L. A., 48
Folding paper, method of, 165
Foot pedal, design of, 220, 222
Foot rest, 213
Forms for, instruction sheets, 360, 362, 363
  motion-analysis data, 87
  motion picture data, 83
  simo charts, 93
  standard practice, 246
  stop-watch studies, 257, 263, 274, 282
Formulas for, gear hobbing, 301
  milling, 292
  soldering cans, 311
Full-hook grasp, 108

G

Gauging hard rubber washers, 116
General Electric Company, 56, 60, 73, 185, 333, 364
Get, time for, 335
Gilbreth, F. B. and L. M., 1, 4, 8, 12, 13, 14, 15, 16, 23, 62, 65, 66, 72, 81, 88, 111, 145
Gisholt lathes, 31, 237
Grasp (therblig), check list for, 112
  definition of, 64
  example of, 108
  four types of, 334
  full hook, 108
  pressure, 108
  symbol for, 63
Grommets, 158

H

Habel, O. W., 222
Hand motions, abrupt changes in, 165
  classification of, 161
  continuous curved, 165
  of varying lengths, 162
Hand tools permanently positioned, 224
Hand wheels, design of, 241
Handles, design of, 233

Hardy, James A., 222
Health of Munition Workers Committee, 139
Heating factory buildings, 141
Height, of chair, 213
  of desk, 178
  of table top, 210
Hobbing gears, standard time for, 301
Hold (therblig), check list for, 131
  definition of, 66
  example of, 130, 149
  symbol for, 63
Hotel, rearrangement of departments in, 31
Hours of work, 139

I

Illumination, adequate, 200
Incentives, 252, 330
Individual differences, 269
Industrial Engineering Laboratory, University of Iowa, 74, 156
Industrial Welfare Commission of California, 210, 212
Information, securing, 261
Inspect (therblig), check list for, 129
  definition of, 65
  example of, 203
  reaction time for, 129
  symbol for, 63
Inspection, of bottles, 209
  of cloth, 208
  of electric fan blades, 209
  of electric meter mechanisms, 201
  of polished surfaces, 208
Instruction sheet, for lacing tennis shoes, 363
  for packing chocolates, 362
  for turret lathe work, 360
International Business Machines Corporation, 28
Iowa, University of, 74

J

Janitor work, 48
Jigs, principles of motion economy related to design of, 216, 222

Jigs and fixtures, 161
Job, specifications for, 245
Job analysis, 1, 22
Job Conditions form, Standard, 246
General, 247
Johnson and Sons, Inc., C. S., 177
Judgment of analyst, 272

K

Kitchen layout, 34
Koch, B. S., 28
Koepke, C. A., 4
Kymograph, 131

L

Labor, commodity, 250
value of, 250
Labor accomplishment, 250
Laboratory, motion study, 73, 74
Laundry work, 45, 137, 192
University of Iowa, 198
Lawrence, Ivan C., 242
Length, of rest periods, 140
of working day, 139
Level of performance, 272
Leveling method, 272
Lighting, 141, 203
Link-forming operation, 96
Loops, film, 248
Lowry, Hotel, 31

M

Machines, arrangement of, 180
MacKenzie, John M., 122, 154
Macy's Department Store, 87, 111
Magnet armature, drawing of, 27
manufacture of, 28
Making the motion pictures, 79
Management, principles of, 9
Massachusetts State College, 4
Master tables of time data, 288, 301
Materials handling, analysis of, 37
Mayo, E., 107, 142, 143
Measurement, of labor, 250
of therblig time accurately, 131
Merck and Company, 181

Metal containers, methods of painting, 42
Metal spools, inspection of, 203
Method of doing work, improvement of, 143
Methods, analysis of, 1, 22
Metropolitan-Vickers, 4, 58
Microchronometer, 72
Micromotion study, aid in improving methods, 54
aid in teaching, 55
classes in, 57, 58
definition of, 14
list of equipment for, 77
training in, 58
two purposes of, 54
Midvale Steel Works, 7, 9
Milling, data for, 292
machine, 299
Minimum time, 268
Minnesota, University of, 4
Minnesota Mining and Manufacturing Company, 242
Mogensen, A. H., 60
Momentum, effective use of, 163
in dipping candy, 167
Mop, specifications for, 49
Mopping, methods of, 48
Morrison, James, 179
Motion, economy, principles of, 145
Motion and time study, definition of, 1
economy of, 17
effect on worker, 252
extent of use, 17
four parts of, 1
history of, 7
part of industrial engineering, 4
refined use of, 19
setting time standard, 3
simplest use of, 20
standardization of operation by, 2
techniques, 17
types of, 17, 18
Motion pictures, "before" and "after," 60
ease of making, 71
for improving rating ability, 278

Motion pictures, not micromotion
study, 60
records, 248
Motion study, applied to every member of organization, 59
beginning of, 13
cooperation resulting from, 60
definition of, 2
Gilbreth's use, 12
laboratory for, 73
right and left hand charts for, 40, 41
Motion-minded, 55
Motions, classes of hand, 161
Mullee, W. R., 116
Mundel, Marvin E., 152

N

New York State Labor Laws, 113
New York University, 59, 167, 227
Noise, reduction of, 141
Norem, Bert H., 154
Number of cycles to be timed, 266

O

Observation, board, 257
sheet, 257, 263, 274, 275
Observations, number of, 266
Observer, position of, 257
Office work, 177
Operating-room setup, 177
Operation analysis, 37
Operator, selection of, 79, 259
training of, 3, 359
Overall time, 267
Oxygen consumption, rate of, 135

P

Packaging small parts, 154
Packing bench, 181
Packing papers, description of operation, 165
simo chart of, 101
Painting with spray gun, container
covers and bottoms, 42
rectangular cans, 24
refrigerator units. 128

Paper folding, 165
Part, blank from punch press, 328
bolt and washers, 147
can, rectangular, 311
change gear, 307
link for typewriter, 96
magnet armature, 27
mounting spring for refrigerator, 373
tool adjusting screw, 298
wood screw, 374
Percentage method of leveling, 272
Perception, 200
Persing, L. P., 364, 365
Personal allowance, 278
Phillips recessed head screw, 236
Photoflood lamps, 82
Physiological changes resulting from
work, 134
Physiological cost of doing work, 135
Pin sets, 121
Place, time for, 335
Placing the camera, 80
Plant layout, 28
Point, definition of, 276
Polishing, silverware, 172
typewriter parts, 172
Porter, David B., 59, 227
Position and pre-position (therbligs),
check list for, 127
definition of, 64, 65
examples of, 117, 227
symbols for, 63
Position of operator, 257
Possibility charts, 102, 105
Posture, 213
Pre-position, see Position
Pressure grasp, 108
Principles of management, 9
Principles of motion economy:
1. The two hands should begin as
well as complete their therbligs
at the same instant, 146
2. The two hands should not be idle
at the same instant except during rest periods, 146
3. Motions of the arms should be in
opposite and symmetrical directions, instead of in the same di-

rection, and should be made simultaneously, 146

4. Hand motions should be confined to the lowest classification with which it is possible to perform the work satisfactorily, 161

5. Momentum should be employed to assist the worker wherever possible, and it should be reduced to a minimum if it must be overcome by muscular effort, 163

6. Continuous curved motions are preferable to straight-line motions involving sudden and sharp changes in direction, 164

7. Ballistic movements are faster, easier, and more accurate than restricted (fixation) or "controlled" movements, 169

8. Rhythm is essential to the smooth and automatic performance of an operation and the work should be arranged to permit easy and natural rhythm wherever possible, 170

9. Definite and fixed stations should be provided for all tools and materials, 174

10. Tools, materials, and controls should be located around the work place and as close in front of the worker as possible, 175

11. Gravity feed bins and containers should be used to deliver the material as close to the point of assembly or use as possible, 185

12. "Drop deliveries" should be used wherever possible, 189

13. Materials and tools should be located to permit the best sequence of therbligs, 192

14. Provisions should be made for adequate conditions for seeing, 200

15. The height of the work place and the chair should preferably be so arranged that alternate sitting and standing at work are easily possible, 210

16. A chair of the proper type and height to permit good posture should be provided for every worker, 213

17. The hands should be relieved of all work that can be performed more advantageously by the feet or other parts of the body, 216

18. Two or more tools should be combined wherever possible, 225

19. Tools and materials should be pre-positioned wherever possible, 226

20. Where each finger performs some specific movement, such as in typewriting, the load should be distributed in accordance with the inherent capacities of the fingers, 228

21. Handles such as those used on cranks and large screwdrivers should be designed to permit as much of the surface of the hand to come in contact with the handle as possible, 233

22. Levers, crossbars, and handwheels should be located in such positions that the operator can manipulate them with the least change in body position and with the greatest mechanical advantage, 237

Problems, 371
Process charts, 25, 26, 28, 29
  outline for making, 36
  symbols for, 23, 24
Proctor and Gamble Company, 48
Production, curves, 138
  studies, 286
Projector, 76
Pull, strength of, 239
Punch press, inclined, 321

Q

Quality classification on die and tool work, 328

R

Rating, skill and effort, 273
Rating factor, definition of, 273
Reading, eye movements in, 202
Recording stop-watch readings, 265
Refrigerator door-knob assembly, 220
Reinhard, W. A., 192
Relation of time standards to wage incentives, 250
Release load (therblig), check list for, 130
  definition of, 65
  examples of, 130, 147, 189
  symbol for, 63
Repetitive timing, 264
Rest periods, 140
Rethreading machine, 222
Rhythm, 170
Richards, Roscoe C., 198
Rubber washers, gauging, 116

S

Saginaw Steering Gear Division of General Motors, 222
Sandals, belting, 51
Scales in elevator, 31
Scope, 4
Screwdriver, combination, 225
  electric motor driven, 228
  handles for, 233
  motor driven, foot-operated, 218
  plain, 234
  pre-positioning devices for, 227, 229
  spiral, 235
  study of pre-positioning, 228
Screws, packaging, 154
Sealy, M. P., 111
Securing time study information, 261
Seeing, adequate conditions for, 200
  time for, 202
Select (therblig), check list for, 107
  definition of, 63
  example of, 107
  symbol for, 63
Selecting the operator, for micromotion study, 79
  for stop-watch study, 259

Selecting time values, 268
Semi-automatic lathe operation, 19
Sensitive drills, standard data for, 289
Setting rates, methods of, 251
Shaw, A. G., 4, 58, 366
Shipping-department operations, 181
Shirt finishing, 193
Shoveling, Taylor's investigation of, 11
Simultaneous gets and places, times for, 342
Simultaneous motion-cycle chart, 93
  modified chart, 102
Simultaneous motions, 146
Skill and effort rating, 273
Slide rule, 259
Smith, R. E., 192
Sockets, radio tube, 160
Soldering cans, time standards for, 311
Soldering iron, foot-operated, 217
Spectacles, use of, 202
Spencer, Floyd R., 317
Spencer, P. R., 170
Spiral screwdrivers, 235
Spools, inspection of, 203
Spray painting, of container covers and bottoms, 42
  of rectangular cans, 24
  of refrigerator unit, 128
Standard practice, 245
Standard times for get and place, 336
Standardization, 245
Stats, H. E., 31
Steps in making stop-watch observations, 268
Stop watches, 255
Stop-watch study, determination of allowances, 278
  determination of time standard, 281
  division of operation into elements, 261
  equipment required, 255
  forms for, 257, 263, 274, 275, 282, 283
  rating skill and effort, 267
  recording and filing data, 286
  securing information, 261
  selection of operator for, 259
  technique of, 260
  time-recording machines, 256

Stop-watch study, timing and recording data, 262
Strength of pull, 239
Surgery, motion study in, 177
Symbols, therblig, 63

T

Table, new design of, checkers, 184
  laundry, 199
Taylor, F. W., 7, 9, 11, 140
Therbligs, best sequence of, 192
  colors, 63
  definition of, 62
  symbols, 63
  time values for, 333
  use of, 107
Time-recording machines, 256
Time standard, determination of, 281
Time standards, for constant elements, 288
  for die and tool work, 317
  for drill press work, 289
  for gear hobbing, 301
  for light assembly work, 333
  for milling, 292
  for soldering cans, 311
  for variable elements, 291
Time study, *See* Motion and time study
  analytical work of, 7
  constructive work of, 8
  narrow interpretation of, 16
  Taylor's definition of, 7
Time values, abnormal, 268
  computing, 281
  establishing by formula, 288
Tiredness, feeling of, 134
Tool and die work, standards for, 317
Tools, 11, 225
Training apprentices, 58
  in colleges and universities, 59
  inspectors of metal spools, 204
  new employees, 58
  operators, 359
Transfer sheet, 87
Transport distances, corrections for, 337

Transport empty and transport loaded (therblig), check list for, 117
  definition of, 64, 65
  example of, 112
  length of, 113
  time for, 162
Trays for bolts and nuts, 185, 187
Typewriter keyboard, 232
Typist's desk, 178

U

Unavoidable delay, 65, 280
Uniform finishing, 198
Use (therblig), check list for, 129
  definition of, 64
  example of, 127
  symbol for, 63

V

Vacuum tool, 52
Variable elements, time standards for, 291
Ventilation, 141
Vibration, reduction of, 141
Visual perception, 150, 200
Viteles, M. S., 141

W

Waffle-iron assembly, 349
Wage incentive application, die and tool work, 330
Walking on level, 136
Washers of varying thickness, grasping, 109
Wechsler, D., 269
Western Electric Company, 142, 156
Westinghouse leveling method, 272
Whitson, Lee S., 242
Williams, A., 361
Window washing, 53
Wink, definition of, 88
Work, one- and two-handed, 157
Work place, 11, 14, 28, 107, 113, 148, 154, 155, 201, 204, 205, 337, 375, 377
Working area, 175
Working conditions, 2, 140
Wright, Frank Lloyd, 177
Written standard practice, 2, 245